Wordsmithy

WORDSMITHY

HOT TIPS FOR THE WRITING LIFE

Douglas Wilson

canonpress
Moscow, Idaho

Published by Canon Press
P.O. Box 8729, Moscow, ID 83843
800.488.2034 | www.canonpress.com

Douglas Wilson, *Wordsmithy: Hot Tips for the Writing Life*
Copyright © 2011 by Douglas Wilson.

Cover design by David Dalbey.
Interior design by Laura Storm.
Printed in the United States of America.

Library of Congress Cataloging-in-Publication Data

Wilson, Douglas, 1953-
 Wordsmithy : hot tips for the writing life / by Douglas Wilson.
     p. cm.
 ISBN 978-1-59128-099-6
 1. Authorship. I. Title.
 PN145.W54 2011
 808.02--dc23

                                        2011028091

12 13 14 15 16 17 18   10 9 8 7 6 5 4 3 2

For Toby Sumpter,
a good friend with good words.

CONTENTS

In the world of public speaking, it is a commonplace for young aspirants to the lectern to be told something like "tell them what you're going to tell them, tell them, and then tell them what you told them." This admirable advice, strong on repetition, is counsel I intend to follow here. Repetition is a sound pedagogical device, even for those who do not think of themselves as thick-skulled, in whose ranks we might have to include at least some aspiring writers.

In this introduction, I would like to give a summary overview of the seven main exhortations I would like to deliver. In the main body of this small book, I would like to expand on these seven points, extracting seven more points out of each of them. And then in the conclusion, I will harmoniously allude to the whole business once again. But the conclusion will be so graceful, you'll scarcely notice it.

The Anglo-Saxons had a great word for the right word, the word that you need right now, when another one simply would not do. That word is *wordriht*. Think of it as the *mot juste*, not that *they* would put it like that. Who could imagine Beowulf talking that way to Hrothmund, *n'est-ce pas?* No one really, although French did come into English via the Norman invasion, and Norman is short for Northman, a bunch of whom had at an early time in the proceedings come down into France from Beowulf's neck of the woods. Still . . . another bit of advice that I should have put in this book would be to "avoid tangents." Don't get distracted. Stay on point.

So in no particular order of importance, I would encourage those who want to learn the *wordriht* life to approximate something like the following:

1. Know something about the world, and by this I mean the world outside of books. This might require joining the Marines, or working on an oil rig or as a hashslinger at a truck stop in Kentucky. Know what things smell like out there. If everything you write smells like a library, then your prospective audience will be limited to those who like the smell of libraries.

2. Read. Read constantly. Read the kind of stuff you wish you could write. Read until your brain creaks. Tolkien said that his ideas sprang up from the leaf mold of his mind: your readings are the trees where your fallen leaves would come from. Mind mulch. Cognitive compost.

3. Read mechanical helps. By this I mean dictionaries, etymological histories, books of anecdotes, dictionaries of foreign phrases, books of quotations, books on how to write dialogue, and so on. The plot will usually fail to grip, so just read a page a day. If you think it makes you out to be too much of a word-dork, then don't tell anybody about it. Let's keep it between you and me.

4. Stretch before your routines. If you want to write Italian sonnets, try to write some short stories. If you want to write a few essays, write a novel, or maybe a novella if you are pressed for time. If you want to write haiku, then limber up with opinion pieces for *The Washington Post*.

5. Be at peace with being lousy for a while. Chesterton once said that anything worth doing was worth doing badly. He was right. Only an insufferable egoist expects to be brilliant first time out. Some writers—those who live charmed lives—have been brilliant first time out, but this happens so rarely that we shouldn't care who they are. You can't copy them anyway. You *can* copy those who *got* good.

6. Learn other languages, preferably languages that are upstream from ours. This would include Greek, Latin, and Anglo-Saxon. The brain is not a shoebox that "gets full," but is rather a muscle that expands its capacity with increased use. The more you know, the more you *can* know. The more you can do with words, the more you can *do*. As it turns out.

7. Keep a commonplace book. Write down any notable phrases that occur to you or that you come across. If it is one that you have found in another writer, and it is striking, then quote it, as the fellow said, or modify it to make it yours. If Chandler said that a guy had a cleft chin you could hide a marble in, that should come in useful sometime. How could it not come in useful? If Wodehouse said somebody had an accent you could turn handsprings on, then he might have been talking about Jennifer Nettles of Sugarland. Tinker with stuff. Get your fingerprints on it.

Know when to stop.

CHAPTER ONE

A VERITABLE RUSSIAN DOLL
of Writing Tips

The first tip was to get out more.

> Know something about the world, and by this I mean the world outside of books. This might require joining the Marines, or working on an oil rig or as a hashslinger at a truck stop in Kentucky. Know what things smell like out there. If everything you write smells like a library, then your prospective audience will be limited to those who like the smell of libraries.

A writer should have some kind of real life ballast. Here are seven tips that will help explain that first tip. And, weather permitting, we may do the same thing with the other six as well. Each of our first seven tips is a Russian doll, lined up on a mantelpiece for you, and when we take each one apart, we should find seven additional points inside each one. At least you should find them if we did this right.

Real life *duties* should be preferred over real life tourism.
Taking care of your preschoolers or being deployed with the
Seventh Fleet is far to be preferred over purchasing a backpack
and heading off to find America, or even worse, yourself.

Look at the world, and try not to look at yourself looking at the world. Your readers may well be interested in your
description of the world—and they will learn plenty about
you in the process—but they will not be all that interested in
your descriptions of yourself directly, even though you may be
using the outside world as the scenic backdrop for your junior
high melodrama of a tortured and misunderstood soul.

When you discharge your duties in the real world you are
learning the concept, and this helps you understand how to
discharge your duties to your readers. In the task of writing
and reading, the initiative in doing one's duty lies with you,
the writer. You are the one who started the whole thing by
writing whatever it was you wrote, and so the responsibility
is yours. You started it. Your duty as a writer is the same as
the respective duties of the plumber, the knee surgeon, the
computer repairman, and the architect, which is to *make it
work*. Moreover, your duty is to make it work for the customer,
which in this case is the reader. Readers have responsibilities
too, and that would be a fine topic for another book, but in
the meantime your job is not to make them do *their* duty raw
as they read your writing. Your job is to make it as pleasant
as you can for them.

So when you are out and about during your stint in the
Marine Corps, or wherever you are, you are learning two

things. You are learning about the world and the people in it, about whom you will write, and you are learning how to do your job in the service of others, which is what you need to continue to do as you undertake the writing life. Knowledge of how to do your duty in one area transfers readily to another area.

The right kind of ambition is impatient to get on with it, which means that the aspiring writer would like to graduate from college at twenty-two, marry at twenty-three, and land a major book deal at twenty-four. While the right kind of ambition is good, it rarely works like that. And even if you *did* have a major book deal at twenty-four, you would hardly have a vast reservoir of experiences to draw from. There was that time when you went sledding with your college buddies and broke your finger. Anything else? Maybe a little autobiographical note might illustrate this. I have wanted to "make books" since around the sixth grade, and I published my first book when I was in my late thirties. My point is that the time in between was not wasted—submarine service, marriage, college, bringing up three kids, starting a school for them, and so forth. This kind of life experience is not distracting you from your appointed task of writing. It is, rather, the roundabout blessing of giving you something to say.

TAKEAWAY POINT

Get some life experience, the kind of experience that a responsible human being gets.

RECOMMENDED READING

Gene Veith, *God at Work* (Wheaton: Crossway, 2002).

❧ 2 ❧

Authenticity in writing will only arise from authenticity in living. Ideas that occur to you in the course of your life should be jotted down in your notebook, which we will discuss later, but only so long as you remember that the world does not exist to provide raw material for your notebook. The world you are observing has every right to continue on just as it was even if you never get published.

One of our great problems today is that we have gotten caught up in our culture-wide quest for authenticity. We want our jeans authentic (pre-ripped at the factory), we want our apples authentic (grown locally instead of somewhere else), we want our music authentic (underground bands nobody ever heard of), we want our lettuce authentic (organically manured), we want our literature authentic (full of angst), we want our movies authentic (subtitles), and we want our coffee tables authentic (purchased from a genuine peasant while we were on some eco-tour). In short, we are a bunch of phonies. We are superficial all the way down.

We are not going to get out of this snare until we see the quest for authenticity for what it is—a hypocrisy factory, cranking out tight-weave superficiality by the yard.

Now of course, there is a sense in which the word *authentic* should not be a problem. If a manuscript expert said that a recently discovered eighth-century manuscript was authentic, he means that it is not a forgery. Great, and no problems. The same thing goes for paintings, and so on. But somewhere between that and a crusty old farmer who has an authentic soul because he grows tiny peas for the local farmers' market, we have lost our way. The word *authentic* has lost its authenticity and has become a nebulous term of praise, loudly used by those who are in the process of chasing their *zeitgeistian* jack-o'-lanterns.

This quest for authenticity, in its current configuration, is actually a quest to feel superior to other people, and because *everybody* has gotten in on this very attractive proposition, this presents a considerable marketing challenge. As a consequence, we have low sales resistance, no shortage of authenticity-mongers, and lots of niche markets for different manifestations of superiority. These good folks will sell you a smaller carbon footprint, a burlap tote bag, a slate shower, a Che poster, an indie movie that only the true-hearts understand, a trip to the rain forest, a bit of jewelry for your nose, and lots and lots and lots of other stuff.

Of course, an honest man knows how to hold back when everybody else is galloping off after the latest thing. But since Rousseau, at least, the latest thing has usually been some virulent form of the authenticity fraud.

Our public literature is not immune to this foolishness and is indeed one of the principal carriers of it. So if you ever get published, you should have vowed beforehand, at the very least, to do nothing to propagate it any further and to insult it at every opportunity. Quit acting real. Get real.

TAKEAWAY POINT

Live a real life, the kind God watches. Beware the authenticity fraud.

David Brooks, *Bobos in Paradise* (New York: Simon & Schuster, 2000).

Thomas Frank, *The Conquest of Cool* (Chicago: University of Chicago Press, 1997).

Christian Lander, *Stuff White People Like* (New York: Random House, 2008).

Andrew Potter, *The Authenticity Hoax* (New York: Harper-Collins, 2010).

Always remember that your writing will have a message. It ought not to be a clunky message, ham-handedly delivered, but it *will* have a message. It will have a point. Even a nihilist writer, showing the thin smoke that constitutes all things, is trying to make the point that there isn't one.

Anybody who has been out in the world with his eyes open for longer than ten minutes knows that there is always an answer in response to the question, "What's *his* game?"

But we are confused on the point. One of the staples of discussion about basic aesthetic principles is that art has to exist for its own self and cannot be prostituted to advance any particular cause or point of view. Perfect nonsense, of course, but that doesn't keep it from being repeated *ad nauseam*.

There is a truth buried in all the nonsense, as there often is. Propaganda typed with two thumbs *is* contrary to true aesthetic sentiment, because the art is treated as simply a sugar-coating to enable the consumer to swallow the message. The amalgamation is nine parts message to one part thin veneer art. But clunky art carrying a message tells us nothing whatever about whether high art can do the same thing. Virgil wrote *The Aeneid* to advance a political purpose. So?

As any good rhetoric teacher should be able to tell you, when people are focusing on your rhetoric, it means you are failing in your rhetoric. Like Ovid said, it is art to conceal art, and I would add that it is art to half conceal the deep message. True artists know how to do this deftly, and message-mongers do not. But doing it deftly and with wisdom should never be confused with not doing it at all.

Now the standard line in today's writing community is that the artist is beholden to no one, that art for art's sake is the only law in the world of artistry, and away with your mundane concerns. So contemporary art tries to pretend it can float above the world, seeking to provide us all with a sense of the transcendent, but only achieving the kind of heights attained by a child's lost carnival balloon. If former President Bush had been chump enough to approach America's artistic community with a request that they use their artistic gifts to help with the war on terror, the howls of outrage would match what would happen if you took away Michael Moore's cinnamon bun. The artistic *haut monde* would be as indignant as a room full of wet cats. The insult to art in its pristine state would be discussed in the galleries of New York for *months*. Plays would have been written about it, and songs composed. *High dudgeon* would be a phrase that I believe we could use to describe the resultant bedlam.

Yet in the first year of Obama's reign, the honchos at the National Endowment for the Arts set up a conference call with a bunch of artists and generally cool people, in order to ask them to sign on as artistic helper bees for Obama's

United We Serve agenda. Now *wait* a minute. What happened to the independence of all True Art? What happened to the "beholden to no man" shtick? It was here just a minute ago. Somebody needs to paint a picture of high artistic hypocrisy—but good luck getting funding.

So the independence of art from worldview and worldview concerns is a myth. Every work of art is produced within a framework of worldview assumptions. Those assumptions include values, goals, and standards. If a worldview is being subverted by a work of art, then its values, goals, and standards are being challenged by another set. This is another way of saying that propaganda (things to be propagated) is inescapable. It is not *whether* certain values will be propagated by art, but rather *which* values will be propagated. And, of course, returning to an earlier point, each worldview will have its adept Baryshnikovs and each worldview will have its two-left-feeters.

And this helps us to understand what we tend to excuse for the sake of the message. Dispensationalists who know how to write good prose are embarrassed by the *Left Behind* series. There will be a number in the middle who wouldn't write that way themselves, but they will put up with it because it reinforces certain things that they like having reinforced. Bad prose coupled with good message, in their view, comes out okay for the most part. Let's overlook the prose this time, shall we?

But the same thing happens in other directions. There are Christians who are not so much interested in advancing a lurid eschatology as they are interested in pushing the boundaries of Christian cultural norms. The message *they* want is that of shocking their Great Aunt Milly with some vampire lit. The message is the boundary challenge, and for the sake of that challenge, they can tolerate prose every bit as bad as poor premillennial rapture prose.

So when you have some kind of wretched art that is all the rage, the first thing to do is *look for the subtext*. It is always there, and pointing it out always gets you in trouble. Then brace for the reaction. We like having our little illusions.

Your writing advances a particular view of the world. Pretending that it doesn't just confuses everybody, starting with you.

RECOMMENDED READING
C. S. Lewis, *That Hideous Strength* (New York: Scribner, 1996).
C. S. Lewis, *The Abolition of Man* (Toronto: Macmillan, 1965).
George Orwell, *All Art Is Propaganda* (Boston: Houghton Mifflin Harcourt, 2009).
Rousas Rushdoony, *Politics of Guilt and Pity* (Fairfax: Thoburn, 1970).

4

Use your conversations to hone your writing voice, and not the other way around. Your native voice in writing is probably closer to the way you most naturally choose to speak than anything else. So you want to use this opportunity to import reality into your writing, instead of importing your writing into your reality.

If your everyday conversation is sloppy and scattered, a highly disciplined writing voice will come off like some kind of schizophrenia. And that is if you manage a highly disciplined writing voice, which is less likely if you tolerate verbal slack in your life elsewhere. Speaking is less formal than writing, but you should have a goal of being recognizably the same person in your speaking and writing. The timbre of your writing voice should be the same kind of timbre as your speaking voice. But in order to keep artificiality out, you should start by disciplining how you speak.

All of us were speakers before we were writers. Begin with the foundations. If you develop your writing voice in a distinctive kind of way first, and then try to harmonize it with your speaking voice, that is like jacking up a house to pour a foundation under it. It can be done, but there are better ways. As you think of metaphors, use them in conversation. As you learn more about language, apply it in speech first. Then transfer what you have learned to your writing. Pay attention to all the words you use every day—especially the words that are coming out of your mouth.

TAKEAWAY POINT

You are a wordsmith. Remember that you are in the smithy all day long.

RECOMMENDED READING

Owen Barfield, *History in English Words* (Barrington: Lindisfarne Books, 1967).

5

When you are out and about, you are watching the gaudy show called life and are trying to learn from it. This is harder to do if you are busy being the star of the show. As Yogi Berra said, you can observe a lot by just watching.

You can often tell if someone is busy being the star of his own show by the ear buds, which are worn in situations that don't really call for them. In fact, the only reason someone would be wearing them in *that* situation is if they needed a soundtrack for their own personal movie, starring *them,* as they walk down the avenue looking at reflections of themselves in the shop windows. This is not the discipline of the effective writer.

Interesting people are *interested* people. Interesting writers are interested writers. But there is a caution here. Ambrose Bierce once defined a bore as someone who talks when you wish them to listen. Someone else should not be simply dismissed as a bore just because he doesn't want you to keep droning on and on. Writers are a famously catty bunch and, while many famous and gifted writers have been (or have gotten) this way, it can be safely said that to whatever extent they gave way to the impulse to be petty, their writing suffers.

As a writer, you should want to be interesting. The way to do this is by being interested. But you have to really *be* interested and not just playing at it. One of the good ways to avoid playing at it is by going off on reading jags, just because you feel like it. It is better to read books you are genuinely interested in, which you may or may not be able to use in your writing, than to slog through books with a middling interest, knowing that everything will be useful. The latter is fine, of course, especially if you are writing an assignment, but your deep interests should always have a dog-eared place on your nightstand.

It is not a violation of this principle to know that being genuinely interested is interesting, provided you are both.

Being interested is interesting.

RECOMMENDED READING

G. K. Chesterton, *Tremendous Trifles* (New York: Sheed & Ward, 1955).

Thomas Peters, *The Christian Imagination* (San Francisco: Ignatius, 2000).

Virginia Postrel, *The Substance of Style* (New York: Harper-Collins, 2003).

6

Live an actual life out there, a full life, the kind that will generate a surplus of stories. Don't go slumming in order to garner a few superficial observations. A two-week camping trip doesn't make you a mountain man, and a three-week job does not constitute the kind of life experience platform that will bear the weight of a lifetime of writing. If you want to say a lot, you need to have a lot to say.

It is not possible to have the inputs be thin and the outputs thick. He who sows sparingly, the apostle Paul once observed, will reap sparingly. While writing is a part of life and *can* be looked at, it is mostly a part of life that is used for looking, and not for being looked at. This noble little book is an exception to the rule. For the most part, your eyes should be used for seeing, and you should spend very little time in Meta-ville looking at your eyes looking at things.

The more you get into what you are doing, whatever it is, the more lived experience you have to draw on. This is not to be undertaken like a research visit to the library. Picture your writing corpus as the mouth of a great river, and all the life you have experienced as the various tributaries that feed the river.

But you ought to be actually living the experience, not just spelunking in the lives of ordinary people while the other end of the rope is tied off in your writer's study. If there is any way to avoid it, don't identify yourself as a writer. There is a variation of the Heisenberg uncertainty principle here. If you step into a situation with that tag, you affect and skew the situation you are stepping into—especially if you are published. If you are not published, then you are just striking a pose, which is a nuisance to everybody in another way.

Mark Twain once defined a classic as a book that everyone wanted to have read, but which no one wanted to read. In a similar spirit, lots of folks want to be "a writer" because they have had a few great ideas for a television script. They want to be a writer but are not all that thrilled about actually writing. They don't want to write, they want to have written. So if you haven't done anything yet, don't talk as though you have. If you *have* done something, then don't talk boastfully or carelessly as though you have either—as much as honesty permits. This is just another way of urging you to fit into the world you want to describe. You don't want the people you know to feel like they are just so much raw material for your project.

Invest in the kind of experience that multiplies.

RECOMMENDED READING

Theodore Dalrymple, *Life at the Bottom* (Chicago: Ivan R. Dee, 2003).

Theodore Dalrymple, *Our Culture, What's Left of It* (Chicago: Ivan R. Dee, 2005).

7

Enjoy yourself. If you enjoy what you are living, you will enjoy writing about it. And if you enjoy writing it, the chances are greatly increased that the readers will enjoy reading it. Angst, anguish, and lots of despair is the kind of thing that whiners buy, and the problem with having whiners as your reading constituency is that whiners are not known for their loyalty to anything. That would include your next book, remember.

Writing is a form of teaching, even when it is not being didactic in some formal kind of way. And the most contagious form of teaching is when an instructor loves his material in the presence of others—whom he also loves. We have all heard someone tell a joke before when the joke wasn't all that funny, but the joke teller was wheezing, trying to get through it. Chances are that his audience was caught up in the experience too, enjoying the enjoyment that the joke teller had in his joke.

There are some writers that I want to read no matter what they are talking about—because they are the kind of writers who write about things they love. And if, for their next book, they decided to love something really odd, that's fine by me. They love it, and by the time I am done with their book, so shall I.

Love what you observe, love what you write, and love those who read it.

G.K. Chesterton, *Orthodoxy* (New York: Image Books, 1959).

CHAPTER OVERVIEW

TAKEAWAY POINTS

Give yourself to the world and the duties God assigns to you along the way. Despise sham authenticity above all things. Own your perspective. Apply what you are learning to all your words. Take an interest. Run a surplus. Love what you do.

RECOMMENDED READING

Douglas Jones and Douglas Wilson, *Angels in the Architecture* (Moscow: Canon Press, 1998).

CHAPTER TWO

READ

Until Your Brain Creaks

The second tip concerned the writer's reading habits.

> Read. Read constantly. Read the kind of stuff you wish you could write. Read until your brain creaks. Tolkien said that his ideas sprang up from the leaf mold of his mind: your readings are the trees where your fallen leaves would come from.

So then, what about it? How should writers read?

The first thing is that writers should be voracious readers. We live in a narcissistic age, which means that many want to have the praise that comes from *having* read, without the antecedent labor of actually reading. Wanting to write without reading is like wanting to grind flour without gathering wheat, like wanting to make boards without logging, and like wanting to have a Mississippi Delta without any tributaries somewhere in Minnesota. Output requires intake, and literary output requires literary intake. We already noted this principle with regard to experiences of life, lived out as a wildcatter in the oil fields, or something. We now come to apply it to input through books.

You learn about life from other writers who have learned about life, but you, as a writer, are also learning something else. You are learning the craft. How did he *do* that? How did he create that effect?

As a writer who reads voraciously, you are like a chef who makes a point of eating in a lot of other restaurants. You should know what it is like to be on the receiving end. When you read widely, you are in a position to identify with the readers who will be picking up what you write. You know what irritates you, you know what makes you laugh, you know what makes you want to pick up this author's next book. You are simply gathering grist for the Golden Rule mill—do as you would be done by. Reading a great deal means that you are "done by" a lot, and you then have an experienced measurement with which to evaluate how you are doing by others.

TAKEAWAY POINT

Spend a lot of time reading. The impact of this reading is not something you need to catalog and track. Just let it happen.

RECOMMENDED READING

C. S. Lewis, *An Experiment in Criticism* (Cambridge: Cambridge University Press, 1969).

Read widely. Reading shapes your voice, and if you want a wide, experienced voice, you have to get out more. Reading solely within one genre is a form of literary provincialism, and it will provide you with a distinctive but unhelpfully narrow accent.

The timbre of your voice will be affected in good ways by every place you have been, bookwise, and so you should make a point of reading novels, histories, collections of poetry, comedies, biographies, theology, and plays. Don't be afraid to have twenty books going at once.

I said just a moment ago that reading shapes your voice; you should have some sort of plan to shape it as it develops. Aside from your name on the cover of the book, your voice should be your most distinctive signature. Those who give themselves to learning the craft of writing wisely will therefore not be content with vague, indistinct results. The point is not to read widely so that your voice will be sort of a mutt descended from them all. The point is to read widely enough to know what delights you, what you would like to imitate, and what you want to stay away from. You will want to become like some writers, you will want to cherry pick from others, and you will read others as a salutary warning. For myself, I have long wanted to write like H. L. Mencken, if Mencken had loved Jesus, or like Chesterton, but a Chesterton who hadn't wanted to defend the papacy or the dubious spectacle of Thomas Aquinas levitating. In rejecting the mistakes of Chesterton, I want to do it as Chesterton would have. He didn't have a lot of use for the Puritans, and here I am a

Puritan who wants to write like Chesterton. What to do? Well, quote someone else you would love to write like . . . Lewis!

> But there is no understanding the period of the Reformation in England until we have grasped the fact that the quarrel between the Puritans and the Papists was not primarily a quarrel between rigorism and indulgence, and that, in so far as it was, the rigorism was on the Roman side. On many questions, and specially in their view of the marriage bed, the Puritans were the indulgent party; if we may without disrespect so use the name of a great Roman Catholic, a great writer, and a great man, they were much more Chestertonian than their adversaries.[1]

Reading widely will also deliver you from the curse of writing instruction that tries to keep students from ever doing anything distinctive. If you "write by rule" only, then, as Quintilian once put it, you will come up with something that is equally free of both vice *and* virtue, like a verbal tapioca pudding made with skim milk. Our world already has too much verbiage in it that comes off like it was written by a committee or a computer—or maybe a committee of computers.

Certain basic rules for writing *are* important, but it is way too easy for students to think that successful writing is a matter of not breaking any rules. So here is the most basic rule. Be yourself. Don't be boring. And if *you* are boring, try to deal with that first.

> Dr. Dimble looked out of the window. "There is my dullest pupil just ringing the bell," he said. "I must go to the

1. C. S. Lewis, *Selected Literary Essays* (Cambridge: Cambridge University Press, 1969), 116.

study and listen to an essay on Swift beginning, 'Swift was born.' Must try to keep my mind on it, too, which won't be easy."[2]

And we must not forget Aravis in *The Horse and His Boy*, who was really taught how to tell a story as a child, just as our children are taught to write essays. But people wanted to hear the stories, whereas Lewis had never heard of anybody who wanted to read the essays.

If you have listened to a lot of blues, then just three notes will give away the distinctive guitar of B. B. King's "Lucille." If you have read a lot of C. S. Lewis, then you should be able to recognize the timbre of his voice after just a paragraph—even if it were a paragraph you had never read before. Our ability to do this kind of thing should not be surprising. We can recognize a friend a block away, even if we have never seen him down that street before.

So if you read widely, you will become accustomed to many different voices. You will accumulate a great deal of experience with all of them. And out of that, your voice will be born and will be able to grow naturally.

TAKEAWAY POINT

Read widely and pay attention to all the different voices out there. Which one fits you like a ten-dollar suit? Which one doesn't?

RECOMMENDED READING

G. K. Chesterton, *The Everlasting Man* (San Francisco: Ignatius, 1993).

2. C. S. Lewis, *That Hideous Strength* (New York: Scribner, 1996), 33.

C.S. Lewis, *Surprised By Joy* (New York: Harcourt, Brace & World, 1955).

H.L. Mencken, *Newspaper Days* (Baltimore: Johns Hopkins University Press, 1940).

P.G. Wodehouse, *Leave it to Psmith* (Woodstock: Overlook Press, 2003).

3

Read like a *reader* and not like someone cramming for a test. If you try to wring every book out like it was a washcloth full of information (and nothing but information), all you will do is slow yourself down to a useless pace. Go for total tonnage, and read like someone who will forget most of it. You have my permission to forget most of it, which may or may not be reassuring, but you *will* forget most of it in either case.

Most of what is shaping you in the course of your reading you will not be able to remember. The most formative years of my life were the first five, and if those years were to be evaluated on the basis of my ability to pass a test on them, the conclusion would be that nothing important happened then, which would be false. The fact that you can't remember things doesn't mean that you haven't been shaped by them.

Every word you use should have countless little dents in it— let us call it something fancy, like the patina of wise usage—but the fact remains that you were two-years-old when you first learned what that word means, and it is now under multiple layers of native-speaking connotations. The fact that you cannot remember applying that connotative coat of meaning does not mean that it is not happening. Read widely and your vocabulary will be hand-rubbed, like the finish on a costly piano.

If you *can* remember everything about a word, it means you don't really know it all that well. The example I like to use is that if you were to ask me what the Greek word καὶ meant, I would promptly tell you that it means "and, even, also." And what that prompt reply should tell you right off is that I don't really know Greek. Let me illustrate. Take one of the English words in the definition, *even*. What does *that* mean? Well, I know the word, but I can't rattle off a tidy set of lexical definitions. I don't even know how many entries are in the dictionary for that one. Hold on, let me check . . . okay, I'm back. In the dictionary I consulted, there were twenty-six definitions, including the adverbial use represented by καὶ. There was only one of the twenty-six that I did not know—and not surprisingly it was a mathematical definition, and no, not the one about even and odd numbers. I know that one.

Why could I rattle off the lexical definition for καὶ and not for *even?* The answer is that I am not a fluent speaker of Greek, and I am a native speaker of English. The way you get to this point is by constant immersion and exposure, *most of which you will not recall.* So not being able to recall something is not automatically a fault.

Now someone may reply that this is all very well, but that they don't know what a particular Sanskrit word is either. They don't know anything about it. How is that ignorance different? It is ignorance *simpliciter,* as opposed to so *much* knowledge that the "knower" doesn't know how to sort it out, or where to start. Let us not affirm the consequent. Pure ignorance of a language cannot give lexical lists for specified vocabulary, and neither can a native speaker. A cow has four legs and so does a cat, but a cow is not a cat, or so *I* maintain. However, a sophomore with one semester of whatever language it is can get one hundred on his vocab quiz, and good for him.

Bringing it back to reading, we test students right after they read something mostly to ensure that they have in fact read it. From this, many have drawn the erroneous conclusion that the only good that can be extracted from the reading is that which can be displayed on or measured by such a test. This is wildly inaccurate. Most of the good your reading and education has done for you is not something you can recall at all.

Well, actually, sometimes learning something in your home language does jump out at you, and you can remember learning it. I still recall my astonishment as a boy upon figuring out what the word *facetious* was. I had *thought* I had known it before, but in my mind it was supposed to start with a *v*—vacetious. Heh.

At the same time, mark every striking thing that you read. You won't remember everything you read, and you won't even remember everything you mark. Nevertheless, it is not a sin to remember *some* things or to mark them in such a way as to be able to find them again. I use blue highlighters on everything, to such an extent that one of my granddaughters assumed, reasonably enough, that this is what I use whenever I am "coloring."

But you are not cramming for a test. You are simply marking things because this is a good way to read with your eyes open. You read widely to be shaped, not so that you might be prepared to regurgitate.

Read like someone who can afford to forget most of what you read. It does not matter because you are still going to be shaped by it.

RECOMMENDED READING

Jacques Barzun, *The Culture We Deserve* (Hanover: Wesleyan University Press, 1989).

James Taylor, *Poetic Knowledge* (Albany: State University of New York Press, 1997).

Douglas Wilson, *The Paideia of God* (Moscow: Canon Press, 1999).

Read like a lover of books and not like someone who wants to be seen as knowledgeable, or well-read, or scholarly. Read because you want to, not because you need to. Actually, you need to as well, but you need to want to. You also need to want to need to, but I am rapidly getting out of my depth.

There is a temptation to deck your prose out, festooning it with references to all the people who are currently being cited by the smart set. Flannery O'Connor is always good for this. A writer can't be afraid to use what he is gathering but must constantly resist the temptation to show off what he has gathered. Always distinguish use, and the tools of the trade, from vainglory.

Speaking of Flannery O'Connor, when I was reading *Wise Blood,* it struck me how *seriously* O'Connor took her fundamentalist misfits. She was a Roman Catholic, and yet we find that her literary (and very Southern) genius really saw Jesus in the angular, raw Tishbite street preachers. She expects us to see the same thing. And if we are ordinary readers, that is precisely what we do see. But if we are Flannery fanboys, smoking our pipes like a pig chewing on a root, that is the very last thing we could possibly see. Hers was the famous comment that the South was Christ-haunted, and she really believed it. "Jesus been a long time gone," which is why He is still here. She would see Jesus in that plowman turned preacher, and some of her fans would only see someone who would never had read Flannery O'Connor.

A lot of aspiring writers quote the right people, but they do so like Mary Bennett in *Pride and Prejudice.* They quote Austen like Mary quoted *her* eighteenth-century bromides, and were Austen here to see them do it, she'd slap them right into her next book, and it wouldn't be pretty.

TAKEAWAY POINT

Use what you have read. Don't show off with what you have read.

RECOMMENDED READING

C. S. Lewis, *The Screwtape Letters* (New York: Macmillan, 1962).

Dorothy Sayers, *The Mind of the Maker* (San Francisco: Harper & Row, 1941).

 5

Pace yourself in your reading. A little bit every day really adds up. If you only read during sporadic reading jags, the fits and starts will not get you anywhere close to the amount of reading you will need to do. It is far better to walk a mile a day than to run five miles every other month. *Plod.* Make time for reading, and make a daily habit of it, even if it is a relatively small daily habit.

Speaking of plodding, let me expand my observations on that. A question I frequently get, and which I am generally reluctant to answer, is a question about time management. How do I get everything done? I don't like to answer this for three reasons. First, I *don't* get everything done. The done stuff is visible enough, but the undone stuff is sitting on my desk, staring at me malevolently. Secondly, I am a firm believer in distinguishing principles from methods, and I am afraid that if I talk too much about what I do, or the way I approach things, people in completely different circumstances or with different sets of gifts will think that I am saying that this is *the* way, which it isn't. And third, it seems awkward and self-centered to talk about yourself like you were a template of some kind, as though you were trying to explain to people how you got to be so wonderful. That kind of attitude evokes the *ick* response, and I don't ever want to look like I am doing that.

That said, this is a book on how to do certain things, and despite misgivings, I can only explain the way I do it. As already stated, I believe firmly in plodding. Productivity is more a matter of diligent, long-distance hiking than it is one-hundred-yard dashing. Doing a little bit now is far better than hoping to do a lot on the morrow. So redeem the fifteen minute spaces. Chip away at it. For example, I usually have a stack of books that I am working through on a catch-as-catch-can basis. Don't despise a page or two of each book every time you sit down to read. And do the same kind of thing with writing—if you only have time for a little bit, then *do* a little bit.

Second, maintain boundaries for everything: boundaries that suit the circumstance and protect your family. I have read enough books to know that the "Acknowledgements" section frequently includes a tribute to the wife and kids, who always let Dad go off to the study for the interminable time it took to produce the book. This is a reasonable thing to acknowledge, of course, but I would encourage writers not to overdo it— the disappearing that is, not the acknowledging. When an extra load develops, try to have it land on you and not on the family. If it *has* to get done now, then get up at five, and nobody else pays. So if you need to, get up at five, but always try to go home at five.

Think of it this way. A 60-hour work week is an honest job and a significant load, but a lot of the problems that come to people who work this much happen because of *where* those 60 hours are placed. Apportion 40 hours to your regular job, the calling which pays the bills, and then 20 hours for your half-time job of getting a writing career started. It is possible to work those 60 hours and still have lots of time left over for family. A week has a total of 168 hours in it. Sixty hours of work leaves 108, and 8 hours of sleep a night take away another 56 hours, leaving you with 52 hours a week to play tag in the backyard with the kids.

Third, you should measure progress by the extended video, and not by the snapshot. Set specific goals for getting things done, but allow for daily or weekly fluctuations. For example, in 1979, when I first began to work on my reading seriously,

I set a goal for my weekly reading, as measured by the month. I wanted to read an average of one to two books a week, calculated by how many I finished in a month, which would be somewhere between four to eight books. Set hard but reasonable goals, and measure them in reasonably extended time units.

Fourth, use and reuse everything. Act like a Sioux with a superstitious fixation on using every last part of the buffalo. I know that my blogging pace sometimes creates the illusion that I do little other than sit here typing like a madman with my hair on fire, but that is really not the way it is at all. Prepare things with an eye on reusing them in the future, and make sure to use (any useful) work from the past. This is how articles I have written are shaped into books, sermon outlines are shaped into books, Bible study outlines from fifteen years ago are lightly edited into continuous prose and turned into blog posts and may one day find their way into a book, and interesting quotations from books I have read are posted on my blog with a view to using them as the research background on future books.

In the evenings, Nancy and I hang out with the kids and grandkids, who come over frequently. I play the guitar, read, and so on. It is a full and busy life, but we work hard at preventing it from becoming frenetic. I hate frenetic, which returns us to the previous point on the fruitfulness of plodding. Living this way, we have found that it adds up.

TAKEAWAY POINT

Plod intelligently. Plodding generally goes in the same direction, while pottering doesn't.

Annie Dillard, *Pilgrim at Tinker Creek* (San Francisco: Harper, 2007).

6

As a general pattern, read quality literature, and go "slumming" occasionally to remind yourself what quality is and why quality matters. And when you go slumming, enjoy yourself. Don't act like you just came down to check out the rubes and cornpones. In the writer's restaurant, you should know what first rate *cordon bleu* is and, at the same time, not be above enjoying an elephant ear or a funnel cake at the state fair.

"Iron sharpeneth iron; so a man sharpeneth the countenance of his friend" (Prov. 27:17). In a similar way that conversation sharpens a man's countenance, conversation with men throughout history sharpens a man's mind. You don't want to hang out all the time with lazy friends—bad companions corrupt good morals. If this is the case, and it is, then a point should be made to seek out profitable companions in a disciplined fashion throughout your life with books.

Set a lifetime pattern of reading books. Set a course of reading, and adopt general criteria which will guide your reading. I would recommend one to two books a week. If you began this when you were thirty and joined the choir invisible when you were seventy, you would have read, over this course of time, between 2,080 books and 4,160 books. It is quite true that you run the risk of learning something, but these are the risks a writer must take.

Read attentively and with your eyes open, but *not as though* you are cramming for a test. The reason you should not read as though studying for a test is that, as we have already noted, the vast majority of what you learn (with great profit) you will not be able to recall. Read with a pen, pencil, or highlighter so that you can mark things of interest in a way that will help you find them again, and keep your reading intelligent and interactive.

Generally speaking, read canonical literature. The amount of books in the world is vast, and your reading should be filled with purpose and intent. You are not wandering around aimlessly in circles, which would be easy to do if the books you read were to be selected at random. Canonical reading provides you with the protections of a collective wisdom.

Anyone who wants to write in the English language needs to focus on the canon of Scripture. Read, reread, and reread again. This is of course something that all Christians should do, but it is also something every writer should do. For shaping the cadences of your mind, there is nothing like the Authorized Version.

Read widely in the Western canon, which means reading the sorts of books that educated men are presumed to have read. Your reading should therefore include Homer, Virgil, Shakespeare, Dante, Donne, *Beowulf,* and so forth.

But as we began this section by noting, you should also read, as you feel like it, non-canonical books. I am not referring to terrible writing here, or the "guilty pleasure" of reading a Harlequin romance every night. The fact that a book is not canonical does not make it a lousy book. In fact, it may be far superior to one that is in the canon. Reading lousy books is occasionally edifying, but do not make a practice of it. Life is short.

As you read, allow your reading to cluster around your interests. For example, say you are interested in practical economics. What better way to work through this than to read, over the course of a year or so, twenty books on the subject? When you are done there, move on to something else which interests you. And if nothing interests a man, then he should give up writing and get a job watching television. What goeth on in the writer's life, he wots not.

But don't be a snob.

TAKEAWAY POINT

Love what is noble. Associate with the lowly.

RECOMMENDED READING

Robert Alter, *Pen of Iron* (Princeton: Princeton University Press, 2010).

Harold Bloom, *The Western Canon* (New York: Riverhead Trade, 1995).

 7

Read widely enough so that you are not provincial, but not so widely that you become some sort of deracinated cosmopolitan. Walls that are too narrow can stifle all thought and originality. Walls that are not there at all leave you defenseless. Marauders of literary fashion come galloping in, and there you are.

Loyalty of some sort is inescapable, and so if a writer doesn't have a sense of people and place, he will tend to substitute some literary school or other. Belonging to a particular stylistic school is perfectly necessary, of course. Once you start writing, your use of the passive voice will either be closer to Jane Austen's or to Ernest Hemingway's. If you are going to write, you have to write *something*, and you will have to do it in some way. And presumably, you would do so for a reason.

But the problem of deracination is still a serious one. If you have been paying attention to the earlier advice about living an actual life among other people, you will have been doing so as a Christian, then a family man, then an American, and then a writer, and so on, just as your friend the software engineer is a Christian first, a member of a different family, a Korean, and then a software engineer. All idolatries are sinful, as when a particular nation is put before Christ, but some idolatries are pathetic, as when a peculiar literary preference is.

You can tell when the writer's guild has tiptoed off with someone's loyalties. The hapless victim starts apologizing for the literary sin of his Christian brothers, that sin being failure to belong to the current literary school, and the apologizer does this when it is completely unnecessary and uncalled for. If it weren't so funny, it would be sad. "Why can't Protestant Christians write?" the lament goes up. "We have to do better than this, people!" with "better" defined as receiving the accolades of the denizens of the nearest MFA program at the nearest state university, in which the lamenter is currently enrolled and learning *lots* of stuff.

To which I would respond by pointing to Chaucer, Tyndale, Beza, Spenser, Marvell, Donne, Herbert, Defoe, Shakespeare, Bradstreet, Bunyan, Taylor, Milton, Johnson, Buchan, and Lewis. Not bad, I would say, but please remember that we're just getting started. But I admit I included Bunyan on the list in order to draw the inevitable sneer. You see, Bunyan wrote *allegories* where the people had names like Talkative, and Hate-Good, and Faithful, and Pliable. You can almost see the labels sticking out of the back of their coat collars. Right, but that doesn't keep Bunyan from being one of the great literary geniuses of our civilization, a man who practically invented dialogue in the modern sense.

Lewis remarks on the marvelous ear that Bunyan had for this kind of thing:

> Such passages seem to me the essential Bunyan. His prose comes to him not from the Authorized Version but from the fireside, the shop, and the lane. He is as native as Malory or Defoe. The Scriptural images themselves take on a new homeliness in these surroundings.[1]

And I should remark in passing that one of the reasons why Lewis was such a marvelous writer is that he was not threatened by the academic pretensions and pufferies that regularly surround aspiring writers, urging them to try to fit in a little better. Lewis had the same kind of ear that Bunyan did. Here is something he noticed about Elizabethan writers:

> They talked more readily than we about large universals such as death, change, fortune, friendship, or salvation; but also about pigs, loaves, boots, and boats. The mind darted more easily to and fro between that mental heaven and earth: the cloud of middle generalizations, hanging between the two, was then much smaller. Hence, as it seems to us, both the naivety and the energy of their

1. Lewis, *Selected Literary Essays,* 140.

writing. Much of their literary strength (when at the end of the century they became strong) is bound up with this. They talk something like angels and something like sailors and stable-boys; never like civil servants or writers of leading articles.[2]

When Lewis says that the Elizabethans never wrote like civil servants or the writers of leading articles, you can tell where his sympathies are.

Ko-Ko from *The Mikado* once referred to this problem, as he was assembling his "little list" of potential executionees— "Then the idiot who praises, with enthusiastic tone / All centuries but this, and every country but his own."

TAKEAWAY POINTS

Be true to your people, not to your school. Have a people to be true to.

RECOMMENDED READING

John Bunyan, *The Pilgrim's Progress* (New York: Penguin, 2009).

CHAPTER OVERVIEW

TAKEAWAY POINT

Just read. Get around. Try things on. Most of what shapes you will be forgotten. Don't show off, but don't be coy either. Plod. Be high-minded and lowly-hearted. Love your people.

2. C. S. Lewis, *English Literature in the Sixteenth Century* (Cambridge: Cambridge University Press, 1964), 62.

RECOMMENDED READING

Rachel Jankovic, *Loving the Little Years* (Moscow: Canon Press, 2010).

Rebekah Merkle, *England Swings* (forthcoming).

J. R. R. Tolkien, *The Lord of the Rings* (New York: Houghton Mifflin, 1954).

Michael Ward, *Planet Narnia* (Oxford: Oxford University Press, 2008).

N. D. Wilson, *Notes from the Tilt-a-Whirl* (Nashville: Thomas Nelson, 2009).

CHAPTER THREE

WORD FUSSERS

and Who-whomers

In my recent seven-fold set of admonitions for writers, my third bit of advice was this:

> Read mechanical helps. By this I mean dictionaries, etymological histories, books of anecdotes, dictionaries of foreign phrases, books of quotations, books on how to write dialogue, and so on. The plot will usually fail to grip, so just read a page a day. If you think it makes you out to be too much of a word-dork, then don't tell anybody about it.

Under this head, allow me to break it out into seven separate elements, but with a brief caution first.

Having eggs doesn't mean that you know how to make the omelet. But if you don't have the eggs, it doesn't matter if you *do* know how to make the omelet. Writing is like cooking, and words are your ingredients. In order to write well, you need to have those ingredients, and you need to know those ingredients. And having them means collecting them, and it also means studying them once you have them.

That said, here we go.

1

Read boring books on writing mechanics. Include grammars, books on how to write dialogue, books on how not to write dialogue ("I dropped my toothpaste!" he said crestfallenly), and books about finding good agents and how to blow away those who read query letters. Writing is a vocation, and there is a body of professional literature out there—which is uneven in quality, just like every other kind of book. Read a lot of it anyway.

Somebody needs to tell you where to put the comma. If you read the dire warnings of prescriptivists with whom you do not agree (note my use of "with whom"), then that's all right. You are a writer, and you work with words, and you don't have to agree with everybody. It is still a benefit to know what people think. Oscar Wilde once defined a gentleman as one who never insulted somebody else *accidentally*. In a similar spirit, a competent writer wants to be the kind of person who is never guilty of a solecism accidentally. If you do it, do it with your eyes open.

Say what you will, there is a difference between someone who does not agree with the grammarian in tight shoes and the person who simply does not know what is going on. Master the rules before you assume that you have the right to break them. If you proceed directly to the slob option, then the problem is simply laziness. Take the question of the serial comma. In a list, do you put a comma in before the final and?

Do you say "blackberries, blueberries, and strawberries"? Or do you say "blackberries, blueberries and strawberries"?

As you study these issues, you will discover that there are frequently good reasons for these rules. Unfortunately, there are often good reasons both ways. Justin Taylor, editor of Crossway, cites the example of one writer who wanted to thank "my parents, Jesus and Ayn Rand." See what happens when you leave out the serial comma? But Andy Le Peau, at InterVarsity, points to a different kind of example. Suppose someone were to dedicate his book to "my mother, Ayn Rand, and God"? Now the serial comma creates the idea that Ayn Rand is in apposition to mother, which it presumably wasn't.

For my money, the serial comma is the way to go, unless it isn't.

TAKEAWAY POINT

Writing well is more than mechanics, but it is not less.

RECOMMENDED READING

James Scott Bell, *Plot & Structure* (Cincinnati: Writer's Digest Books, 2004).

Susan Rabiner and Alfred Fortunato, *Thinking Like Your Editor* (New York: W. W. Norton & Co., 2002).

William Strunk and E. B. White, *The Elements of Style*, 4th ed. (Boston: Allyn & Bacon, 1999).

Francis-Noël Thomas and Mark Turner, *Clear and Simple as the Truth* (Princeton: Princeton University Press, 1994).

Nancy Wilson, *Our Mother Tongue* (Moscow: Canon Press, 2004).

2

Collect and read dictionaries. First, read regular old dictionaries. Take a couple of minutes every day to read a page. Highlight fun words you didn't know before, and write them down somewhere else. I read a paperback American Heritage once, up into the M's, but then I lost it in a move or something.

There are other kinds of dictionaries you should also want to read. Read dictionaries of odd and unusual words. Read dictionaries for specialized vocations or settings. Find out what *abaft the beam* means, so you can describe somebody's Ford F250 in that spot. Or read baseball dictionaries. There's a good idea.

Read books of proverbs and clichés. A proverb is frequently a cliché that went into retirement to get its groove back, and you may be the one to bring it into circulation again. Read books of clichés so that you learn to notice and avoid them, or the phrases that sound just like them. But don't get overly precise—make a distinction between clichés and linguistic roughage. Some phrases are used all the time but are not really clichés (e.g., on the other hand), while others may be entirely your own and come off sounding just like a cliché (e.g., her eyes were limpid pools reflecting the full moon). Closely related to books of proverbs would be books of lists and rules, like Paul Dickson's assorted books. It was from Dickson that I learned the Gadarene Swine Rule—just because a group is in formation doesn't mean it knows where it is going.

But for real color, and for the highest levels of usability, read dictionaries of slang. There are many of them out there, and they have high levels of linguistic fiber for your diet. C. S. Lewis once commended the Elizabethans for their use of color in language, a virtue, he said, which they apparently bequeathed to their American cousins. Speaking of Thomas Nashe, he said this:

> [The appeal of Nashe's writing] is almost entirely to that taste for happy extravagance in language and triumphant impudence of tone, which the Elizabethans have, perhaps, bequeathed rather to their American than to their English descendants.

Dictionaries of American slang are a great repository of this kind of thing. Along the way you may discover that some of your expressions are really quite vulgar, which would explain that expression on your mother's face all these years, and maybe you ought to stop using them.

TAKEAWAY POINT

Dictionaries are books. Why can't we read them?

RECOMMENDED READING

Mrs. Byrne, *Mrs. Byrne's Dictionary* (Secaucus: Citadel Press, 1974).

Paul Dickson, *Words* (New York: Delacourte, 1982).

Jonathon Green, *The Cassell Dictionary of Slang* (London: Cassell, 1998).

Jeffrey Kacirk, *Forgotten English* (New York: William Morrow, 1997).

Read books of complaint about the decline of our language by word fussers and who-whomers, and read the hilarious refutations of those word fussers by word libertines. You can learn a lot from *both*. Anyone who can't learn from a word fusser ought to have their head examined. A word fusser is anyone who would have a problem with the previous sentence.

The antinomians believe that grammars and dictionaries are descriptive *only*, and that they should simply record what's going on out there. If every English speaker takes it into his head to start saying, "Her and me think going to the mall would be the very goodest thing for she and them," well, then, as the Beatles taught us, let it be.

Standing against the libertines, the civilized believe that grammars and dictionaries should be prescriptive and lay down laws for proper usage. This, and only this, stands between us and the beasts that perish.

Not surprisingly, both sides have a point. Certain grammatical rules *are* arbitrary, but the need to have these arbitrary rules is *not* arbitrary. Someone has rightly said that manners are to be understood as love in trifles. And because spelling, grammatical coherence, and standards for writing are necessary for clarity of communication, clarity in communication is therefore an act of love. A sign of respect in one language may not be a sign of respect in another, but a particular sign of respect is necessary somehow. The American military salutes with the palm down, and the British military salutes with the palm out. Which way it goes is arbitrary, but *that* it goes is not arbitrary. And within each military culture there needs to be agreement and standardization—otherwise the point of coordinated communication is lost. To give up on standards within language is to give up on language itself. To insist that these standards be treated as the law of the Medes and Persians is to make the crucial task of maintaining standards risible.

A writer should know the effect he is having, which means that he should know what the standard usage is and how he is likely to be received if he writes it that way. Within these confines, schoolteachers and editors should feel as prescriptive as they like. The one thing they are not allowed to do is to act like certain rules of subject/verb agreement were delivered to Moses on Mt. Sinai. It is prescriptive, sure, but not *that* prescriptive.

Jonathan Edwards was one of the most educated men of his day, and he wrote some things that wouldn't make it past the lowest tier scrub editor in the seediest publishing firm in Manhattan. To fire off with a "he don't" was for him the work of a moment. And the contraction *ain't* isn't proper anymore, but it used to be okay. It is short for *amn't,* and *amn't I* is a darn sight more proper than *aren't I.* Usage determines this kind of thing, but it is a long stretch from agreeing that usage determines linguistic manners to saying that linguistic manners are unnecessary. That is like pointing out that we use forks, and the Chinese use chopsticks, and that therefore getting food to your mouth must be unnecessary.

Linguistic casuists do a valuable work, and yet they suffer deeply for their pains. Apostrophe abuse in particular is a vexation to them. If I put a sign over our front door saying, "Welcome to the Wilson's," you would be justified in asking yourself, "the Wilson's *what?* Is *house* implied?" In the meantime, the libertines would be pointing out that some languages don't even *have* apostrophes, and so it is apparently not part of the fundamental order of nature. If we can dispense with them, then surely we can move them around if we want. Yes, and if they have been moved for three centuries, you may consider the point made. But in the meantime, you need strict schoolmarms around to whack your knuckles and tell you that the reason your query letters are all getting round-filed is because of that apostrophe in the return address. It would violate a decent editor's conscience to mail anything to "the Smith's," even if doing it with a self-addressed, stamped envelope. The Smith's failed writing career is not stated, merely implied.

TAKEAWAY POINT
Nothing like a good argument to help you sort things out.

RECOMMENDED READING

Jim Quinn, *American Tongue and Cheek* (New York: Penguin, 1980).

John Ivan Simon, *Paradigms Lost* (New York: Penguin, 1980).

Lynne Truss, *Eats, Shoots and Leaves* (New York: Gotham, 2003).

 4

Read etymological histories, histories of idioms and phrases, and dictionaries of word roots. Every word in the English language has countless little dents in it, which contribute to the patina. But don't fall for the etymological fallacy, which assumes that any meaning of a word in its history must be a meaning of the word now. Rather, etymologies should help you with the flavoring, helping you pick a word with traces of oak, licorice, charcoal, or tobacco in it.

Why do "He could not get to sleep, even with sleep medicine" and "He could not get to sleep, *not* even with sleep medicine" mean the same thing? Why does "Don't be surprised if he doesn't get well one of these days" mean that we should not be surprised if he *does* get well? Why do "I couldn't care less" and "I could care less" mean the same thing? Who is in *charge* of this language? Not only that, we park in driveways and drive on parkways.

When you rummage in old etymological dictionaries, you will probably create more of these questions than you can answer, but these are the sorts of questions that are fun to not be able to answer. Why do we pronounce the word *one* as though it began with a *wuh?* And what sound does *ough* make? As somone once noted, "A rough, dough-faced, thoughtful ploughman strode through the streets of Scarborough; after falling into a slough, he coughed and hiccoughed." This should be read by the learned as "A ruff, doe-faced, thawtful plowman strode throo the streets of Scarboruh; after falling into a sloo, he coffed and hiccupped." Quite a language we have here.

The word *belittle* was coined by Thomas Jefferson, and we ought to applaud him for it. Did you know that *dandelion* comes from the French *dent de lion,* tooth of the lion? Does it matter, you ask? Of *course* it matters. *Backing and filling* is not something a backhoe does to that trench in your yard—it was a sailing term. Backing meant letting the sail blow toward the stern, against the mast. Filling was letting the sail fill out naturally, toward the bow.

Sideburns were named after the Civil War general, Ambrose Burnside, who was something of a dandy and sported them. But nobody knows how the *side* and the *burn* got switched.

TAKEAWAY POINT

Whenever you get to know anything, you want to know where it's been.

RECOMMENDED READING

John Ayto, *Dictionary of Word Origins* (New York: Little, Brown, 1990).

N. F. Blake, *A History of the English Language* (New York: New York University Press, 1996).

Wilfred Funk, *Word Origins and Their Romantic Stories* (New York: Grosset & Dunlap, 1950).

T. F. Hoad, *The Concise Oxford Dictionary of English Etymology* (Oxford: Oxford University Press, 1986).

H. L. Mencken, *The American Language* (New York: Alfred Knopf, 1919).

Joseph Shipley, *Dictionary of Word Origins* (New York: Dorset Press, 1945).

5

Read books and manuals that help you gain mastery of your word processing program, whatever that is. You may not become a techno-geek, but you really should be computer-savvy, at least when it comes to using the tools and software that you will use on a daily basis.

Various technologies are simply servants, available to work for you. While some people have always had servants, some of them have always had trouble managing the servants. Just having the servants does not solve your problems—in fact, it can multiply your problems. I estimate that my iPhone is the equivalent of having one hundred thousand servants. The problem is that about ninety thousand of those servants of mine are sitting on their butt all the time. What *can* be done is amazing, and yet the limit on what actually gets done is usually to be found in the person who has to provide the direction and oversight.

The same kind of thing goes for your laptop or desktop. The capacity that a basic computer provides for organizing research, doing research, tracking notes, correcting spelling, formatting pages, keeping track of footnotes, and so on, is quite astounding. If you want to write, then you should want to write with all the available help you can round up. But it is not enough to round up the help: you must read up on the help.

If you use Word, then read Word manuals. If you use Google Books, then study what Google Books can do. If you read a lot, which we have already covered, you should be connected to something like Goodreads.

This is advice that does not come easily to me. I was born in 1953, which means that my natal day was closer to the nineteenth century and the administration of William McKinley, than to the present day and the reign of the Obama. So if I do not take naturally to the digital age, I may be excused. But even though I may be *excused,* I am still trying to write books in the digital age, and this means I am in the market with a bunch of other writers born after 1980 (let us call them "punks"), who were all born knowing how to use anything electronic. So this is not optional. If you find yourself struggling with it overmuch, then get some geezerware.

A carpenter has to think about the hammer sometimes, and not just the house.

Robin Williams, *Your PC is Not a Typewriter* (Berkeley: Peach-pit Press, 1995).

Read books of quotations and anecdotes. Charles Williams once sniffed at encyclopedias as being "slums of the mind," and I would probably be able to find that quote if only it had been included in a book of quotations. As it is, I will have to allude to his point somewhat vaguely. I think that being above those sorts of collections is being overly precious.

Some people collect things, and other people can profit greatly by browsing in those collections. So read collections of Chesterton quotes, Churchill quotes, and Samuel Johnson quotes. Read books of general quotations. Read books of anecdotes. Read books of presidential anecdotes. Read collections of great toasts.

There is no shame in viewing a great picture in a museum. The fact that it has been collected somewhere by somebody does not put it off limits for you.

At the same time, if you read only these collections and never a real book, then what you are doing is making Charles Williams' point for him. What you are doing is creating the illusion of having read widely when you have done nothing of the kind. If someone were to read *Bartlett's Familiar Quotations* only, he would never be at a loss at dinner parties, and he would always be ready with a quip. But this is simply an abuse that should not negate a judicious use of the collector's art. If someone refused to look at a picture of a painting in a coffee table book because he wanted to wait until he could see it in its home gallery, then he is being overly scrupulous.

Willie Sutton was purported to have said that he robbed banks "because that's where the money is." Why read books of quotations? Because that's where some great lines are.

Paul Dickson, *Baseball's Greatest Quotations* (San Franciso: HarperCollins, 2008).

Clifton Fadiman, ed., *The Little, Brown Book of Anecdotes* (Boston: Little, Brown, 1985).

Edmund Fuller, ed., *2500 Anecdotes for All Occasions* (New York: Avenel Books, 1978).

Richard Langworth, *Churchill by Himself* (New York: Public-Affairs, 2008).

Ned Sherrin, *Oxford Dictionary of Humorous Quotations* (Oxford: Oxford University Press, 1995).

7

Read wordcraft books. Wordsmiths love to write, and a lot of them love to write about how they write. Other writers love to read about how accomplished writers write. They buy any book in that genre by the quarter ton, or so I am told, and here's hoping. Their advice ranges from how to ungarble syntax to counsel on the discipline of actually writing. Read books on plot structure, on writing dialogue, on pestering editors, on writing memoirs, on editing your own stuff, and so on.

I try to be reading at least one wordsmithing book all the time. The writers of these worthy volumes will frequently include samples from other writers to illustrate their point. At the time I wrote this book you are reading now, I was in the middle of *The Art of War for Writers*, and here is an example James Bell cited from the hard-boiled tradition that just made me happy.

> The sun that brief December day shone weakly through the west-facing window of Garret Kingsley's office. It made a thin yellow oblong splash on his Persian carpet and gave up.

These advice books by writers are not like the reference books mentioned above, the ones where you have the grammatical transmission taken completely apart and laid out on the workbench in front of you. These are books on the writer's life, on his inspirations, on his tricks and techniques, and so forth.

TAKEAWAY POINT

If you want to learn how to cook, do more than read recipes. Listen to other cooks tell stories from the kitchen. You need recipes and stories about recipes.

RECOMMENDED READING

Leonard Bishop, *Dare to Be a Great Writer* (Cincinnati: Writer's Digest Books, 1988).

Christopher Booker, *The Seven Basic Plots* (New York: Continuum, 2004).

H. L. Mencken, *My Life as Author and Editor* (New York: Knopf, 1992).

Arthur Plotnik, *Spunk & Bite* (New York: Random House, 2005).

CHAPTER OVERVIEW

TAKEAWAY POINTS

Learn basic mechanics, and learn them well. Read dictionaries like they were books, for they are. Follow the arguments among the grammarians, that their battles might do the world some good. Study the genealogies of words. Learn how your words are processed. Browse collections. Listen to how the cooks talk about the kitchen.

RECOMMENDED READING

James Scott Bell, *The Art of War for Writers* (Cincinnati: Writer's Digest Books, 2009).

John Gardner, *The Art of Fiction* (New York: Vintage, 1985).

Blake Snyder, *Save the Cat!* (Studio City: Michael Wiese Productions, 2005).

CHAPTER FOUR

BORN FOR THE CLERIHEW

My fourth bit of advice for aspiring writers was:

> Stretch before your routines. If you want to write Italian sonnets, try to write some short stories. If you want to write a few essays, write a novel, or maybe a novella if you are pressed for time. If you want to write haiku, then limber up with opinion pieces for *The Washington Post.*

As with the others, this point can also be separated into seven things to think about.

This helps to keep content vibrant. If someone specializes in only one form of writing, the chances are good that he will master that structure, and the content he produces to fit within that structure will become pretty predictable. After that has been happening for a while, a school of thought will arise blaming the structure and demand freedom from such limitations and constrictions. But that is like noticing that your tap water smells like sulfur and therefore replacing your table pitcher.

When it comes to this, cross-pollination is good. Hybrids are good. Mutts are good. If, in order to be whatever it is you are writing, the structure has to be there, then the only thing that changes is the content. And when you have been to a number of other places, the content of your conversation is more interesting. Who would you rather listen to: someone who has been around the world three times on a oil freighter, or someone who never came out of his basement—even if he had really sweet bandwidth down there? In this case, the world and the exotic locations are the forms of writing that you need to visit, whether or not you intend to live there.

When you are experimenting with crossing over from one genre to another, the point is to focus on different forms. Because poetry is form intensive, it is a great place to start. If you try your hand at essays instead of your usual articles, you are not limbering up enough. But if you move from essays to sonnets, the challenge of fitting into a different form will be quite striking.

TAKEAWAY POINT

The limitations of form are verbal traction. Get some traction.

RECOMMENDED READING

Clement Wood, *Poets' Handbook* (Garden City: Garden City Publishing Co., 1942).

Lewis Turco, *The New Book of Forms* (Hanover: University Press of New England, 1986).

2

If you are in a position to do so, which usually means that you are young enough, make sure to get a thorough and broad liberal arts education. I am astonished at how many young Christians want to be writers and how few of them want to mess with all the prerequisites, which look suspiciously to them like work.

A good liberal arts education will acquaint you, like it or not, with a broad spectrum of writing genres, and as you are working through them, try your hand at writing your own. It also provides grist for the mill—you know enough to have something to say. If you took a number of average nineteen-year-olds who want to be writers and said, "Great, here's a contract," and then asked them what was on their mind and what they had to say, many of them would have to say that their sole insight is that they want to be writers.

This book is directed at those who want to cultivate the kind of soil in which a writer might grow. This is an admirable thing to do, but once upon a time entire cultures were dedicated to the cultivation of this kind of soil. Now you have to get a do-it-at-home-yourself kit and a grow light.

Think of it this way. Where did C. S. Lewis and J. R. R. Tolkien come from? How did that generation of amazing writers arise? Individual genius is certainly part of the answer, but the foundational answer is cultural and educational. The glory of that civilization was rudely interrupted by the catastrophe of the First World War, but we have more than enough evidence to conclude that civilization is capable of great things.

My point is not that a restored liberal arts education in the Christian tradition will produce alums who are all, head-for-head, fantastic writers. A liberal arts degree is not a vocational degree. It trains future citizens how to live in the world with understanding and express their thoughts ably and well. It trains them to be free men and women. This means that, in such a context, those students who have the native capacity to be great writers can just give themselves to growing. They won't have to busy themselves trying to create their own soil to grow in first.

One of the advantages that a liberal arts education provides the future writer is that it gives the student something called *assignments*. These are books, readings, projects, essays, and so forth that the student would not have undertaken if left to his own devices. But if he is assigned something he would never have picked up on his own, he may well discover that he has a taste and a talent for it.

TAKEAWAY POINT

With all your getting, get wisdom.

RECOMMENDED READING

Douglas Wilson, *The Case for Classical Christian Education* (Wheaton: Crossway, 2003).

3

You may discover that your wordsmithing gift was centered in the wrong spot. You always had some facility with words, and so you thought you needed to write the kind of stuff that followed closely the forms you were taught when you first learned how to write. You are like a duckling out of the egg that bonds with the family dog.

But if you spread out more, you might discover that you were not destined to become master of the English comp essay, but rather that you were born for the clerihew. For those who are interested, a clerihew is a bit of short comic verse, containing a couple of rhymed couplets, mentioning somebody famous. To wit:

Percy Bysshe Shelley
Wrote a poem about jelly.
It was before he drowned
That he wrote "Prometheus Unbound."

Or perhaps—

Mr. Cecil B. de Mille,
Sorely against his will,
Was persuaded to leave Moses
Out of the Wars of the Roses.

And concluding with—

The sad feature
About Nietzsche
Was that the creature
Thought he was a teacher.

Or perhaps you were not born for the clerihew.

When you are trying other forms, try the ones that will keep you humble. Don't just try the ones that can be made to sound humble but involve back-handed pride. If you tell someone that you have attempted to write the story of Plato's account of Atlantis, following the forms of *Paradise Lost,* but that you sometimes think that you are not up to the challenge, then she will think (and it *will* be a she that you told this to) that you are just bragging and walk away disgusted. Or, contrariwise, she will be impressed, and the two of you will deserve each other. No, what I mean by forms that will keep you humble are humble forms. Try writing thirty limericks, and see if you can do it.

TAKEAWAY POINT
Branch out. Experiment. Go to a part of the menu where you have never been before, and order something there.

RECOMMENDED READING
E. Clerihew Bentley, *The First Clerihews* (Oxford: Oxford University Press, 1982).

Trying your hand at different forms helps to fend off flattery. Without this literary discipline, it is terribly easy to want to write screenplays, and because there is a minor industry dedicated to flattering people who want to write screenplays, you are a potential sucker for every writers' workshop pitch that comes down the road. They tell you in these workshops that you should write what you know, but it turns out that all you know are writers' workshops.

People want different kinds of unrealistic things. Some unrealistic desires are flattered by society, and others are not at all. When little boys want to play in the NBA, they will find that the adults have built an impressive system that will enable them to have a run at it. But only one boy in one hundred thousand actually makes it. Playing other sports would help get him out of the realm of institutionalized flattery. It is the same with the keyboard sports, which is why you should really have a go at the Petrarchan sonnet. *Nobody* is gonna flatter you there.

Having urged aspiring writers to try their hand at many different forms of the writer's art, I must now introduce a necessary cautionary note. Competence in one area is not something that transfers automatically to another.

Examples of those who have failed to recognize this crowd instantly into our minds. The fact that Michael Jordan was one of the greatest basketball players ever does not mean he can play professional baseball. The fact that someone can play baseball, a mean second baseman for the Yankees, say, does not make him an expert on the latest superglidefusion razor blades. The fact that dad flips a Saturday morning flapjack in a manner second to none does not mean that he should be allowed to prepare the soufflé for the big dinner. And the fact that a writer has sold a bazillion copies of one kind of writing does not mean that anybody wants to read his other stuff. Expertise in the possum hunter's cookbook genre does not mean that a writer will have the nuanced ear that is needed for haiku.

What might happen is the inadvertent creation of a new genre entirely—as may have happened, who knows, with redneck haiku. Speaking of which, through the magic of Google, we can summon up an example almost instantly:

In early morning mist,
Mama searches Circle K for
Moon Pies and Red Man.

So my advice is that writers should fool around in their workshop with all kinds of writing. They should not expect a huge market for all of it, even if they are hauling in the big bucks in one particular area. If they are not hauling in big bucks for any of their writing, they should consider their forays into alien genres the way a boxer considers his pushups.

But the world is a funny place. Usually this problem arises for writers because they made it big in an area they were pretty good in, and then they want to branch out into more artistically respectable directions—in which they display no talent whatever.

Suppose someone hit the *New York Times* Bestseller List with his *Chevy Malibu Repair for Dummies,* and then he wants to follow it up with his photos of Yosemite captioned with prose poems inspired by the antics of the family cocker spaniel named Cutes (Ansel Adams meets Annie Dillard meets T. S. Eliot). His publisher is a man of little faith. He can afford to humor the big author but is not looking forward to the banter at the next New York publishers' wine and cheese get together. But he needn't worry—his friends there have *their* versions of the same kind of thing, say a teen-aged fantasy writer who thinks he is a cross between the author of *Beowulf* and Tolkien on one of his good days. And who said so to a reporter.

But sometimes the problem goes the other way. Sometimes someone makes the big time in an area where they are not all that good, but in other areas they are quite good.

Take Eugene Peterson. As a capable wordsmith of thoughtful, devotional prose, he is very good. For example, his introduction to *Tell It Slant* exhibits all the consonance you could ask for when considering his words and his subject matter. And though I differ with one of the basic points he was making there, he nevertheless made it very well. The man can write.

It was his 2002 colloquial rendition of the Bible, *The Message*, where Peterson really made it as a writer. But translating the Bible means translating the Psalms, and the Psalms are one of the poetic glories of all human history. Now Peterson's conviction is that "give us this day our daily bread" and "pass the potatoes" come "out of the same language pool."[1] He wants continuity of language whether we are studying the Bible or fishing for rainbow trout.[2]

The misfire result is that in *The Message* Psalms he has taken a collection of Hebrew glories and crammed them full of English clichés—lie through their teeth, within an inch of my life, the end of my rope, only have eyes for you, down on their luck, every bone in my body, sit up and take notice, rule the roost, the bottom has fallen out, free as a bird, kicked around long enough, my life's an open book, at the top of my lungs, nearly did me in, sell me a bill of goods, wide open spaces, stranger in these parts, hard on my heels, from dawn to dusk, skin and bones, turn a deaf ear, eat me alive, all hell breaks loose, raise the roof, wipe the slate clean, miles from nowhere, and, as they say on the teevee, much, much more. If

1. Eugene H. Peterson, *The Message* (Colorado Springs: NavPress, 2002), 2.
2. Ibid, 4.

clichés were candied fruit, walnuts, and raisins, the Book of Psalms in *The Message* would be a three-pound fruitcake.

So let this be a cautionary tale. The fact that you have written spy thrillers that have Tom Clancy's publicist worried does not mean that you should take up the project of translating *The Odyssey* into an extended chain of limericks.

TAKEAWAY POINT

Stretching yourself in various ways, preparing for what you do, does not mean that you have profound expertise in those stretching exercises. A football player stretching before a game is not therefore a gymnast.

RECOMMENDED READING

Judson Jerome, *The Poet's Handbook* (Cincinnati: Writer's Digest Books, 1980).

5

The gift of language is one of the most versatile tools imaginable. Not exploring what it can do exhibits an incurious frame of mind, one not suited to the life of writing. A writer in any form needs to be constantly inviting the reader to see *more,* to open his eyes *wider.* But if the writer only uses two buttons on a remote with 150 buttons, if he uses a Swiss army knife for cutting bits of string, and *only* for cutting bits of string, and if his sense of culinary exploration is limited to brown gravy or no brown gravy, then he is not excited enough about life to be exciting to anyone else when he writes about it.

G. K. Chesterton once said, "There is no such thing as an uninteresting subject; the only thing that can exist is an uninterested person." H. L. Mencken agreed with this, saying, "There are no dull subjects. There are only dull writers." And if you are really interested in a subject, you will be fascinated by it, and when you are fascinated by it, you will be going back to your workbench of words constantly, looking for ways to describe this thing that has your attention. When you do that, you have the reader's attention.

Take a nondescript phrase—like "the gray rock was in the sunlight"—and see how many ways you can recast it. The sunlight shone on the gray rock. The rock was gray and sunlit both. The sunlight just made the rock grayer. The rock was black before the sun rose, but then turned gray. And so on.

If you don't know what something does, try it out. If that doesn't work and everybody laughs, then try it another way. Don't let laziness or fear get in the way.

TAKEAWAY POINT

As long as you live, if you continue to ask this question of language, "What else can it do?" you will always find an answer.

RECOMMENDED READING

Ian Bradley, ed., *The Complete Annotated Gilbert and Sullivan* (Oxford: Oxford University Press, 1996).

Ogden Nash, *Selected Poetry of Ogden Nash* (New York: Black Dog & Leventhal, 1995).

❧ 6 ❧

Allusion is lovely, and experience with other forms brings the ability to use that device pervasively. This in turn sets high expectations for the reader—in that you are expecting him to pick up on it—and this is a way of respecting your readers. And when you respect your readers, they will come to respect you.

Outright quotation can have this effect also, but it is easier for quotation to go wrong and seem pretentious. Allusion is for the reader who picks up on it, and if he does, he is "in on it." If he does not, the whole thing just whistled by his head. He missed the allusion, but nobody cares. This is not the same thing as missing the French that the author just quoted at the reader without translating it. In this latter case, the reader is being excluded from something, and he can see your fence *and* the no trespassing sign. The same goes for Latin.

If you are writing for an educated audience and, to take an example, you use the phrase *mutatis mutandis,* you are not showing off—you are communicating. You are using words to do what words are supposed to do. It reminds me of the time that someone complained to William F. Buckley about all the unusual words that he would employ. His reply was that the words were not unusual to *him.* Words are there for a reason, and foreign phrases can often do the trick that more homey phrases cannot. But if you are blogging about your adventures as a shopping mom, and you write about your purchase of a 48-pack of corn dogs at Costco, and you describe them as *de provenance étrangère,* it had better be a joke. Unusual words or phrases (foreign and domestic) are a barrier to understanding, unless the point is to communicate to the reader that you know something they don't. Then they understand what you are doing *quite* well.

But I just used the phrase "foreign and domestic," which comes from the enlistment oath for the U.S. military. It comes from the place where the recruit is swearing to defend the Constitution against "all enemies, foreign and domestic." To allude to that phrase by means of a snippet from it gets you better mileage. Unusual words or phrases are not called enemies, and still less are they called enemies of the Constitution, but you do get a whiff of enemies into the phrase without having to say it outright. If someone misses it, that's fine. They probably have other important things to think about. But if it is caught, then great. Free fun.

Allusion helps you write for different audiences at the same time, and to do so without insulting half of them. It is like reading *Winnie-the-Pooh* to a collection of children and adults. The children appreciate it on their level, and the adults on theirs. One master of easy allusion was P. G. Wodehouse, who could easily bring in references to aunts coming down like wolves on the fold, and those who picked up Byron enjoyed it more, while those who did not were not all that concerned about it.

TAKEAWAY POINT

Good writing is like a great cathedral. The echoes are lovely.

RECOMMENDED READING

P. G. Wodehouse, *The Code of the Woosters* (New York: Overlook Press, 2000).

❦ 7 ❦

I have long said that good teaching consists in loving the subject you are teaching in the presence of students whom you also love. They have not yet met for some reason, so you are introducing two good friends of yours to one another, and in such a way that your affection for both is apparent to the other. In the case of writers, the students would be your readers, but what would be your subject? The subject really needs to be words, and words wherever you might be able to find them. Lesser loves may then be disciplined and ordered in accordance with this overarching love. Ultimately for Christians, this means that our love begins with the Word. We are people of the Word, and therefore we are people of words. Because we are people of words, we may, later on, be people of essays, poems, blog posts, screenplays, and novels.

Love is not just intensity of feeling. Winston Churchill once complained that a pudding had no theme, and just like a pudding, love needs a theme. It needs to be coherent and directed. In order to be directed, it has to be arranged in the hierarchy correctly. Scullery maid words must not be allowed to think they are the princess, and the princess is not supposed to behave like a wanton. It is a bad deal when servants ride and nobles walk (Eccl. 10:7).

But in egalitarian societies, it is assumed that to arrange things into a hierarchy at all is a way of showing contempt for anything that is relegated to a position of inferiority. But the older way of thinking was capable of delighting in the whole hierarchy. In the world of the egalitarians, inequality of rank means inequality of worth, but this should not be our approach at all. Archangels and roly-poly bugs occupy the same universe. They have different house numbers, but they live on the same street.

Love sanctifies, and in order to sanctify it is not necessary to pretend you are dealing with something else. A lofty description is no more to be preferred than an earthy one, so long as love for the words, the readers, and the subject is present. Those posers who think that grime is more authentic than cleanliness do fail in how they write, but the problem is not the words they use—the problem is that love is not the motive.

TAKEAWAY POINT

Love what you observe, love what you write, and love those who read it.

RECOMMENDED READING

C. S. Lewis, *Preface to Paradise Lost* (Oxford: Oxford University Press, 1942).

CHAPTER OVERVIEW

TAKEAWAY POINTS

Limits liberate. Learning is grist for the mill. Get out a book of poetic forms and walk on the wild side. Do not treat your sketch book rejects as museum-ready. Extend your prose further than you think it can go. Listen for echoes in the cathedral or, to change the image, if your allusions were amped, set the reverb to eleven. Love.

RECOMMENDED READING

John Milton Gregory, *The Seven Laws of Teaching* (Lancaster:
    Veritas Press, 2004).

CHAPTER FIVE

THE MEMOIRS
of Old Walnut Heart

My fifth bit of advice for writers was:

> Be at peace with being lousy for a while. Chesterton once
> said that anything worth doing was worth doing badly.
> He was right. Only an insufferable egoist expects to be
> brilliant first time out.

But let's unpack this a bit.

 1

Concert pianists can do what they do because they practiced scales for years. So most of the music that comes from them over the course of their lives gets thrown away in the practice studio. The quality of what you keep will be directly proportional to how much you are willing to throw away. Drills, scales, and exercises should not be something you consider beneath you.

It makes sense to us to make a big deal out of it if we discovered a new sketch pad that Leonardo DaVinci hid in his basement, but it should also make sense to us that Leonardo did not make a big deal out of it. If we found the commonplace book belonging to the author of *Beowulf*, we would be excited to study it—finding out just why he decided to use *hwaet* in that particular place. But this is because we all know that *Beowulf* is an important poem, as tested by centuries, and somebody could probably get a PhD on *hwaet* placement out of it. We don't know that about our scraps and jottings, and if we save them all just in case, we are likely being delusional.

What you delete from your computer, what you take out of your prose, is as important as what you leave in. It is not a loss. When you take away that unnecessary adjective, the removal adds to the ambience surrounding that noun. When you write a page and delete the whole thing, there is a sense in which it is not deleted. The better writer who remained behind is still there. In this sense the analogy to a musician practicing scales is most apt. The point is not to create so many yards of music. The point is to create a particular kind of musician, one who, when called upon, can do what he is expected to do. Writers who throw their scraps away are leaving a better writer behind, and that was the point, wasn't it?

But in order to throw scraps away, you have to be able to recognize them. You have to think about language, what it can do, what it cannot do, and how a disciplined approach to language is a disciplined approach to being human. The apostle James tells us that a man who can control his tongue can control the rest of his body as well. This goes double for the man who is putting what the tongue does into a more permanent setting.

Nothing worthwhile ever comes without practice. But practice is still just practice.

Walker Percy, *The Message in the Bottle* (New York: Farrar, Straus and Giroux, 1954).

If a striking expression hits you, don't hold back just because you are writing an email to your sister. If you think, "I need to save *that* kind of thing for my memoirs," you are a stingy writer with a heart like a walnut, and you won't have any memoirs to save it for. Who wants to read the *Memoirs of Old Walnut Heart?* Writing ability is a developed and honed skill, and the more you develop and hone it, the more of it you will have. Writing as well as you can in every setting is the way to have reserves to draw on when it comes to writing for publication. Pianists don't have a limited number of C major chords they are allowed to play in the course of their lives. They aren't afraid of running out.

Writing is not a zero sum game, and so you shouldn't be afraid of using up all the colorful adjectives. Extending yourself in *any* situation is the best way to be able to extend yourself in *every* situation.

Zero sum thinking is the result of people thinking that God is parsimonious. A bigger piece of pie here means a smaller piece of pie there. But our world is a world in which pies grow, and those who give are those who receive back again. John Bunyan once said of a man, "some thought him mad/the more he gave, the more he had." A use of language which overflows causes language to overflow still more, thirty, sixty, and a hundredfold.

God blesses giving, so every use of language, down to the lowliest tweet, ought to be thought of as a gift to others. But when we give, we do not run out of what we are giving. If we are giving language that is thought through, language that is edifying, that is calculated to bless the other, then what on earth makes us think that God would let us run out?

Writers do not live in isolation or write in a bubble. Their craft will reflect the kind of world they believe themselves to be in. The recommended reading for this section is (perhaps surprisingly) two books on economics, because money reveals, more quickly than anything, what kind of world you think you are living in. There are two basic approaches to life—one in which the world is a world of scarcity, given to us by the skinflint god, and the other in which the world is a world of endless possibilities, bestowed on us by a loving Father. Guess which world is more conducive to works of real and lasting imagination. You become like what you worship— and a writer's world, over which he is the subcreating "deity," is a world that will reflect *him*.

TAKEAWAY POINT

Good writing grows and multiplies, like the loaves and the fishes. And pie.

RECOMMENDED READING

Jay Richards, *Money, Greed, and God* (San Francisco: Harper-One, 2010).

John Schneider, *The Good of Affluence* (Grand Rapids: W. B. Eerdmans, 2002).

Make sure you don't have a faulty and deterministic view of talent. The older clunkity-clunkity view of genetics was sadly simplistic, holding that your genius, if you had any, had been packed into your genetic suitcase, and if it had not been, you were wasting your time trying to unpack it. Now your genetic package certainly has *something* to do with what you will be able to do, but your range of opportunities does not come to you fully assembled. Your genetic givens interact with your situation, and what you do with what you're given will help determine what you are able to do. While it remains true that you can't put in what God left out, it is also true that God put a whole lot more into most of us than we are currently using.

Older materialistic approaches to science wanted everything to be deterministic and predictable, and so we have been told, in countless ways, that people are "hardwired" for certain things, that they are "programmed" to function in this way or that. Like all effective lies, this contains an element of truth. Each person reading this is either male or female, and the reasons for this are genetic. Each person reading this is doing so with eyes that are a particular color, and not another color, and the reasons for this are genetic. But facile thinking about genetics has resulted in people becoming fatalistic about their entire lives, thinking that their choices, discipline, behavior, etc. cannot really affect their ability to perform certain tasks . . . like writing. This is false.

Our genetic make-up interacts with our environment, in just the way that God designed, so that we *grow*. We don't just "unfold." We are not just privileged to create certain artifacts, like whatever story we are writing. We are also privileged to cooperate with God's Spirit in creating the person *we* are becoming. We are, in part, writers of our own story. The exhaustive sovereignty of God over all things, including every aspect of the future, is undeniable. But it makes no sense to ask what percentage of this scene in the play was "Shakespeare" and what percentage was "Hamlet." Every option that adds up to 100 percent is incoherent. The scene is 100 percent Shakespeare and 100 percent Hamlet. So the sovereignty of God extends over an interactive process, one in which the genetic you is choosing, and another you is becoming.

We need to think about this like adults. Someone who has no fingers due to a genetic birth defect is not going to be able to "choose" to become a concert pianist. But the basic package that most of us have includes the ability to do far more than we usually assume we can do. This includes a capacity for writing. Education matters, experience matters, practice matters.

TAKEAWAY POINT

Do what you would love to be able to do someday.

RECOMMENDED READING

Jonathan Edwards, *The Freedom of the Will* (New Haven: Yale University Press, 2009).

David Shenk, *The Genius in All of Us* (New York: Doubleday, 2010).

❧ 4 ❧

If you are good with practice runs, if you are okay with not being as good as you are going to be, if you see the need for playing in the minors, then it should follow that you are emotionally prepared for negative feedback. If you enter your first pie in the county fair while knowing it will not get the blue ribbon, then you should also be eager and ready for your friends to tell you *why* it didn't win the blue ribbon. What is true of your life overall should also be true of your writing life. Criticism should be received as a kindness (Ps. 141:5).

Writers are known for their egos. I just now googled (is that a great verb or what?) the phrase *writer's ego* and garnered almost eight million hits. There is a delicate balance here. You do have to have a thick skin. But this does not mean that you are deaf to all appeals. You have to have that rare combination of thick skin and a tender heart. Most writers get it backwards and have a tender skin and a thick heart. This means that criticism gets a spectacular reaction but no substantive changes. The writer and his friends have the addition of a little more drama for their lives, which they probably didn't need, but nothing gets accomplished. Rather, when someone offers criticism, there should be very little drama and an eager and substantive desire to learn from the criticisms.

Every critic, however ill-informed, represents a point of view which is likely not limited to just him. Others like him will pick up your book in the bookstore and put it down again. Or they will read three chapters of it and write a scathing review on Amazon. Taking note of the criticisms is not necessarily the same thing as agreeing with them. A writer is talking to a large number of people, and it is necessary to anticipate the ways in which they might not understand you. C. S. Lewis once said this about readers: "I sometimes think that writing is like driving sheep down a road. If there is any gate open to the left or the right the reader will most certainly go into it." Assume for a moment that this is what your critic has done. That is no reason to refuse to close the gate you left open. Sometimes you will disagree with your critic, but you can always gain from him. This includes published critics, who are sometimes able to make a living from being ignorant. So a published critic went through an open gate . . . that is still no reason to keep the gate open.

Don't overreact and don't underreact. Lewis said of J. R. R. Tolkien that his reaction to criticism was one of two responses—he would either ignore the criticism completely, or he would tear the whole thing up and start over. There is a middle way.

TAKEAWAY POINT

Critics, whether right or wrong, well-meaning or malicious, should be listened to with care.

RECOMMENDED READING

Deborah Tannen, *I Only Say This Because I Love You* (New York: Ballantine Books, 2002).

 5

Speaking of criticism, your enemies will sometimes be more accurate, more perceptive, and more to the point than your mom. Be willing to learn from anyone, regardless of their evil motives for pointing out your deficiencies. The "misunderstood" writer is a stock character, and so don't be that stock character. Assume that every critic, even one with a black cape and handlebar mustache, has something you can learn from. This point especially needs to be remembered when you start getting published, or are at least public enough to garner attention. Once you start getting reviewed, negative reviews should not be treated by you as simply revelatory of the blackened state of the reviewer's soul.

The previous point was that an enemy might show you ways in which you are being misunderstood. That is valuable for writers who want to head off misunderstandings. But this point is that your enemies will sometimes *understand* what you wrote. Your adoring sister didn't take it that way, because she was filling in the deficiencies in what you wrote from numerous childhood conversations that the general reading public doesn't have access to. And with regard to the public record of what you actually wrote, your adversary has you dead to rights.

If it is not what you meant, but is still what you *said,* then take the opportunity to fix it at the first opportunity and to acknowledge it before that. If you said what you meant, but it turns out that you were wrong, then the same thing applies. Acknowledge it and fix it. Credit your adversary in the footnote. Do this whether or not your adversary is the kind of person who will acknowledge that you have done so. Right is right and outranks both of you.

TAKEAWAY POINT

The animus of others can be a useful magnifying glass to help you find things in your writing that need correction.

René Girard, *The Girard Reader* (New York: Crossroad Herder, 1996).

Openness to criticism is not the same thing as that faux-humility that prepares to inflict itself on everybody with absolutely no reason to do so. We all know the type. Someone gets up to sing for the church dinner and spreads out a safety net for himself before singing one note. "I am sorry about this . . . haven't had any time to practice this week . . . just getting over a cold . . . was only just asked to do this at the last minute." When this goes on for a bit, the sentiment of the audience soon becomes, "Then why didn't you say *no?*"

My father-in-law actually lists this one among his pet peeves. One time, many years ago, during his career as an Air Force pilot, he was attending at a banquet at which a junior officer got up to address a room full of brass. He began his talk with the disclaimer, "You know, there are a whole lot of people who know a whole lot more about this subject than I do," and my father-in-law slumped. But then the young man continued, "but I don't see any of them here." My father-in-law perked right up and was prepared to listen to someone who was clearly ready to be there.

Openness to criticism is not the same thing as apologizing for breathing. If you shouldn't be there, don't be there. If you shouldn't have written it, then delete the file. Nobody will care. But if you *should* be there, if God has called you to the writing life, then put it out there and offer no apologies for having done so. Then, don't be defensive when you get the feedback. Don't criticize it yourself beforehand, but when the criticism comes afterwards, listen. Take notes.

If, when you set out to write, the foremost question is, "Who do I think I am?" then you are getting off on the wrong foot. Or there is a variant of this, which is, "What if *they* are wondering, 'Who does he think he is?'" This approach takes the view that your writing is a litter on which the servants carry your ego about. But it is the other way. Your ego, such as it is, bears the weight of your writing. You carry it—it doesn't carry you. The point of writing is that you have something to *say*. It is not so that your precious ego will have said something. In order to write effectively, you have to assume the station of someone who is called to write.

TAKEAWAY POINT

Do not think of yourself more highly than you ought. But don't undershoot either.

RECOMMENDED READING

Dave Harvey, *Rescuing Ambition* (Wheaton: Crossway, 2010).

7

Remember that relative competence cannot be universal, and that this applies to your critics, reviewers, editors, and publishing houses as much as to you. There will always be a bell curve spread, but do not make the mistake of overvaluing what the bell curve actually tells you. The bell curve explains *relative* placement. The next time you make a medical appointment, it may be helpful to recall that exactly one half of all American doctors graduated in the lower half of their class.

Whatever the industry standard is, half of the publishing houses are going to be in the lower half of it. This doesn't make them bad, but it *does* mean that 90 percent of them will not be above average.

If you are going to be a writer, you should want to be a writer who excels. It also means you should want an agent who excels, an editor who excels, a publicist who excels, and a publishing house that excels. Happy the man who gets all of them to line up, which is, given the nature of the case, sort of like having a glorious comet appear on your fiftieth birthday, promising you another fifty fruitful years.

A writer should have some working idea of what these others in the publishing business are for. He doesn't have to be an agent, but he should know what an overtaxed agent is supposed to do—besides not returning phone calls. He should not be afraid to have opinions about what publishing houses do in making their decisions, and then he should weigh those decisions when making *his* decisions about what houses to go with.

There are many examples, but here is one. It is a current industry practice to project sales of any proposed title, a practice that can be standardized and bureaucratized, just like financial and political and global warming analysts do. And like these three examples, the predictions will almost universally be wildly off. Alfred Knopf once asked, "Why can't we publish only best sellers?" Our lives are a mist, and we cannot predict the future (Jas. 4:14). We can, however, use computer modeling to conceal our helplessness. We can publish enough books such that the random successes will carry the others, and we can predict wildly erroneous sales figures for all of them so that we feel useful in the meantime.

So a writer should be realistic and, to the extent possible, he should want to work with realistic people.

TAKEAWAY POINT

In your little career kayak, ride the white water of creativity without smashing into the jagged rocks of incompetence.

RECOMMENDED READING

Michelle Howry, ed., *Agents, Editors, and You* (Cincinnati: Writer's Digest Books, 2002).

Nassim Taleb, *The Black Swan* (New York: Random House, 2007).

CHAPTER OVERVIEW

TAKEAWAY POINTS

Give yourself to practice, knowing what it is. Expect your abilities to grow and develop. Do what you cannot do yet. Critics are full of information, even malicious critics. Don't be conceited, and don't fight conceit with faux-humility. Understand that half the published world is below average.

RECOMMENDED READING

René Girard, *I See Satan Fall Like Lightning* (Maryknoll: Orbis, 2001).

CHAPTER SIX

ANCIENT ROMAN TODDLERS

Back in my callow youth, just a few chapters ago, when I set out seven basic pointers for writers, the sixth one was

> Learn other languages, preferably languages that are upstream from ours. This would include Greek, Latin, and Anglo-Saxon. The brain is not a shoebox that "gets full," but is rather a muscle that expands its capacity with increased use. The more you know, the more you *can* know. The more you can do with words, the more you can *do*. As it turns out.

And so here are some additional thoughts on that.

 1

God approves of translation, and by this I am referring to the process of translation. Obviously, some translations are better than others, and some are atrocious. But God approves of the attempt. The work itself is a good work. Good things come out of the process of moving house from one set of linguistic thought forms to another. Jesus taught His disciples in Aramaic, but God wanted the original that we have received to be a Greek translation of that teaching. The canonical text of the Lord's teaching is a *translation* and not what originally came from the Lord's mouth. This means that God approves of translations. We ought not to accept, therefore, the idea that something is always lost in translation. Sometimes, sure. But there are also many times when something is *gained* in translation.

For you as a writer, translating something you have written into another language can be a great way of sharpening your writing. This applies even if the translations you undertake are, like mine have been, pretty rudimentary. This need not be an occasion for putting on airs—I am just saying that it might benefit you to take one of your *the cat sat on the mat* sentences and put it into Hebrew.

TAKEAWAY POINT

A man with a watch knows what time it is. A man with two watches is not quite sure. A man with seven watches has the best idea.

RECOMMENDED READING

Alexander Humez and Nicholas Humez, *Latin for People* (Boston: Little, Brown, 1976).

✶ 2 ✦

Learning languages is a very good way to learn *your* language, even if you don't go on to speak fluently whatever language it was you thought you were learning. Languages that you learned and then forgot are still good for you. I speak here as the experienced one—during the course of my life, I have been subjected to a year of French, two years of Spanish, two-plus years of Greek, two-plus years of Latin, a year of Anglo-Saxon, and now some Hebrew. This has not turned me into a cosmopolitan, but it *has* made my English more colorful, which is a *trez beans* kind of thing.

Learn a foreign language. If you already did, but learned it like everybody learns Spanish in high school and then forgot it, pick it up again. Or learn a different one, for real this time. If you have a choice, I would recommend a language that is upstream (with regard to vocabulary) from modern English, which would limit your choices to Greek, Latin, and Anglo-Saxon. Diehards can have a go at Indo-European, which nobody knows, but there are some word root dictionaries that can help you gesture helplessly in that direction.

Greek and Latin open up the formations of many modern English words. *Laudare,* "to praise," for example, gets you laud, applaud, laudatory, and so on. And Anglo-Saxon is a different kind of blast. *Attercop* is Anglo-Saxon for spider, which I thought told us something fun about Bilbo, and *rimcraft* is arithmetic, and of course *merscmealuwe* means marshmallow.

TAKEAWAY POINT

Learn to love the rumble bumble of words.

Henry Beard, *Latin for All Occasions* (New York: Villard Books, 1990).

Eugene Ehrlich, *Amo, Amas, Amat and More* (New York: Harper & Row, 1985).

Eugene Ehrlich, *Les Bons Mots* (New York: Owl Books, 1997).

Eugene Ehrlich, *Veni, Vidi, Vici* (New York: HarperCollins, 1995).

Jennifer Speake, *The Oxford Dictionary of Foreign Words and Phrases* (Oxford: Oxford University Press, 1997).

Learning different languages helps a writer get a firm grasp of grammar in the abstract. All languages need to *do* certain things—which means they need verbs. All languages are describing what's out there in the world, which gives us the nouns, and so on. And then the nouns do things. Either John is hitting the ball, or the ball is hitting John, and we need various devices to determine what kind of incident this actually is. My own government school education was pretty inadequate when it came to English grammar, and it wasn't until I learned about case endings in other languages that certain practices in English started to make sense to me.

Different languages place their adjectives differently, but all languages *have* adjectives. It has become customary in recent years to speak disparagingly of abstract thinking (and there are times when it *should* be disparaged), but our ability for abstraction is an essential part of being human.

The possibility of translation shows us this. There must be something called "meaning" that is independent of the linguistic body that houses it. Without this abstract meaning, we could not get from one language to another—the essential meaning, not having a space suit, would die out there in between the two spaceships of language. In English we can say "A man loves a woman." In Latin that would be *Vir feminam amat*. In order to be able to effect this transfer, there has to be an abstract carrier of $m > w$. Call it an abstract space suit if you like, but the meaning survives.

Learning different languages enables a writer to understand what this abstract language must be like.

TAKEAWAY POINT

Try to understand what a grammar for an abstract language might do.

RECOMMENDED READING

Douglas Wilson, *The Paideia of God* (Moscow: Canon Press, 1999).

 4

At the same time, be judicious and thoughtful in what you transfer from one language to another. All languages require some means for identifying the direct object, but not all languages have the same skeletal structure in every respect. In the eighteenth century, during the ascendancy of the English dictionary makers and grammarians, it was foolishly thought that Latin was superior to English, and that things which *couldn't* be done in Latin, like ending sentences with prepositions, *shouldn't* be done in English. This is where we get the absurd rule that one must never, ever, end a sentence with a preposition. As Winston Churchill put it, "That's the sort of nonsense up with which we shall not put." There are times, even in English, when to do so is not euphonic—"Where you be *at?*"—but English has the kind of skeletal structure that allows for a judicious little preposition right there at the end of the sentence.

Another dumb thing was that it was thought that because Latin infinitives, being one word, could not be divided with an adverb, this meant English infinitives should not be so divided. But that followeth no way. *Laudare* cannot be a split infinitive, but *to praise* most certainly can be, and if your sentence scans better with *to loudly praise,* then let 'er rip. All this said, fussy grammarians need friends too, and so you may seek out and encourage them. Drop them a little note, telling them that they are your very favorite fussy grammarian, out with whom you like to hang. And if anybody winced there at my use of a plural pronoun for an indefinite singular, then may I suggest counseling?

It seems odd to say that this kind of thing flows from one's view of history, but back in the day when our first grammars and dictionaries were being written, it was assumed that Latin was superior to English, Greek to Latin, and so on, right on back to the Garden of Eden. Linguistic history was therefore a history of decline. To make progress in language study was therefore to go *back*.

But the idea of decline is just that, an *idea*. What if the world is progressing and improving? What does that do to your views of what is happening to language? Chinese should be respected and honored as an ancient tongue, but it must also be admitted that keyboards with five thousand keys are cumbersome.

There is a hidden assumption held by most of those who care about effective communication. That hidden assumption is that things used to be better than they are now. Those who are carefree about what language might be doing out there on the street are those who are not too particular about where the comma goes. And those who do care where the comma goes find it convenient to postulate a golden age back when schoolmarms really knew how to whack the knuckles, unlike today. But suppose for a moment that changes might bring improvements, and seriously consider that as a possibility. Not all openness to change is linguistic antinomianism.

TAKEAWAY POINT

In comparing languages, make sure you distinguish principles and methods.

RECOMMENDED READING

Arthur Herman, *The Idea of Decline in Western History* (New York: Free Press, 2007).
Douglas Wilson, *Heaven Misplaced* (Moscow: Canon Press, 2008).

5

All this is being recommended as an aid to English. But if you have an opportunity to become fully *fluent* in another language, take it. Just don't confuse good grades in a college language class with fluency. When it is working well, a couple years of study will usually get you *fluidity* within a very limited range. Two years of Latin study, with good grades and everything, does not mean that you "know Latin." The average

English speaker has a working vocabulary of about twelve thousand words. The average honors graduate of two years of Latin study knows about two thousand words. We can cede him some extra points because he will be able to make sense out of various cognate words. So do not confuse fluidity in a very limited classroom environment with fluency in the street. You are not the ultimate urbane sophisticate for having gotten two notches above the levels of ancient Roman toddlers.

Now this is not intended as a slam, and in some respects I grant that it doesn't fit the bill exactly. A twenty-year-old with a limited vocabulary is not the same thing as a two-year-old with the same vocabulary. The twenty-year-old, for example, is fluent in another language, and this means that he *knows* something about what he does not know. In a discussion I had with a colleague about this, he offered the better example of an Indian student with school English. But such a student who arrives here is not just missing idiom and accent. He is also missing about 80 percent of the vocabulary he is going to wind up using. Back in India, he is an English speaker. Here, he simply has a good start.

Language students, before they head upriver to live among the natives, are simply getting a jump on a good start. A good Latin student can speak literary Latin with very few mistakes, true enough. But he is doing so with a vocabulary range provided by the limited universe of the textbook. This is what I am calling fluid—not fluent. The stage is *set* for fluency, if he goes on—which is what this is encouraging folks to do.

I have been a strong advocate of restoring the study of ancient languages to our schools, and many classical and Christian schools are pursuing this in their curricula, and all to the better. We need to be grateful for this, but at the same time not think we have gotten farther than we have gotten. I have been a college Latin student, one who got good grades for two years of it, and I *know* how little I knew. I have studied French, Spanish, Greek, Latin, Anglo-Saxon, and now Hebrew. I know how small those cages are, because I have done hard time locked up in a bunch of them. And I know how spacious English is. I know the comparative sizes of the former to the latter.

In the land of the blind, the one-eyed man is king. In the land of the illiterate, the semi-literate is the scribe. In a society that has abandoned the serious study of the classical languages, it doesn't take much to surpass everybody else. So the goal here needs to be genuine fluency in another language and, for a writer, preferably one of the languages upstream from modern English—Latin, Greek, or Anglo-Saxon.

TAKEAWAY POINT

Classroom knowledge is good, but if you have the opportunity to go further, seize it.

RECOMMENDED READING

Victor David Hanson and John Heath, *Who Killed Homer?* (New York: Encounter, 2001).

 6

One key to good writing is to have a wide-ranging vocabulary. I have recommended collecting dictionaries of unusual words, but this can be on the artificial side. An organic way to grow your vocabulary is by means of learning the languages that dumped a lot of their vocabulary into our current usage. This means Latin, which accounts for about 50 percent of our current vocabulary, Greek which is responsible for about 30 percent, and Anglo-Saxon, which feeds the rest. *Dico* means *I speak* or *say* in Latin, and we get dictate, dictator, benediction, diction, and so on. *Eikon* is Greek for *image,* and we get the icons on your desktop, icons in front of churches (which we shouldn't have), and iconoclasts, which is more like it. And when you study Anglo-Saxon, you discover that the riders of Rohan were simply Vikings who had lost all their boats.

When you pick up new vocabulary in the course of language acquisition, you tend to *handle* it better than if you simply picked up an unusual word from a collection of unusual words. You usually have to do translation exercises and drills, and this helps keep the word in that part of your brain that remembers things.

Words are the bricks with which you build. Buy the bricks before starting on the wall.

RECOMMENDED READING
Hans Ørberg, *Lingua Latina* (Newburyport: Focus Publishing, 2006).

7

This certainly involves extra work, but it doesn't take up any extra room. The brain is more like a muscle and less like a storage area. If you really want to be a writer, you should want to write a lot. If you want to write a lot, then you need to be in training. You are preparing to run marathons, not emptying a suitcase. Learning new languages, acquiring new vocabulary, keeping yourself in various forms of constant logocentric discipline is one of the best things you can do. And language acquisition is nothing if not logocentric discipline.

TAKEAWAY POINT
God created part of your brain for the use of words. Exercise it.

RECOMMENDED READING
John McWhorter, *Our Magnificent Bastard Tongue* (New York: Gotham Books, 2008).

CHAPTER OVERVIEW

TAKEAWAY POINTS
The more you know about language, the more flexible you are. But this is not the knowledge of the pedant: learn to love words the way pirates love gold. Well, maybe not quite like that. Learn the abstract and spiritual side of language. Distinguish principles and methods. Classroom knowledge is just the first step. Words are bricks, not buildings. Discipline your mind in the love of words.

RECOMMENDED READING
Lawrence Vance, *Archaic Words and the Authorized Version* (Pensacola: Vance Publications, 1996).

CHAPTER SEVEN

UNCOMMON COMMONPLACES

My last bit of advice on the *wordriht* life was:

> Keep a commonplace book. Write down any notable phrases that occur to you or that you come across. If it is one that you have found in another writer, and it is striking, then quote it, as the fellow said, or modify it to make it yours. If Chandler said that a guy had a cleft chin you could hide a marble in, that should come in useful sometime. If Wodehouse said somebody had an accent you could turn handsprings on, then he might have been talking about Jennifer Nettles of Sugarland. Tinker with stuff. Get your fingerprints on it.

 1

The writer's life is a scavenger's life. A little here and a little there, diligently pursued, and pretty soon you have a lot of material. When you come across a striking phrase (and if you are reading properly this will happen a *lot*), make a note of it. Use it yourself in conversation. If there is no opportunity to use it in conversation, or in something you are writing, then you need not worry because you wrote it down in your commonplace book. You can always use it later.

As a rare concession to Stuff White People Like, I recommend getting the smaller pocket-sized moleskine notebook (moleskine.com). They are easy to keep, easy to find, and easy to write in. You are not compiling anything in logical order but are rather just putting them down in the order you come across them. Even if you don't wind up using most of what you record, it is still a helpful mental exercise to write down striking phrases that you find in other writers.

P. G. Wodehouse wrote nearly ninety books, and I am currently about halfway through them. I have read him assiduously over the years, but about five years ago I decided to read through the whole corpus. Overlook Press is issuing some fine hardback editions, and so I always have one Wodehouse handy. When I am about halfway through that one, I order the next one. As I read, I highlight words or phrases that strike me. When I am done with the book, I sit down with it and my commonplace book and jot down anything that I think I might find to be useful later on. Not surprisingly, much of my commonplace book comes from Wodehouse—here are sample entries from where I have it opened now: "flickered at the edges," "mass of inert porridge," "dusty high road," "burning words of love into her alabaster ear," "come off the boil a bit," "cut and thrust," and "badly dressed leper." There is a lot to work with there.

Write notes to yourself, and keep them where you can find them.

RECOMMENDED READING
P. G. Wodehouse, *Carry On, Jeeves* (Woodstock: Overlook Press, 2003).

2

It is dishonest to take the wit and wisdom of others and represent it as your own. That is form of theft. But it is *not* dishonest to have your expressions reflect the fact that you have spent a great deal of time with witty, wise people. At the same time, be scrupulously honest in your usage. If you are quoting Churchill or Chesterton (and why wouldn't you?), then say, "As Chesterton put it . . ." If the expression is distinctive, but you don't want to look like you live in Footnoteville, write, "As the fellow said . . ." Sometimes you cite by name, and other times you just point away from yourself. You would not say, "As somebody once said, 'When in the course of human events . . .'" You *could* say, "She had just enough brains, as the fellow said, to make a jaybird fly crooked." This last one is from Wodehouse, and he is also well known enough to cite, if you feel like it. But one of the reasons why I often generalize when using Wodehouse is that he was obviously a scavenger of American slang from the thirties. When I use that kind of expression, I am just keeping the ball in play.

Some of what you read is another author handling the common currency. If he does this in a way that makes it *distinctively* his, then at a minimum you should not take credit for it (except what small credit comes your way for having known about it), and you perhaps may want to cite him in full.

This lets everybody know that you are not taking credit for the *bon mot* yourself. But if you are a mere copyist, instead of being an intelligent and engaged imitator, then, whenever you let fly, it will just be a *bon not*.

Thou shalt not steal.

P. G. Wodehouse, *Right Ho, Jeeves* (Woodstock: Overlook Press, 2000).

These concerns have led to the saying that if you steal from one person, it's plagiarism, but if you steal from many, it's research. This is a bit glib (leaving out the issue of intent), but there is still a point to be taken there. All the books out there, all the articles, are simply an enormous conversation. To quote others is to demonstrate that you are listening. If you have modified the phrase, you have made it your own, which you have the authority to do. If you did not modify it, or did not modify it significantly, then you should in some way acknowledge it as the contribution of another person in the conversation. If the phrase is striking, but you picked it up from general conservation and have no idea who originated it, then general attribution is indefinite, but appropriate. If you jump into a hacky sack game, you don't always have to ask who manufactured the hacky sack itself. Just kick it.

Words being what they are, this requires judgment calls of a fairly subjective nature. Just make sure they are honest judgment calls. Suppose I come across the phrase "silly young juggins" in a book (which, in fact, I have). Suppose I want to use it. What do I do? I don't have to give attribution for the word *juggins* by itself, for this author did not coin that word. *Silly juggins* doesn't really scan well. *Young juggins* is better, but in a case like this I would probably modify it significantly. *Silly young juggins* is too insignificant to quote, and yet too distinctive to just pick up and use. In this case, I would imitate and come up with something like *solemn little juggins*. See? Everybody's happy.

You are managing an antique shop, but it should be an honest antique shop.

RECOMMENDED READING
P. G. Wodehouse, *Lord Emsworth and Others* (Woodstock: Overlook Press, 2002).

4

Having a commonplace book does not mean that you will use everything in your commonplace book. If you are like me you will probably use about 20 percent of what you have written down. The previous points in this section have had to do with the 20 percent; the point I'm addressing now has to do with the usefulness of the 80 that never goes anywhere.

Having a collection of memorable quotations and metaphors helps your mind function in those grooves. If you traffic in metaphors, collecting them, enjoying them, you run a much better chance of contributing your own in due time. He who walks with the wise will be wise, Scripture saith, and he who walks with the witty will eventually start to pop off himself.

You are shaping a particular turn of mind.

TAKEAWAY POINT
Collections do not leave the collector unaffected. The art of collecting results in a certain turn of mind.

RECOMMENDED READING
P. G. Wodehouse, *Galahad at Blandings* (Woodstock: Overlook Press, 2009).

5

Don't be afraid to learn from your own typos. For example, my joke earlier in chapter seven (*bon not*), was originally a typo. If you can't use it immediately, put your own typos into your commonplace book. Reserve a special place for them, a place of honor. If your commonplace entries are dragging a little, type faster and see what you can come up with.

TAKEAWAY POINT
There are no accidents. You can learn from anything.

RECOMMENDED READING
P. G. Wodehouse, *Uncle Dynamite* (Woodstock: Overlook Press, 2006).

✵ 6 ♣

Don't shy away from any striking phrase, even if it has been promoted into a cliché. One of the elements of writing that is most delightful to the engaged reader is the element of surprise. And one of the ways to surprise the reader is to set up an expectation that you then veer away from at the last minute. A stitch in time saves the penny earned. Or something like that.

There is a joke about the lady who didn't like reading Shakespeare because it was "full of clichés." Clichés became what they did because they were originally phrases that worked. People saw that they worked, picked them up, and worked them to death. If one's good, two's better. After a while this gets tired, so many of the clichés go into semi-retirement. From that place you can cull through them and see if any are ready to come back, or if others can be modified to provide a twist on the familiar. This is what was done once, for example, when academics were once described as the "bland leading the bland."

TAKEAWAY POINT

You do not create ex nihilo. You rearrange and recombine. You are the same old flour and eggs in search of a new recipe.

RECOMMENDED READING

P. G. Wodehouse, *Blandings Castle* (Woodstock: Overlook Press, 2002).

❋ 7 ❋

When you collect phrases, points, metaphors, and what-not in this way, you are, as Cicero used to put it, loaded for bear. By linking "loaded for bear" with Cicero, incidentally, I am providing another example of the previous point. And here is another example of the same kind of change-up pitch from Wodehouse. This comes from *A Pelican at Blandings*:

> She was thinking of Alaric, Duke of Dunstable, and a stylist like Gustave Flaubert, with his flair for the *mot juste*, would have described her as being as mad as a wet hen.[1]

This last point is an important part of what the ancient rhetoricians called copiousness. One time G. K. Chesterton, the rolypologist, was patted on the stomach by his adversary, George Bernard Shaw, a beanpole of an infidel, and was asked what they were going to name the baby. Chesterton replied immediately that if it was a boy, John, if a girl, then Mary. But if it turned out to only be gas, they were going to name it George Bernard Shaw. Now we hear that story and marvel at his amazing quickness. And it may well have been such, a prodigy of the moment. But I also wouldn't be a bit surprised to find out that Chesterton had *that* particular pistol loaded beforehand and concealed on his person. When copiousness is active, you not only know how to respond in the moment, but you can also see the possibility of such moments coming and prepare for them beforehand.

1. P. G. Wodehouse, *A Pelican at Blandings* (London: Herbert Jenkins, 1969), 109.

Your commonplace book is just a staging area. You are collecting things in order *use* them, to get them into your mind and heart and thence into your writing. Someone once commented on how information can get from a professor's lecture notes and into a student's notebook, without passing through the mind of either. You don't want that kind of thing. Remember Charles Williams' comment cited earlier about encyclopedias being the slums of the mind. This is where he has a good point. It is a fair slam when such things are used in a way that enables information to circulate without passing through your mind. You don't want to come off like someone who gets his wisdom from collections of inspiring quotes found in his dentist's waiting room. As Lao Tzu once put it . . .

TAKEAWAY POINT

When you find a good one, look for multiple places to use it. You should be like a ten-year-old boy with a slingshot who just found a really round rock.

RECOMMENDED READING

P. G. Wodehouse, *Uncle Fred in the Springtime* (Woodstock: Overlook Press, 2004).

CHAPTER OVERVIEW

TAKEAWAY POINTS

You are a writer. Don't just write for others, write to yourself. In all your gathering, do not steal. You are handling the goods of others, so do so honestly. As you collect things, the act of collecting affects you and is not limited to possession of whatever it was you collected. Be willing to learn from anything whatever. Think of words as ingredients that can be combined in endless recipes. When you find something really worthwhile, look for multiple places to use it.

RECOMMENDED READING

P. G. Wodehouse, *The Clicking of Cuthbert* (Woodstock: Overlook Press, 2002).

This has been a book of advice for writers, and so it has been full of "do this, not that," and "avoid this other thing." I have been admittedly prescriptive, while at the same time I have tried to lean against too much prescription or prescription that could be administered in a wrong-headed and absolutist way.

The prescriptive element legitimately comes in when the language of educated people is described for someone who wants to be equipped to join the ranks of such people. Aspiring writers want to get published, and they naturally want to learn "the rules" for getting published. But the world is not like that. There are principles, sure, but these principles are not "rules" in the common sense of that word. So, when we do not hedge the practice of prescription with constant warnings and qualifications, prescriptive rules come to be set down as though they existed in their own authority, in their own realm. The rules of grammar come to be reified. The rules of particular schools of stylistic thought are made into artificial absolutes and suspended from the skyhook that creative writing workshops have bolted in place above their respective universities. Ambrose Bierce observed the problem:

God said: "Let Spirit perish into Form."
    And lexicographers arose, a swarm!
Thought fled and left her clothing, which they took,
    And catalogued each garment in a book.

The world of actual language use is so complex and so messy that only God understands the English language. Only God is fluent.

In literature and art, the Romantic movement was a revolt against neo-Classicism of the late seventeenth and eighteenth centuries. The neo-Classical approach was precise, meticulous, rationalistic, and fussy. The neo-Classicists were addicted to living by rule. When we cite Wordsworth—"we murder to dissect"—we are putting forward the sentiments of a Romantic over against this tidy approach. Quit the head work, and try the gut.

Now when Christians object to revolutions, this is not to be taken as disapproval of everything the revolutionaries say and do. Whenever two unbelievers quarrel, they may both say some very insightful things about the unsightly habits of the other. So the Romantics had a point in their quarrel with the neo-Classicists, just as the neo-Classicists had a point in their quarrel with the Romantics. Men who do not know God must always lurch and wobble. We see the same thing in our day. The postmodernists are very good at pointing out the pretensions of the modernists. And the modernists are very good at pointing out the incoherence of the postmodernists.

In a real sense, this is a manifestation of the same pendulum problem that unbelievers always face. Nietzsche pointed to the difference between an Apollonian view of the world (rationalistic) and a Dionysian view of the world (experiential), and we should note how the unbelieving world always reacts away from one and into the excesses of the other. Nietzsche wanted this swing to help him account for the creative fusion that led to Attic tragedy. But these fusions always come unstuck. Stability in this scenario is never an option. Only in Christ can anything hold together.

And so these exhortations should be understood as exhortations to a writing life, with emphasis on that word *life*. The writer must know something about the world outside books—whether his or the books of the others. At the same time, he must also be thoroughly acquainted with the world inside books. Words on a page are part of real life. They cannot be substituted for the whole, but they cannot be taken from it either. Without words, we can only stand around, grunting and pointing.

Writing is not solo work. We are explorers, sure enough, but we have maps. Those who have gone before us have accumulated a vast amount of information about words, which they have helpfully gathered in easy-to-find locations. Much of it is alphabetized, and so there is no excuse for not finding what you need.

If you want to do what you really want to do, a good way of practicing is by picking up writing tasks you never thought of doing. This means that some of your exercises will be a sight to behold, and this will be true even in those select areas where you return to achieve immortality for your writing name. So make your peace with not being the best right from the get-go writer that ever was. Somebody has to be that guy, but it probably is not you or me.

The brain is more like a muscle that expands its capacity with increased use, and not very much like an attic crowded with boxes. The more you know, the more you *can* know. Take every advantage of every opportunity to learn your native language better, as well as any opportunities to learn other languages that will contribute to your writing. There is an old joke that asks what we call someone who knows three languages. Trilingual, right? Two languages? Bilingual would be that answer. What do we call someone who knows only one language? Right . . . an *American!* Well, if you are as offended by this joke as I am, then let's get out there and show *them*.

Be a verbal packrat. Keep a commonplace book. Write down the notable phrases that occur to you, as well as the ones you come across. Modify them and make them yours, or quote them in a context that makes them yours.

And, as was said quite a bit earlier, know when to stop.

Many thanks to Stephanie Kay.

30782751R00071

Made in the USA
San Bernardino, CA
29 March 2019

The
Warning

KATHRYN CROFT

Bookouture

Published by Bookouture in 2018

An imprint of StoryFire Ltd.

Carmelite House
50 Victoria Embankment
London EC4Y 0DZ

www.bookouture.com

ISBN: 978-1-78681-657-3
eBook ISBN: 978-1-78681-656-6

For our beautiful Amelie

PROLOGUE

I don't know who I am. Not really.

People might pity me if they knew this, but it's okay – it means I can be anyone I want to be, can make anyone believe anything I want them to. Where's the sadness in that?

Isn't that how the whole world has become now? Everyone living their lives through social media, creating a fake world where everything is perfect. What I do is no different.

I'm casually swiping through Tinder when I see his face: the bright, blue-grey eyes, slightly downturned, shy and appealing; the flick of dark hair falling across his forehead. Something stirs within me and I'm captivated, like I've never been before, on the app or anywhere else.

I stare at him for too long, absorbing every detail of him, ignoring the calls for me to go downstairs.

'In a minute,' I call. 'I just need one more minute.' One more minute to look at the person who will change my life.

I swipe right.

We are a match.

Excitement rises in my stomach as I imagine the first words that will pass between us. Then I almost forget about going downstairs as my mind conjures up scenarios of far more than this.

ONE

Zoe

I should be used to it by now, the heavy silence that always fills the house, even when we're all at home. It's been three years, yet I always have the television or some music on in the background and often speak too loudly, just to remind myself that I'm still here, that I'm not a ghost floating around, in some sort of limbo state because I've lost my child.

Nothing prepares you for that.

I close my eyes and I can see Ethan. It's hard to recall exactly how old he is in this scene playing out in my mind – probably ten – but I remember it clearly. I'm watching them in the garden; Ethan is talking animatedly to Harley, his wide smile stretching across his face. I can't hear what they're saying but Harley throws his head back and laughs at something his brother says. Then Harley grabs him into a bear hug and they topple to the grass. That's Ethan. Always making us laugh. Jake is soon at my side and we smile at each other and clutch hands because we both feel blessed.

The image evaporates as quickly as it appeared. There is no Ethan any more, and I'm standing here alone, in a different house and a different time.

Harley appears at the kitchen door and breaks the silence. 'Is Dad home?' he asks, the narrowing of his eyes telling me he already knows the answer. In the beginning, most of his disappointment, when Jake didn't appear home until late into the night, was because he needed him, needed his father around. Jake had always been there before, when we were a complete family, a constant and reliable figure, until he no longer could be. It must have been hard for Harley to adjust to the sudden change in his dad. Now that he's nineteen, though, I'm pretty certain it's more about my son feeling bad for me.

'He's got an important meeting with Liam,' I tell him.

Don't get me wrong, I'm not some spineless woman who lets her husband get away with never being at home; I just know how hard Jake works to make his graphic design business a success. I also know that it's his way of dealing with the absence we all feel, even though we're in a different house – a different city, even. I've often wondered if London is far enough from Guildford to make a difference, but we came here so Jake could set up a business with his old university friend Liam. Besides, if we'd moved further away I would have felt as though I was betraying Ethan.

Harley raises his eyebrows. 'Another meeting? Okay.'

I continue stirring the beef stew I've thrown together. Harley and I have had this conversation before, and I've pointed out to him that he needs to give his dad a break. Yet here we are, always coming back to this place. This time I try to make light of it. 'Oh, you'll be the same once you're a doctor, Harley,' I tell him. 'In fact, you'll be working night shifts and double shifts. That won't leave much for a social life in the beginning.' I pat his arm.

He smiles. 'I know all that. It's worth it to save lives, though, isn't it, Mum?'

This is why I'm so proud of my son. After Ethan's accident, Harley struggled so much with his grief that he had to take a year off before starting his A levels. Somehow, he pulled himself together, and now he's determined to do some good in a world that can show so much cruelty. I admire his strength and determination; I don't think, at his age, I'd have been able to focus like he does. I suppose it's his way of coping.

'How's Melanie?' I ask, aware of how loud my voice is in comparison to Harley's. He's always been softly spoken, something that belies his inner strength.

Harley pours himself a glass of milk from the fridge; I've never understood how he can drink so much of the stuff. 'You can call her Mel, you know. No one calls her Melanie – not even her parents.' He chuckles.

'I know. Sorry.' The truth is I have no idea why I address her so formally; she seems a lovely girl and is besotted with Harley. 'So how are things going with you two?'

'Well, we're not planning on eloping to Vegas just yet, so don't worry!'

I laugh, knowing this is something I'm unlikely to have to worry about. Harley's head is screwed on too tightly to do something so impulsive.

'Why don't you invite her here for dinner tomorrow evening? I'll make something special, and it's Saturday, so Dad should be able to come home early. What do you think?'

As soon as I've said this, I wonder if I'm pushing too hard. Perhaps they're not at the stage in their relationship where they want to spend time with each other's parents. Does any young person ever? It's been a few months since they met, though, so they must like each other a lot. I study Harley's face but see no sign of doubt or discomfort.

'I'll ask her,' he says, with a shrug. 'Not sure what she's up to, though.'

'Well, let me know. Anyway, I'd better get on with dinner or there'll be nothing for tonight.'

'Want help with anything?'

It's a tempting offer, but Harley's been at college all day and I'm sure he could do with a break. 'Help me tomorrow instead,' I tell him.

As I watch him head upstairs I feel that familiar ache. He wasn't supposed to be an only child.

Jake gets home just after 10 p.m. and finds me asleep on the sofa. 'I'm so sorry, Zoe,' he whispers. 'We had so much to get through and I couldn't leave any sooner.'

I pull myself up and bury my head in his chest, breathing in his comforting scent. It always reminds me how lucky we are to have made it through those dark months together. 'It's okay. Have you eaten? I would have saved you some but Harley was extra hungry and wolfed down your portion.'

Jake doesn't smile at this, even though he should. He would have before. 'Liam and I ordered a pizza,' he says.

'Ah, now I understand why you didn't come home for dinner. Pizza trumps beef stew any day, doesn't it?'

We both chuckle but the moment of levity is short-lived. It's almost as if we feel bad enjoying ourselves and have to stop ourselves laughing too long about anything, even three years later. Ethan wouldn't have wanted this. He was only fourteen, but he had a cheeky sense of humour. If he could see us now, he'd tell us we were being boring. He would instruct us to laugh as much as we could.

'Think I'll have a shower before bed,' Jake says, standing up. He doesn't need to explain why; it saves him time in the morning so he can make the most of the day.

'You should take a weekend off once in a while,' I say. 'We could go somewhere with Harley. After he goes off to medical school in September, how many more chances will we get to do things as a family?'

The word always feels strange now that Ethan's no longer here. We are a family, but an incomplete one.

Jake nods. 'You're right, we should do that. We'll go away somewhere for a weekend. I'll sort something out.' Neither of us has to point out that it will be nowhere near a lake or river – nowhere close to a beach, even.

'Also, I've invited Melanie – Mel – here for dinner tomorrow evening. Can you get home earlyish?'

For a second, I think Jake will say he can't, that he'll offer up a hundred reasons why it's just not possible, but then he surprises me. 'Yeah, that should be fine. So, is it getting serious between them?'

'You know Harley, he's a boy of few words, but I think they like each other a lot.'

'Or she does at least.'

'What does that mean?'

Jake scrunches his face. 'Oh, nothing. Isn't it just the way with young love that one person always falls harder? And every time we meet her it seems as though she's all over him while he's a bit more laid-back.'

I tell him I disagree. 'He's just a bit more reserved, that's all. He always has been. Anyway, you can't be talking from personal experience, as that's not how it was for us, was it? It may have been a while ago but I seem to remember things being pretty equal between us.'

Jake smiles, and I'm glad that thinking of our early days together can still make him feel happiness. 'Yeah, you're right,' he says. 'We were lucky, weren't we?'

He's right – a blind date set up by my best friend Leanne could have been a disaster, and it had taken a lot of persuading for me to agree to it in the first place, but Jake had quickly won me over with his kindness and sense of humour. For too long, though, the happiness and ease of our early years together has been overshadowed by what came later, when Jake hardly knew what to say to me, when he could barely look me in the eye.

'Anyway,' Jake continues, 'Mel's a nice girl and I'm happy he's with her.' He kisses me on the forehead before heading off to have his shower.

Upstairs, I remember that I haven't checked my emails since I got home from work. There shouldn't be anything important; I'm not the emergency contact this evening and I always check work emails before I leave in case a patient needs an urgent query answered. Being a nurse at a fertility clinic means a lot to me and I want to make sure I'm there for the women and men who are going through such a lot to have a family.

On my iPhone, my accounts are merged so I get all my emails in one inbox. I notice there is one from Lynette, a thirty-year-old woman who has been struggling to conceive since she was twenty-six. This is her first IVF cycle and she's anxious it hasn't worked after she had her embryo transferred yesterday.

I type a reply, telling her to try and relax, that she probably won't have symptoms for a while, and when she does they could mean anything. Just hang on until your test day, I advise her, yet even as I send the email I know nothing I say will help her. The waiting is hell for everyone.

The next email is from a patient called Gemma. She's just turned forty, meaning the chances of her IVF cycle working for her are extremely low, so when I start to read the message my heart feels like it's jumping inside my body. *It worked, Zoe! I did the test today and I'm pregnant! We're finally having our baby!*

Moments like this are what I live for. To know that amidst all the failure and grief in the world, amazing things can happen. People can have happy endings.

The only other unread email was sent to my Google account, from someone I've never heard of: m.cole@gmail.com. There's nothing in the subject field, so I expect it to be junk but need to check just in case.

The words hit me like a knife through my chest.

You need to find out the truth about what happened to your son down by the river three years ago. Don't let this rest. Don't believe the lie. It was no accident.

TWO

Jake

The second he walks into the bedroom, wrapped in his bath towel, Jake knows something is wrong with Zoe. She's sitting on the floor by the bed, staring at her phone, her skin pale and her hands shaking.

At first he assumes it must be to do with one of her patients, but that can't be right; Zoe is too strong to fall apart when people are depending on her. He's only seen her like this one other time, and it was when they lost their son. Not before, or since, has he seen her so shaken up.

He sinks to the floor beside her and pulls her into his chest. 'Zoe, what's happened? What is it?'

She stares at him, her eyes wide. 'Here,' she says, shoving her phone towards him. 'Read it.'

Frowning, he takes the phone from her, but the words are a blur without his reading glasses. 'Just a sec.' He reaches across to the bedside table and grabs them.

You need to find out the truth about what happened to your son down by the river three years ago. Don't let this rest. Don't believe the lie. It was no accident.

Jake is confused. 'What the hell is this?'

She tells him she has no idea who the email is from. She doesn't know anyone with the surname Cole. Neither does Jake.

'They're talking about Ethan? Why? I don't get it?'

'What the fuck, Jake? What the fuck?'

Zoe never swears. Especially not the F-word. Jake grabs her hand and tries to think rationally about this. 'Look, it's just some prank. Someone's being an arsehole, trying to screw with us. It's nothing more than that. Let's just delete it.' He's about to do this when she grabs the phone from his hand.

'No! We can't. It… it might be…'

'Might be what? True? Zoe, you can't possibly believe this? We know what happened to Ethan.'

Despite saying this, he has to admit to himself that just for a second – no, less than that, a microsecond – there was a flicker of doubt in his mind when he read those words. But there's no way. He tries explaining this to Zoe, attempting to be as tactful as he can.

'Zoe, listen. It was an accident. Ethan and Josh drowned in the river because they were messing around. It was awful and senseless and they shouldn't have been there, especially in the middle of the night. Ethan would have known very well that he wasn't supposed to be there. There's no more to it; there can't be. The police had no doubts about it and it was fully investigated.'

He remembers that day too clearly, like it was yesterday. Josh had been staying the night and the boys went up to bed at about nine o'clock. He and Zoe had no reason to suspect the two of them had sneaked out in the middle of the night. None of them heard a thing.

Zoe will never say it, but Jake is sure she thinks Josh was the one who convinced Ethan to sneak out. And if he's honest, he probably believes that too, but neither of them will ever say it out loud. It would feel traitorous to do that. After all, Josh's parents are grieving just as much as they are, so why apportion blame? Both the boys should have known better.

It's all thundering back to him now – everything he's worked so hard to ignore, has tried to section away in a corner of his mind that he keeps firmly shut – delivering hard and fast blows that wind him and take his breath away.

Although he will never admit this to Zoe, and can barely register it himself, he's aware that he's been on a constant mission to hide from his grief. Work is the only thing that stops him from feeling overwhelmed – no, suffocated – by the guilt he carries. He couldn't save his child. He failed him in the worst possible way.

'Sometimes the police get things wrong,' Zoe says. 'It happens, Jake.'

He tries to be the voice of reason. 'Let's just take a moment to think about this.' He pauses, waits for her to object, but she doesn't, instead staring at him with those wide, beautiful eyes, as if willing him to produce some words that will explain everything and put this to rest.

'It's been three years,' he tells her. 'If there *was* any truth to this, why would the person who sent this have waited so long? There are some sick people out there who love to see people in pain and do what they can to mess with them. That's all this is. We can't let whoever it is get to us.'

There is silence while she assesses what he's just said, and then she slowly nods. The calm, rational woman he knows is back. 'I know you're probably right, but what if there's just some tiny chance that it's true? I think we should show it to the police, just in case. And if it is just someone harassing me, then that needs to be reported too, doesn't it?'

Jake thought he'd seen the last of the police – or hoped he had anyway. The family liaison officer, Jody, was a nice woman, but it had made him uncomfortable to have her in their house so much, making herself at home as if she lived there, constantly asking them questions. Despite that, though, she really helped Zoe and Harley – when, he has to admit, he didn't have the ability. He is grateful for that. 'Okay,' he agrees. 'We can go early tomorrow morning, before I go to work.'

Zoe shakes her head. 'No, I'll go on my own. I'll be fine. If this is a prank, why should we let this person screw things up for us? I need you home early for dinner with Melanie, so you can't afford to go in late.'

He feels awful about this, but Zoe is right. 'Okay. Just call me after you've seen them and let me know what they say.' He knows she'll be fine without him there; Zoe is independent, headstrong – sometimes too much. She might have had a bit of a wobble, but she'll pull it together by the morning. Still, Jake offers her words he hopes will show his support. 'We'll get through this together, Zoe. Just like we did before.'

Barely.

As he's speaking, he feels his thoughts trying to twist to something else. Something he won't let himself think about.

THREE

Harley

Sometimes he doesn't feel nineteen. He feels more like an older person trapped inside a teenager's body. This must be what losing your little brother does to you, he reckons, although he doesn't remember ever *not* feeling this way.

He sits at his computer, his eyes glued to the website of the medical school he's applied to. The bright pictures full of young, smiling faces make him believe anything is possible, that he can have a future without his little brother in it, that he will seamlessly blend in with those happy faces and stamp out his grief.

Ethan. He'd been everything Harley wasn't: the life and soul of any room, confident, brave. But not as academic, Harley reminds himself. That was where he excelled, although he'd never held that over his brother. There was no rivalry between them. *It would have been better if we'd hated each other, if we hadn't been so close. Perhaps then there wouldn't be such a gaping hole in my life.*

You could say they were doing okay now, as a family. They'd been to hell but somehow made it back and now they were just living their lives. Carrying on. Trying to be normal. But scars don't fade; there is always something left behind. He shudders, not wanting to think about those dark days when they all became completely different people and it felt as though Mum hated Dad, Dad hated Mum and Harley hated everyone.

Now they'd somehow made a new reality for themselves, a quieter, more sedate one, even though Ethan would always exist for them. And Harley was optimistic that the future would be even better, given more time. Dad just needed to get his priorities right and be the person he'd been before: the dad who used to take them out every Saturday afternoon. The cinema. Mini golf. Wherever they'd wanted to go.

But Mum had been weird this morning – distracted, as if she'd been on edge. She'd even managed to burn their scrambled eggs. Her food was never anything other than Jamie Oliver perfect, so he'd known something was going on.

'Are you okay, Mum?' he'd asked her, as she'd tossed the charred remains in the bin and started cracking open fresh eggs.

Her answer had been short and to the point. 'Fine, love. Just feel a cold coming on.'

You didn't have to be a future medical student to notice she had no symptoms of any type of bug. It was probably something to do with Dad. Mum must be so lonely after work, when he's never around and there's nobody to talk to. She never says anything, of course, but Harley sees it. He knows it.

Harley closes down the website and lies on his bed, reaching for his headphones and blasting out Coldplay. *Sorry, Ethan*, he thinks. *I'll be off to medical school soon – the start of my life. It still cuts me up that you'll never get to do anything like that. It doesn't seem fair.*

Thankfully Mel texts him, distracting him from these destructive thoughts. She's checking if dinner's still on, ending her message with three kisses. He smiles. She's so warm and affectionate and sometimes he can't believe she's actually interested in him.

He replies and tells her he can't wait to see her later, even though this isn't exactly true. He's dreading the dinner with his parents; it seems so formal, and something he can do without. And what will his dad have to talk about? He can barely talk to Harley, so it's unimaginable to think of him holding any sort of conversation with Mel. But Mum seemed so happy about it and Harley doesn't want to let her down. Not after everything he put her through after Ethan died. Not only did she lose her youngest son, but her other son began to fall apart right in front of her. He wishes he'd been stronger, that he'd been able to look after her, even though he was only sixteen at the time.

Mel texts again, this time with a picture of her smiling suggestively. Although he's sure she's wearing something, the photo is cut off just below her shoulders so it appears as though she doesn't have any clothes on. He texts back that she's cheeky and adds some smiley faces.

He knows what she wants and he doesn't think he should keep her waiting much longer.

Despite Harley's reservations, dinner was fun. His dad was home early for once and managed to strike up a decent conversation with Mel. In fact, both he and Mum had seemed really impressed with her. Well, what's not to be impressed about? She's cool and down to earth, and over dinner she'd made Mum laugh a lot. It was good to see her laugh.

Now they're lying on his bed, and Mel's cuddled up so tightly against him he can feel the warmth from her body transferring to his, as if she's melting into him. She kisses him hard on the mouth then pulls away. 'Do you like London?' she asks. 'I always wonder what people who aren't born and raised here think of it.'

'Surrey's not that far away. Straight down the A3. It's not like we moved to the other side of the country.'

'Oh, I know. But even different parts of London can seem alien if you're used to another bit of it.'

He knows what Mel means. They live in Putney, south-west London, and other than the West End, he feels weird going to the east, north or west part of the capital. 'London's cool,' he tells her. 'The kind of place anyone can feel welcome and make their home. Eventually.' *Even me*. He doesn't add that he didn't want to come here, that moving from Surrey felt like they were betraying Ethan. Almost like leaving him behind. Mum and Dad had to make a break, though – it was killing them to live in that house, in that street, to have Ethan's ghost all around them. Their marriage barely survived it. He thinks they were all a bit surprised when the big move happened and it made little difference.

Now, though, they're doing okay. They have to be.

'You're so right,' Mel says, stroking his cheek. Her eyes catch on the framed picture of Harley with his brother, which sits on his computer desk. 'Tell me about Ethan,' she says. 'I mean, unless it's hard for you. I'll understand if you don't want to talk about him. He looks like he was so much fun.'

The atmosphere in the room shifts. She's never pushed him to discuss his brother before. It's not that he doesn't want to, it's just that this has come a bit out of the blue. Harley takes a deep breath. 'He was… kind of cool, I guess. Really popular at school and full of energy. Confident. Way different from me. Fun, like you said.'

Mel smiles and clutches his hand, giving it a reassuring squeeze. 'Is that your way of saying he was… cheeky?'

'You could say that. He wasn't a troublemaker, he just, I don't know, had a sense of humour.' As he says this, he wonders if people's perceptions of those they have lost get bent out of shape as time passes. Even though he remembers always laughing when Ethan was around, are his memories of his brother correct, or have they become blurred, mixed up with grief and sadness and pain?

He mentions this to Mel, and she smiles. 'You're so philosophical, Harley. I don't think we truly forget what someone was like, although maybe we do only focus on the good. Actually, I feel a bit awful talking about this because I haven't even lost a grandparent yet. Anyway, I love that about you, that you think so deeply about things.'

His heart almost stops. What is she saying? Surely she didn't mean that she loves him? He gives her a kiss but ignores what she's said. 'Like I said, Ethan was so different to me. I remember always having a book in my hand, while he was more into his bikes or skateboard or whatever the latest thing was.' His breath catches in his throat as an image of Ethan laughing appears in his head. And then he starts laughing too.

Mel stares at him.

'Sorry, I was just remembering how he had such a horsey laugh. Honestly, he really did sound like a horse neighing. It was hilarious. And the more he tried not to sound like an animal, the worse it got.'

And then the moment goes and all Harley feels again is a dull ache across his whole body.

'Growing up, I always wanted a brother or sister,' Mel says. 'It's kind of lonely being an only child. I know that sounds like a cliché, but it really is true. I think I spent too much time with my parents, being their whole world.' She shakes her head. 'It's not good.' Her hand clamps to her mouth. 'Oh God, Harley, I'm so sorry. I just didn't think. I'm so sorry.'

He wraps his arms around her. 'It's okay. I was sixteen when Ethan died, so I did have my childhood with him. Don't worry about it; you don't have to walk on eggshells around me.'

Her whole body, which seconds ago had been tight and rigid, relaxes, and she kisses him again, her lips soft against his. 'Sorry,' she whispers, pressing her body into him. He lets himself get lost in her for a moment.

'Shall we get some fresh air?' he suggests, pulling away. 'I could really do with a walk.'

It's what he used to do after Ethan died, to clear his head and help him feel as if he wasn't going crazy. And as he walked, he'd pretend Ethan was still alive and plan what he would tell him about when he got home. He'd always loved telling Ethan all about his day at school, and even though he was probably boring him to death most of the time, Ethan always listened intently, hanging on every word.

Mel seems surprised at his suggestion to go for a walk. 'Oh, okay.' Harley knows he's disappointed her, that she is more than ready for him, but taking it further would only result in him letting her down, disappointing her even more, he's convinced of that, and he wants her in his life. He *needs* her in it.

After he's driven Mel home, he finds his mum in the living room, curled up on the sofa with her feet beneath her and a book in her hand. She's a bookworm, like him. People always used to comment on how alike they were and how Ethan was more like Dad.

Mum looks up at him and smiles. 'Melanie – I mean Mel – is lovely, Harley. Such a nice girl. I'm so glad you've met someone nice. Oh, I know you're still young and all that, but I was only twenty-one when I met your dad.'

'I know, I know, and it was love at first sight or something like that.' She'll know he's only teasing, although he smiles just to make sure.

'Well, I wouldn't say that. Anyway, the best kind of love is the one that grows, Harley. Well, that's what I think anyway. But what do I know?'

A lot, he thinks. His mum is smart, a deep thinker, just like Mel said he is.

'Do you think you'll stay together when you go off to medical school and Mel goes to uni?'

This is the question he knows is always on the edge of Mel's lips. He shrugs. 'If she wants to. It's a bit hard to think that far ahead though. I just want to get my exams done and enjoy the summer with her, then we can see what happens.'

'You always have been a sensible boy,' Mum says. 'Sorry, make that *young man*. I'm so proud of you, do you know that?'

'Thanks, Mum.'

'Don't be too hard on your dad, though. He's trying his best for us.'

She's probably right, although how does he get past the years his dad practically ignored them, as if they didn't exist? The way he just let their marriage, and family, fall apart. Maybe it was his way of dealing with everything, but he just seemed to make it all worse. 'I try, Mum. I really do.'

'I know. I know.'

He sits beside her and she shifts her legs to make more room for him. 'Mum, are you okay?'

'Oh, yeah,' she says. 'I won't let a stupid cold get the better of me.'

He could point out that she doesn't even have any tissues around, force the truth out of her, but that wouldn't be fair. She was entitled to her own private thoughts. Wasn't everyone?

'Thanks for caring,' she says. 'A lot of teenagers wouldn't.'

And he's back to his earlier thought. He is an older person in a young person's body.

FOUR

Zoe

Somehow, at work on Monday, I'm able to put that email aside and focus on my patients. I've shown it to the police and that's all I can do for now. Although they promised to look into it and try to trace the person who sent it, they didn't seem to think there was any truth in the claim, just like Jake.

'Probably someone's idea of a sick prank,' the young PC had said, but she assured me she'd make it a priority to liaise with the police in Surrey. 'The best thing you can do is try not to give it any unnecessary attention, and definitely don't reply to the email. That's how things escalate.'

I had left feeling determined not to let this person get to me, but those words were too hard to get out of my mind. I couldn't just sit back and do nothing. That's when I made up my mind to take a trip back to Surrey to visit Josh's mum, Roberta. If there is anything legitimate about the email, then surely she will have received one too. My plan is to go tonight after work, even though I have no idea whether the Butlers still live at the same address.

'So what do you think?'

Annette, one of my patients, sits in front of me; by her side is her nervous-looking husband. It's usually the men who are more relaxed at these appointments, although I can understand Nathan's nerves. I've just shown him how he'll start his wife's injections, and his shaking hands – even though we haven't been practising with anything but an empty syringe – tell me it might be a struggle for him.

'Acupuncture can be very beneficial during IVF cycles,' I tell Annette as I pack her syringes into a bag. 'And if nothing else, it's definitely relaxing.'

Annette's eyes widen, full of hope. 'Do you think that would increase my chances of it working?'

I wish I could tell her that it's the answer to all her prayers, that this is what will make a difference for her this time, but I can't promise her anything. Like much of life, it's just a lottery, and all you can do is go through the process, cross your fingers and wait to see what happens. 'Well, there is research to suggest it can help, so I would definitely recommend it,' I tell her.

Beside her, Nathan smiles. 'Let's do it. It's got to be worth a try at least.'

They hold hands while we finish off and I admire the way couples can stick together through this invasive and often soul-destroying process. Silently, I say my usual prayer that it will all work out for them.

At lunchtime Leanne calls my mobile. 'How's everything going?' she asks, and in the background I hear papers shuffling. 'We really are overdue for a catch-up, aren't we?'

Leanne is a solicitor and her long working hours leave little time for socialising, even with her best friend. 'Definitely.'

'How about tonight? I could pop over, bring a bottle of wine. Jake won't mind, will he? He'll probably still be at work anyway.' She chuckles, clearly feeling no discomfort at this joke at Jake's expense. She can get away with it, though; she's known him longer than I have and is the one who set us up all those years ago.

'Actually, I can't. I have to meet up with someone. Sorry.' This isn't exactly a lie; even though I haven't arranged anything with Roberta Butler, turning up at her house means I'm meeting her, doesn't it?

'That sounds very intriguing,' Leanne says.

Now I'm stuck. I hate keeping things from her, but I can't tell Leanne what I'm doing – not yet. I know exactly what she'll say – anything to get me to change my mind. 'Oh, it's nothing, just an old friend.' I keep my explanation short, conscious of the fact that, despite our boys being the closest of friends, and after what happened, Roberta and I have never managed anything like a friendship.

'Shame,' Leanne says. 'Never mind. I'll check my diary and text you some other dates, okay?'

Before she goes, I ask after Ross. She's been seeing him for a couple of months and he's the first man she's been bothered with since her divorce a few years ago.

'He's… nice. Yeah, I like him. Taking it slow, though. I'm not getting burnt again.'

'Sensible,' I say.

After we've hung up, I realise that this word doesn't apply to Leanne's personal life at all. In complete contrast to her work ethic, she follows her heart, not her head, when it comes to relationships. That's how she ended up with a jerk like Seb.

I'm interrupted from this thought by a text message from Melanie, thanking me for dinner the other night. She must have asked Harley for my mobile number. I send a reply telling her she's very welcome and she immediately texts back.

Hope you can come to ours for dinner next time. Mum and Dad would love to meet you x

It's very sweet that she's making such an effort.

This is the first time I've been back to Guildford since we moved to London, and I'm not prepared for the feeling that overwhelms me. It's where I was born and brought up, but all those happy childhood memories are overshadowed now, suffocated by the death of my son.

It takes all my strength to keep driving, avoiding going anywhere near the river as I make my way to the house Josh lived in. Again, I wonder whether the Butlers have moved, forced by the memories to flee their home just like we did. I have no idea what I'll do if this is the case.

When I arrive and walk up the path to the front door, it almost feels as if the boys are still here and I'm just coming to pick up Ethan. Then when I knock, reality hits me and I have to breathe deeply to keep myself together.

Adrian Butler answers the door and stares at me for long drawn-out seconds, a frown on his face. It's as if he does remember me but can't quite believe I'm standing on his doorstep. He seems to have barely changed since I last saw him three years ago, whereas I know I have visibly aged.

'Zoe,' he says, after what seems like minutes.

'Hi, I'm sorry to just turn up like this – it must be a bit of a shock.'

He nods. 'Yes, it is.' He steps back, but doesn't hold the door open to let me in.

'Roberta!' he shouts, turning away from me and walking back into the house. Although I had little to do with him when the boys were alive – it was always Roberta who picked Josh up from our house, or dropped him anywhere the boys were meeting – and I can count on one hand the amount of times Adrian and I have crossed paths, I'm surprised by his reaction.

Hushed whispers fill the hallway and I strain to hear but can't make out the words, only my name. Then Roberta appears at the door, clutching a cardigan around her even though it's June now and has been warm in the evenings.

'Zoe?' she says, staring at me, clearly trying to work out why I could be here. Perhaps she's also surprised by how different I look;

my once long hair is now a short, dark bob reaching only to my chin. 'What... what are you doing here?'

'I'm sorry to just turn up like this, but the mobile number I had for you didn't work.'

'I changed it, ages ago.' She stares at me as if it should be obvious why she's done this. 'I just wanted to change everything, you know? We'd have moved from here too, like you did, if we could afford it.'

'Could I come in? Just for a few minutes. I really need to talk to you about something important.'

She looks me up and down and takes her time to make up her mind. She'll know this can only be about one thing. 'Okay. Come in then.'

Despite the close friendship Ethan and Josh had, I've only been in this house a few times, and never for very long. I quickly learned that it was better to wait for Ethan in the car whenever I picked him up, that my presence in the house somehow made Roberta uncomfortable. Even so, stepping inside now sends a jolt through my body. I can almost hear the boys' laughter, the clomp of their feet as they rush downstairs. They were always whizzing about, full of boundless energy nobody could – or wanted to – tame.

Roberta leads me through the narrow hallway to the living room and gestures for me to go in. I expect to find Adrian in there, but the room is empty, even though the television is on, showing a football match he must have been watching.

'I'll turn this off,' she says, picking up a remote control from the sofa. Her hands fumble on the buttons.

'I don't want to interrupt the match for Adrian,' I say. 'Maybe we could go in the kitchen?'

Her voice is quiet. 'No, don't worry, it's nearly finished and he's going out soon. Meeting his friends at the pub.'

'He seemed a bit shocked to see me – I hope I haven't made him uncomfortable?'

Roberta nods. 'Yes, it's a complete surprise for both of us.'

She sits on the sofa and I do the same. I know she's in need of an explanation, but now that I'm here, I wonder if this is a mistake. She clearly hasn't received an email or it would have been the first thing she mentioned.

'This is about the boys, isn't it?' Roberta says. 'It must be, otherwise you wouldn't be here.'

You would think that two mothers losing their sons, boys who were best friends, would bring them closer together. That makes sense, doesn't it? Not us, though. If anything, it made conversations more awkward, highlighted just how different we are. Within two minutes of first meeting Roberta, it had been obvious she was downtrodden, that both her son and her husband controlled everything she did. Josh seemed to have whatever he wanted and do whatever he liked. No boundaries, no restrictions. It used to cross my mind that she was scared of him. Beneath it all, though, she's a kind woman with a big heart.

'Yes, it is about the boys. Actually, it's really weird but I got an email the other day, from a name I didn't recognise: M. Cole. To be honest, I don't know what to make of it, but I wondered if you'd had one too?'

Roberta frowns. 'I don't know anyone with that name.'

'Neither do I. I think it's probably fake, but you need to see what it said.'

She frowns at me while I reach for my phone and tap my inbox. I read out the message, my voice sounding as if it's not my own, as if I'm a newsreader reporting events.

'I don't get that. What are they talking about? Who would send you that?'

'I have no idea. I've taken it to the police and they're attempting to trace it, although I don't hold out much hope. Whoever sent it must know I would do something about this message, so they must have made sure it couldn't be traced back to them. I've googled M. Cole too and nothing significant comes up.'

Roberta shakes her head, frown lines creasing her forehead. 'Who would do something like this? It doesn't make sense. There's no lie; the boys drowned accidentally in the river. We know that, don't we? Why are they doing this now?'

'I don't know, Roberta. I just had to come here, to see if you'd got one too and also to find out what you thought.'

She shakes her head again. 'I haven't had anything. Let me just check again. My phone's in the kitchen.' She leaves the room and after a moment I hear hushed voices again. She must be filling Adrian in on what I've just told her. Surely that will force him to come in here and join us? Josh was his son too.

While I'm waiting, I recall Roberta mentioning once that Adrian had refused to have any more children, even though she'd wanted a big family. Her revelation had only confirmed my suspicion that he controlled her, that he always got his own way, and it's clear now that nothing has changed.

Adrian doesn't appear with her when she comes back, and her cheeks are red and flushed.

'Are you okay?' I ask.

'Yes, yes. I just don't know what to make of it all.'

She's lying. Her current state is more to do with what Adrian has just said to her than anything else.

The front door slams and Roberta seems relieved, her shoulders drooping as she sits down again. 'I'm so sorry,' she says. 'Adrian hasn't taken this well. He… it took him a long time to come to terms with Josh dying. Not that you ever do. He just, well, he's become a bit withdrawn. Not wanting much to do with people.'

This would make sense if Roberta hadn't just told me Adrian was meeting friends at the pub. I don't mention this; after all, it's not my business how people grieve, and Jake didn't exactly handle it well either.

'Can I read the email?' Roberta asks, leaning forward. 'I just can't wrap my head around it.'

Neither can I, and I've had a couple of days to try. I hand her my phone and minutes tick by as she sits there reading, her long, thin fingers wrapped around my phone. I wish I could know her thoughts, or at least trust that she's honest about them, but from the minute I walked in this house nothing has felt right. Perhaps it's just being here again after all these years, between these stifling walls where nothing's changed, and yet everything has.

Finally, Roberta sighs and hands me back my phone. 'All we can do is wait for the police to trace it,' she says, avoiding eye contact.

'What do you think, though?' I ask. 'Is it just some sick prank? That's what the police seem to believe.'

She nods. 'It must be. We know what happened that night, even though we don't know why they were there or how they ended up in the river. The police would have checked anything suspicious at the time.'

No matter how many times I hear this, my instinct is screaming at me that there's something more. 'But why target just me? Why wouldn't they have done the same to you? Not that I'm wishing this on you – although, however you look at it, it involves both Ethan *and* Josh.'

She considers this for a moment. 'Maybe someone's got it in for you? No offence, but I don't know anything about your personal life, do I? You could have made some enemies.' These words seem out of place, coming from such a timid woman. They are words Adrian might have filled her head with.

Silence fills the room as I struggle to come up with a response to this. Then it hits me that there could be a logical reason Roberta *didn't* get the email. Whoever it was – if they are legitimate – focused on me for a reason, and maybe that's because Josh had something to do with what happened. I won't mention this to Roberta; it's important I find out every detail she can remember about the days leading up to the accident.

'You know, sometimes I struggle to remember those last days with Ethan. I mean, I just can't seem to picture his face properly, no matter how hard I try. I can remember things from before, even when he was a small boy, yet those days before the accident are never clear in my head.'

Roberta leans back, placing her hands in her lap. 'I have the opposite problem. Even now, three years later, it feels like it just happened yesterday. Sometimes I even come downstairs and get three breakfast bowls out. Can you believe that? After three years! It sounds insane, doesn't it?'

'No,' I tell her, reminding myself how unique grief can be.

'I even remember him getting ready to leave the house to go to your place,' she continues.

A tear forms in my eye, and I don't mention that I remember so little about that day. It was just another evening where nothing was out of the ordinary and there was no sign of what was to come. I had no idea those hours would be Ethan's last. I can't even remember the last thing I said to him.

Another thing that can happen when you lose a child is that you question everything you ever did, ever said to them. Were you a good enough parent? Were you too strict? Too lenient? Were you ultimately responsible for what happened to them?

'I'm so sorry, Roberta. I should have known the boys had sneaked out. Something should have woken me and alerted me to the dangerous situation they were putting themselves in. I will never forgive myself for that.'

She doesn't say anything and refuses to look at me.

'Roberta, there's something I need to ask you – and please be honest with me. Do you blame me for what happened? The boys were under my care, after all, so… do you hold me responsible? Because I understand if you do.'

She is quick to shake her head, even though she still doesn't look at me. 'No, of course not. I was angry in the beginning, and probably needed someone to blame, but I quickly realised it could just as easily have happened here. And let's be honest, sneaking out to the river in the middle of the night was more likely to be Josh's idea, wasn't it?'

I'm both shocked and grateful that she's admitted what I've believed all along.

'Ethan was a good boy,' she continues, her voice trailing off. She stares at the fluffy beige carpet, which looks as though it hasn't seen a speck of dust in its life.

'Roberta, what is it? Is there something I don't know?'

'It's… not important,' she says. 'Just something I remembered happened shortly before.'

My body freezes, even though it's stifling in here. 'What? What happened?'

'Do you remember when Ethan was over after school a couple of days before? They'd had sports day and neither of them could be bothered to change out of their PE kits.'

'Go on.'

'They were up in Josh's room and I remember hearing raised voices. Not arguing or anything like that, but it did seem like a bit of a heated discussion.'

I sit up straighter. This is news to me. I can't remember a time when I ever heard the two of them in conflict. 'What were they talking about?'

'It was hard to tell because they had music playing, so I could only catch the odd word, but it seemed like Ethan was trying to convince Josh to do something – or not to do something – I don't know.' She shakes her head 'It's probably nothing at all, and maybe some mums would have gone upstairs to listen, but I'm not like that. I believed in giving Josh some privacy. He was fourteen, growing up, it didn't seem fair to interfere in friendship issues. Besides, they were the best of friends so I knew it couldn't be anything too serious.'

'I'm sure you're right,' I say, remembering the amount of trivial arguments that Ethan and Harley had had themselves, only to end up the best of friends two minutes later.

The front door slams and Adrian appears in the living room doorway.

'You're back,' Roberta says, immediately standing up, as if she's been caught doing something she shouldn't be.

'Changed my mind,' he says. 'I'm not in the mood for the pub now.' He turns to me. 'Zoe, it was nice of you to come here for a visit, but if you don't mind, I think you should go now. I don't want Roberta being upset by the past being raked up.'

Stunned into silence, and annoyed that I won't get to question Roberta any more tonight, I make my way to the front door, Roberta following behind me. Thankfully, Adrian stays out of sight so I quickly fish out a piece of paper and scrawl my number on it. 'Keep in touch,' I say, handing it to her. 'I'm always here if you ever need someone to talk to.'

All the way home my mind is buzzing, digesting all the possibilities. What if this is no prank? And is it possible that Josh had something to do with what happened to Ethan?

FIVE

She used to snoop through my room before the MS rendered her incapable of negotiating the stairs on her own. I never said anything, of course, even though I had every right to. I'm not a child any more, I used to silently scream at her, while I was helping her get dressed or making her some food.

At least she can't do that now. It means this room is finally my own personal space. At my age I should have moved out long ago, I know that, but then who would look after her? She says she wants me to have my own life and would love me to get a place of my own, but behind her words is that desperate sadness that keeps me tethered here.

Never mind. I have a distraction, and he's been emailing me for weeks now, telling me how hot I look in my photo, how he wants to touch my long, silky hair. The thought of it had me splayed out on my bed, picturing all the things I want him to do to me, all the things I want to do to him.

'I've never met anyone like you,' he wrote in his last email. 'Seriously. You blow my mind.'

I had a chuckle to myself at that. He's barely lived, so just how many people has he met? I saved him the embarrassment of stating this, though. I don't want to patronise him and in my photo I don't look that much older than he is.

It's been three days since I last replied to him and he must be going out of his mind. It's not that I don't want to – I'd do it like a shot – but I have to be careful here. I have to make sure we develop a bond that will withstand any issues that may come up. That will *come up. I have to make him desperate for me, unable to picture his life without me.*

Not easily done by email alone, but I have my ways.

The excuses come hard and fast: my mother is sick, I can't leave her on her own (partly true); I've got a nasty flu bug; work is so busy I'm having to do double shifts, so I'm knackered.

He's so innocent that he buys it all, doesn't question me and tries his best to hide his disappointment. I know I can only keep this going for so long; I just hope it gives me enough time.

'Can you at least FaceTime?' he asked me yesterday.

'Impossible,' I told him. 'My Wi-Fi is down and the webcam on my computer is broken anyway.' I could tell he was sceptical, so I threw in something else. 'I've been hurt before, meeting people online, and I don't want to go through that again. Just give me time. We will be together soon.'

That seems to have held him off for a while. And just to make sure he's still interested, I send him a photo, just the top half, no face showing. He immediately responds, saying how beautiful I am.

'Send me one of you,' I ask, already far too excited by the idea.

He doesn't, though – he's too shy.

All in good time. All in good time.

SIX

Roberta

She stares in the mirror and almost doesn't recognise the woman she's become. Her face is haggard and her skin looks like it's peeling off, making an escape. Her mousey hair is limp and sticks to her head and the dark circles under her eyes make her look ten years older. They're worse now, after so little sleep last night. She is only thirty-nine. That's no age at all, is it? Yet here is the ghost of the woman she once was, staring back at her, wondering what happened to her life.

Zoe turning up like that yesterday evening was a shock, damaging the fragile equilibrium in the house, causing Adrian to explode once she'd left and he was free to express himself. For days it has been tolerable, with Adrian mostly leaving her alone, and now this.

'Why is she coming here raking up the past?' he'd shouted. 'It's all nonsense. Our boy died in an accident, that's all there is to it. She must realise that it's some crazy person trying to mess with her, mustn't she? I hope you told her that, Roberta? I hope you set her straight and told her to leave our son out of this?' His eyes had flashed at her; a warning she is used to receiving.

'I… I told her it must be and that the police would have done a thorough investigation.'

He'd nodded, but the expression on his face was far from a pacified one.

'I don't want the past being dragged up, Roberta. I've worked too hard to put it behind me.'

She wanted to scream at him that it had required very little effort because he is not capable of loving anyone but himself. She'd stayed silent, though, just like she always did. She'd learned very early on in their marriage not to stir up trouble.

'You stay away from her, d'you hear me?'

And that was that. End of the conversation.

Roberta reaches for her concealer, covers the black circles, carefully blending the cream in until she looks almost half decent. Almost. Then she hears Josh's voice, as she often does. Not as much as in the beginning, but every now and again it will be there, just to haunt her.

This is all your fault, Mum. Everything was always your fault. At least you could have sent me to swimming lessons, then I would have had a chance to save myself. It's your fault I'm dead.

She will never forgive herself for this.

Adrian comes out of the bathroom, already wearing his work clothes. He works shifts as a Sky television engineer and is on an early call-out today. 'Are you still thinking about that nonsense?' he asks, half-heartedly brushing his hair. It's still very thick and, if he's anything like his father was, she doubts it will ever recede. Did she ever find him attractive? She must have in the beginning, but years of living with him have slowly chipped away at her feelings and now she's numb, dead inside.

It might be different if he wanted her, even just occasionally, but that time passed long ago. Now she tries not to give any thought to what he's doing when he's out late at night and she knows he's finished his appointments. She learned long ago that it's better not to think of these things.

'No. Course not. I was thinking about work.'

He must know she's lying but he chooses not to press her. 'I've left a list of some stuff we need from the shops,' he says. 'You can get it all after work, can't you? I won't have any time.'

Roberta nods. There's no point arguing about it. He will just say that he finishes work much later than she does so there's no way he should have to do the shopping.

'Cheer up, won't you? You'll scare the bloody kids at school. Good job you're just a teaching assistant and not their actual teacher. Ha, you'd have been fired long ago. Poor kids.'

This man is cruel and heartless and she shouldn't spend another day with him, or even another second. But she can't walk away, can she? The tie that binds them keeps her a prisoner.

SEVEN

Zoe

I hear Jake's car pull up outside and prepare myself to deliver the news that I went to see the Butlers yesterday. This is as much to do with him as it is me, and I won't keep things from him, even though I already know what his reaction will be.

On my way downstairs I walk past Harley's bedroom. The door is ajar and I see him sitting at his desk, hunched over his textbooks. My heart surges; he's a good boy, he will make something of his life, despite the awful tragedy that befell us all. I know it bothers him that he's a year behind everyone else, so I try my best to assure him it doesn't matter. People take gap years all the time and it's usually a good thing to have a time out before getting stuck into studying. Especially since medical school and Harley's commitment to becoming a doctor will be his life for the next eight years at least.

Downstairs in the kitchen, I pour red wine into two glasses, and Jake raises his eyebrows. 'You're normally in bed by now. What's the occasion?'

'I just thought we could both do with it. It's been a crazy couple of days.' I hand him a glass.

Jake pulls out a chair at the table and slides into it. 'Yeah, that email. Whoever sent it is one nasty, twisted arsehole, that's for sure.'

There is no point drawing this out so I get straight to the point. 'I went to see Roberta Butler yesterday.'

Jake almost spits out his wine. 'What? You went to Guildford? Why? You haven't been back since…'

'I know. I wanted to check whether she'd got an email too. I just wanted to know if they're only targeting me.'

He thinks about this for a moment and must realise it makes sense. 'I suppose. And did she get one?'

'No. Nothing.'

'There you go then – I was right. It's just someone trying to get to you. If it hadn't been an accident then they would have said the same thing to her, wouldn't they?'

'I've been thinking about that and I don't agree. What if the reason they only sent it to me is because Josh had something to do with it? What if he's somehow to blame and that's what they want me to find out?'

Jake stares at me, slowly shaking his head. 'That's crazy! What are you thinking here? That Josh deliberately drowned them both? Come on, Zoe.'

'No. I don't think that exactly. I don't know. But according to Roberta, the boys had a bit of a disagreement a couple of days before and it's just making me wonder. We don't really know what happened, do we? All we know is that they both ended up dead and we have no idea why.'

'They were fooling around by the river and it was an accident, Zoe. The police said—'

'The police said that because they had nothing else to go on. But they could be wrong. What if we've been wrong this whole time? Don't we owe it to Ethan to find out the truth?'

Jake slides his chair back and it screeches against the floor tiles. 'Hold on a minute, are you saying you believe this email? You're taking it seriously?'

Until this moment I haven't exactly been sure. Now, though, my gut is telling me I need to probe further. And what's the harm if it does turn out to be just a prank? I've got to do this for Ethan, for the whole family.

Explaining all this to Jake is not easy, although by the end he agrees that it can't do any harm to dig a bit deeper and at least get more of a picture of what the boys were doing during those last days.

'So what exactly are you planning on doing, then?' Jake's wine glass is almost empty and he eyes the bottle on the kitchen worktop.

'I don't know. Roberta was a bit weird and not very forthcoming, and then Adrian practically forced me out of the house.'

'Well, you never liked him, did you? He was always okay with me, though. I actually got on with him, even though I never saw much of him. Maybe he just didn't want you dragging up the past.'

I ignore him. 'Anyway, I could try and speak to Roberta again in a couple of days, once she's had time to digest it all. She might remember something important. And I still think it's strange that she never mentioned the boys arguing before.'

Jake shakes his head. 'She probably wasn't thinking about that. And whatever it was, they'd obviously sorted it out because Josh was staying the night at ours.'

Which is why none of this adds up to anything concrete. 'And there's Harley,' I say. 'I could ask him what he remembers about that time. I know it's all a blur for me but it might be different for him. And you know how close the boys were. Maybe Ethan spoke to him about Josh.'

'He would have told us at the time, Zoe. And I don't think it's a good idea to mention this to him and bring it all up again. Remember how fragile he was. He almost didn't pull through.'

Jake is right. Harley still has one more exam to go and I don't want anything messing that up. I won't tell him about the email, not until I've got evidence that there's something in it. 'Okay, I won't talk to Harley about it for now.'

'Just tread carefully if you insist on going back to see Roberta.' Jake frowns. 'I don't like this, Zoe. I don't like it one bit.'

Harley is still studying when I poke my head around his door. 'How's it going?' I ask, startling him so that he swivels round in his chair. 'Sorry, I didn't mean to scare you.'

'You're still up,' he says. 'I heard Dad come home but I thought you were asleep. 'You do realise it's nearly midnight, don't you?' He looks worried, as if there must be something wrong with me.

'I know. I just couldn't sleep. I thought I'd wait up for your dad.' I sit at the end of his bed, smoothing out the slight crumples in the duvet. 'So how's it all going? Only one more to go.'

'I'm actually crapping it a bit, Mum. I've got so much riding on my A levels and I'm really starting to feel the pressure now. Physics is the hardest one.'

'You're good at exams, though – just remember that. I have every faith in you.'

'Thanks. Wish I could say the same for myself. Anyway, I'm determined to do this. I'm not going to let these exams get the better of me. I'm going to medical school, whatever it takes.'

'Just give yourself a break once in a while. You need to have fun, too. Balance is important.'

He smiles. 'I've got Mel for that, haven't I?' His phone beeps just as he says this and he scoops it up. 'That's probably her now.' He checks the screen. 'Yep, it's Mel.' He starts typing a reply before quickly apologising. 'Sorry, Mum. Did you need me for something?'

I'm about to say no when it occurs to me that there might be a way to get Harley talking about Ethan without having to mention the email or cause him any distress. I shuffle up on the bed, closer to Harley's desk. 'I was just thinking of Ethan today. I mean, I think of him every day, of course, but today in particular he's been on my mind a lot. I miss him so much.'

Harley moves his chair closer. 'I know, it's crazy, isn't it? Some days can be kind of okay and you just carry on with things, but then *bam*, it hits you like a punch and feels as if it's only just happened, or is happening all over again.'

I nod. 'Do you remember much about those last days with him? I struggle sometimes to picture what any of us were doing. It's all such a blur.'

Harley sighs. 'It's all I used to think about in the beginning. Going over and over everything. Feeling guilty that I hardly spent any time with him during that last week.'

A vague recollection of this hits me. 'He was constantly with Josh, though, wasn't he? I don't think any of us saw him much.'

'I was so focused on my GCSEs, I barely gave him the time of day.'

'I'm sure that's not true, Harley. You two were always together.'

'We used to be, but I feel like I was growing a bit distant, just focusing on my future and kind of leaving him behind.' A tear forms in his eye and he swipes it away.

'Ethan understood how important school was to you; he was really supportive and proud of you.'

Harley nods. 'I like to think so. I hope so, at least.'

'So you didn't notice anything strange going on with him and Josh around that time?'

Harley's eyes narrow. 'No, why?'

'Oh, I don't know. I just wonder if they ever fell out or anything like that.'

Harley considers this for a moment. 'Well, there was that girl I think they both liked. But I don't know what happened with that.'

My heart almost stops. 'What girl?'

'Daisy, I think her name was. Carter, or something like that. She was in their year at school and I just got the feeling they both might have liked her.'

And now I am the one battling tears. 'I didn't know anything about that. I've never even heard her name before.'

Harley leans forward and pats my arm. 'Mum, no offence but the last person teenage boys want to talk to about girls is their mum. And I didn't mention it because, well, it was Ethan's private business.'

I have always thought I encouraged my boys to be open with me, let them know that they could tell me anything, even if it might be difficult for them. Now I'm questioning everything I ever believed about myself as a parent.

'Don't worry about it, Mum,' Harley says. 'Seriously. It doesn't mean anything.'

'You're right. It's just odd hearing things that I never knew about Ethan. Anyway, I'll let you get back to studying, but you should get some sleep soon.'

He promises he will and I shut his door, standing out in the hall for a moment to gather my thoughts.

Daisy Carter. I need to talk to you.

EIGHT

Jake

He doesn't know what to make of that email, and hates what it's doing to Zoe. You can never be at peace after losing a child, but things were beginning to settle, and they had just about found a way to live with the pain. But where will this end? Zoe's determined to drag up the past and it terrifies him. Why can't she just let sleeping dogs lie?

Jake pulls into the car park, grateful for the half hour commute to his office in Ealing. It gives him time to switch off and become a graphic designer again, not a neglectful dad or workaholic husband. He never thought he'd be that person; he'd relished his role as a father when the boys were younger but Ethan's death stripped him of everything he ever was – father, husband... He'd been incapable of being either and he hated himself for that.

Inside, he's not surprised to find himself the first one in – he usually is – and makes himself a strong black coffee to take over to his desk.

'Hey!'

Someone taps Jake on the shoulder and he turns around to find Cara, Liam's sister, standing right behind him. She only works for them a couple of days a week, but acts as if she's got a stake in their business, that she's indispensable. Jake despises nepotism. Truth is, Cara helps out with admin stuff now and again but she's not organised enough to be useful, and now she thinks they're great friends. All he knows is that Cara is trouble.

'I texted you the other night – how come you didn't reply?' That's another thing about Cara – she's blatantly into him, completely ignoring the fact that he's got a wife. She walks around to the side of his desk and perches on it, her skirt rising up to reveal legs that seem to go on forever.

Jake quickly turns back to his computer. 'I was busy.'

Cara doesn't take the hint. 'I actually thought we could meet up for a drink. Go through my proposals for all the admin changes. I've got some good ideas, Jake, you really need to hear them.'

He doubts this. 'Didn't Liam talk to you about that?' He keeps his eyes on his computer. 'We're not averse to change – in fact, it's a good thing – but in this case we think things are fine the way they are. No point changing what doesn't need fixing, is there?'

Cara rolls her eyes. 'Oh, don't listen to my brother about this kind of thing. Yeah, he's great at designing and all that but he doesn't have a clue when it comes to all the small details you need to run a business.'

And you do? Jake wants to say. 'Well, we're doing a fine job of it so far, so…'

'Don't you have work to do?' Liam's voice travels across from the main door, where he's just appeared. He stares at them both, assessing the situation, how closely Cara is sitting to Jake, and probably coming to all the wrong conclusions.

Cara jumps up and tugs at her skirt, although it makes little difference – there is still more flesh on show than fabric. 'We'll talk about this later, Jake,' she says, squeezing his shoulder. He hopes she notices his body recoiling from her touch. She's an attractive girl, but other than the fact that he's married, there's something not right about her. He just hasn't been able to figure out what it is.

'How are Zoe and Harley?' Liam asks, scowling at Cara as he sits down at his computer.

Liam's a good friend but Jake doesn't talk to him about personal stuff, preferring to keep their friendship business-related. Besides, he's not much of a talker. Liam knows they lost Ethan, of course, but he never brings it up, and neither does Jake. He has to keep his workplace the one area of his life where he can come and not be the man who lost his younger son. He is powerful here, a man in control, making decisions, getting things done for clients. Nothing else comes into it when he's within these walls. There is far too much at stake for Jake to let his personal life cross over and taint this.

It's obvious that Zoe doesn't like this. She wonders how he can switch off so easily, and probably feels like he's turning his back on Ethan. It just isn't like that, though. He wishes he could explain it to her, make her understand exactly why he is the way he is.

'All fine,' he tells Liam. 'Yep, everything's good.'

Liam gives Jake a 'yeah, right' look, but doesn't push it. 'Hey,' he says. 'We've both been working really hard, and you seem to work even longer hours than I do. Why don't you take a couple of days off and do something nice with the family? I can handle things here.'

He should jump at this chance but the thought of it fills Jake with dread. 'No, it's fine. There's way too much to get done and not enough time.'

'You need to slow down a bit, Jake. Seriously. You'll burn out. I know the business is important but you've got to find that work-life balance, you know.'

It's funny to hear Liam say this when he's almost as bad as Jake. Almost, but not quite. Even though they're the same age, Liam's still single – by choice, that is, and he makes sure he finds time for socialising with women. Usually a different one every week. His latest *friend* is called Lily, and she's half his age.

'No, it's okay. I don't need a break.'

Liam leans down close to Jake and places his hand on his shoulder. 'Seriously, mate, you do.' His eyes flick towards Cara, who's making a good show of being engrossed in some filing, pretending she's not listening to their conversation. 'And *she* needs time to cool down, if you know what I mean?'

Jake doesn't bother commenting on this. Instead he thinks about Liam's suggestion, wondering whether he could do it. He owes it to Zoe and Harley; they deserve his time. He has to do it.

But seconds later his mind is a mess again and he knows he won't be able to. Ethan won't be there and he'll feel that gaping hole more acutely than ever without work to focus on. So he puts up that wall in his mind and tells himself that Harley will be busy studying, and he's sure Zoe mentioned she needed to go shopping. It's just not a good time for any of them.

To stop Liam pushing the issue, Jake tells him he'll think about taking the weekend off, and is relieved when the pressure of Liam's hands lifts from his shoulders and he can get back to work. It's the only thing he knows how to be good at.

Just before lunch, he walks in on Cara and Liam in the kitchen, and the raised but muffled voices he heard from his desk suddenly fade.

'I've had enough of this,' Liam says, throwing his hands up at Cara, before he brushes past Jake and heads through the door.

'What was all that about?' Jake asks.

Cara shrugs. 'My darling little brother seems to have a problem with me working here. I have no idea why.' She flashes Jake a wide smile and then trots back to her desk.

The two of them have never been the closest of siblings, but Jake's never felt the atmosphere so tense in here before.

He considers leaving work a bit early, just to get away from Cara, until he remembers that being at home will mean having to deal with that email and the person who is determined to mess with their lives.

Why does he get the feeling everything's about to come crashing down around him?

NINE

Zoe

Daisy Carter.

It didn't take long for me to find her on Facebook, especially as she'd listed the school she and Ethan went to. Her profile picture stares back at me, her flowing strawberry-blonde hair and slightly flirty smile seeming to reflect a belief that she has the world at her feet.

I never felt that confident at seventeen. No, my strength of character took years to cultivate.

Like a lot of teenagers, her profile is public, her whole life laid bare for anyone to spy on. It makes me shudder. Within minutes of browsing through her timeline, I have a complete snapshot of Daisy's life. She still lives in Guildford and is taking her A levels at the local college, rather than at school. According to her profile she 'can't wait to finish exams and start living her life'. You should enjoy it while it lasts, I think, smiling to myself. Wait until you start working, have rent to pay and bills piling up. You might think differently then.

I also learn that Daisy works part time in House of Fraser on the high street. This is too easy. I feel bad for invading her life in this way but I need to speak to her about Ethan and I only hope she's willing to talk to me.

It's too far a drive to just turn up at the shop in the hope of catching her on a day when she's working and not at college, so

I send her a message instead, stewing over which words to use before I finally decide. I rarely use my Facebook account but at this moment I'm grateful I still have it.

Hi Daisy, I'm Ethan Monaghan's Mum. I know we've never met but I was just wondering if I could talk to you about him as I understand you were friends? Thank you.

Now it's just a waiting game.

It's my day off today and Harley's gone into college to revise, so there are too many empty hours lying ahead of me. I called the police again earlier to check on the progress of the investigation, only to be met with barely disguised hostility. I remind myself that these things take time. They will get back to me when there's anything to share.

I scroll through my phone and text Leanne. There's only a small chance that she'll be free to meet for lunch in between clients and meetings, but I need to talk to her. She knows me better than anyone and will tell me if she thinks I'm going insane.

'Wow, this is a nice surprise,' she says, joining me at the table I've been sitting at for twenty minutes. 'Luckily you've caught me on a quieter day.'

We're in Piccadilly Circus, close to Leanne's office. I got the bus here rather than the train and Tube, hoping that a message would come through on my phone from Daisy Carter. Nothing yet, but it hasn't been that long since I contacted her.

I stand up and hug Leanne. 'Thanks for meeting me.'

'You're the one who's come all this way – I should be thanking you! Plus, you've got me out of the office when I probably would have eaten at my desk.'

We sit down. 'How long do you have?' I ask.

'Oh, for you, a good couple of hours. There's nothing back at the office that can't wait a bit. I'll just work later tonight.'

'Thank you, Lea. I really appreciate this.'

'Don't mention it.' She opens her menu. 'I love Thai food. I'm always in here.'

Once we've ordered drinks she wastes no time in getting to the bottom of this impromptu lunch meeting. 'Are you okay, Zoe? It's just that you're usually more of a planner than this. And, actually, I can tell something's wrong. I've known you forever, remember?'

Without a word, I pull out my phone, click on the email and hand it to Leanne. She frowns as she takes it and silently reads the words I've now memorised by heart.

She responds just as Jake and Roberta did. 'What is this? Who sent it?' she says, once she's digested the contents of the email.

I explain the whole story and tell her the police are looking into it.

Leanne grabs my hand. 'Are you okay? It's so creepy, isn't it? You must be devastated, whatever the motivation behind it.'

'Do you know what the worst thing is? Everyone automatically assumes it's just a nasty prank, someone just being malicious. Nobody is even considering the possibility that there could be some truth in it.'

She leans forward, giving me her intense Leanne stare. 'Do you believe what this person's saying?'

'I honestly don't know what to think. There's only one thing I do know – what kind of mother would I be to just let it go? Don't I owe it to Ethan to check it out further?'

The waitress appears again to take our order and I realise I haven't even looked at the menu. Leanne already seems to know what she wants and orders using numbers, while I desperately try to choose something quickly. I settle on a Thai green curry and feel relieved when the waitress trots off and we can get back to our conversation.

'I suppose it's always best to keep an open mind,' Leanne says. 'I just wonder why, if any of it's true, this person approached you in this way. Why keep it anonymous? If they really think some sort of crime has been committed then why not go to the police?'

I've done a lot of thinking about this. 'Because maybe, if they did see something, they shouldn't have been there? Maybe it's someone who is mixed up in it? They've obviously got their reasons for keeping quiet all these years.'

The frown on Leanne's face tells me what she thinks of this suggestion. 'I don't know, Zoe. It all sounds a bit... melodramatic?'

'Maybe you're right,' I admit, knowing I won't be able to rest until I know for sure – whatever it takes to find out. I will do what's right for my son, and for the rest of my family.

'So what exactly does Jake think?' Leanne asks.

Even after all the years Jake and I have been married, it still feels strange that Leanne has known him longer, that they were in each other's lives long before I came along, and shared experiences together that I wasn't any part of.

'He doesn't really believe it, although he's trying his best to be supportive,' I tell her, wondering as I say this just how true it is.

'Whatever you do, just be careful.'

'That's exactly what Jake said.'

'And Harley? Have you told him?'

I shake my head. 'Not yet. He's still got one more exam and I don't want anything messing that up for him. It took him such a long time to recover three years ago and he's finally back on track – I can't let anything disrupt that. Especially if this is all nothing.'

'You must be so proud of him,' Leanne says. 'He's still planning to go to medical school, isn't he? That really is something.'

Her words lift my spirits. Harley definitely is a special boy – young man, actually – and I won't lose sight of him in all this. 'Yes, he amazes us all the time.'

When our food arrives, I change the conversation and ask Leanne to fill me in on her life. She tells me that the man she was seeing – Ross – is avoiding her at the moment.

This surprises me. I can't think of anything about Leanne that would make someone want to avoid her; she's just so easy to be around. 'Why?' I ask. 'What's his problem?'

'In one word: commitment. It's been six months and he probably thinks I'm expecting a wedding proposal. Ha, can you imagine? Me? I love my own space and privacy too much. Ross just doesn't get that, though. He seems to think all women are desperate to settle down, especially one in her late thirties. I've done nothing to make him think that's what I want, though. Nothing at all.'

Leanne and I have spoken about this at length many times, and every word she speaks is honest. It's not that she doesn't like company – she's in a relationship more often than not – but she's happy to have her own home to go back to, a place she doesn't have to share. Jake and I have often joked that we should set her up with his business partner, Liam, but Leanne would never go for such an obvious womaniser.

'Have you tried to set him straight?' I ask.

'Yes, but he can't seem to hear what I'm saying. It's an alien concept to him. Oh well. No real loss, as I barely see him anyway.' I remember that Ross is also a solicitor, and can imagine that finding time for each other is difficult.

I'm about to mention this when a message comes through on my phone. I offer an apologetic smile and scoop it up from the table. It's a Facebook notification: Daisy Carter has replied to my message.

Hey. Yeah, I was friends with Ethan. Happy to help. What is it you want to know?

Relief surges through me. I don't know if Daisy can tell me anything useful at all but at least she's willing to help. Quickly I type a reply, asking if I can pop into her shop to see her when she's working next.

Her reply is immediate. *Am here until 5pm today. In the home section. Come today if you like.*

I slip my phone into my pocket and turn to Leanne. 'I'm so sorry but something's come up and I have to go. That was a message from a girl who was friends with Ethan at school – she said she'll talk to me but she finishes work at 5 p.m. so I have to get to Guildford as soon as possible. I'm so sorry, Lea.'

She is already fishing for her purse. 'No, don't worry, of course you should go. Find out what you can. I'll just finish my food and sort out the bill.'

I lean down and hug her; she is always so understanding. Always there for me. I make a silent vow to make this up to her as soon as I can.

It's nearly four thirty by the time I've made it to Guildford, parked in the town centre and rushed to House of Fraser. The home department is on the fifth floor and when I get there I look around for Daisy.

It's not long before I spot her – long strawberry-blonde hair tied back in a ponytail, eyelashes thick with black mascara, fresh glowing skin which probably doesn't need make-up but is coated in foundation anyway. She's carefully wrapping up some mugs in bubble wrap for a customer, so I stand back, browsing the kitchen accessories until the woman has gone.

'Daisy? Hi, I'm Ethan's mum.'

She hasn't noticed me approach and starts when I speak. 'Oh, I didn't think you were coming. I finish in half an hour.'

I apologise and tell her I've driven down from London, offering excuses she won't care about like traffic and parking trouble.

'Look, I can't really talk now as I've got things to do before I leave, but I could meet you after. I'll only have a few minutes, though. There's a café on the first floor and the shop doesn't close until six.'

I thank her and tell her I'll see her there.

Daisy doesn't arrive until half past five, and until she walks in I assume she has forgotten, or is no longer interested in helping me. But now she is here, sinking into the chair opposite me and dumping her bags on the floor underneath the table.

'Can I get you anything to drink?' I ask, even though I've already finished my latte and the barista has been eyeing his watch every few minutes.

'No, thanks. I'm not really into hot drinks.' She looks around, seeming distracted, as though she would prefer to be anywhere but here, talking to me.

'Thanks for giving me your time,' I say.

'So you said you wanted to talk to me about Ethan?'

'Yes. I've just been trying to get more of a picture of his last few months and weeks really. I never had a chance to do that at the time, and now it's dawning on me that I have no real idea what was going on in his life back then. I mean, I know what was going on at home – but school, for example. I have no idea what was happening there, other than how his grades were.'

I don't expect Daisy to understand this – how could she at seventeen years old? I have to be direct, though, without mentioning anything about the email that has led me here.

'I hope you don't mind me asking this but why now?' she asks. 'It's been three years. You didn't try and talk to me at the time.'

'I'm going to be honest with you, Daisy – I didn't even know about you until my older son mentioned you the other day. Otherwise of course I would have tried to talk to you before.'

Her eyes narrow. 'So Ethan never mentioned me? Well, that's not a surprise.'

'Why do you say that?'

Daisy pulls at the neck of her T-shirt. 'Oh, no reason. It's not strange that Ethan didn't tell you everything that was going on in his life; a lot of kids don't speak to their parents about everything. It's just how it is. I barely speak to mine about much, even now.'

'It wasn't like that with Ethan,' I say, wondering how true this is. 'He did talk to us, it's just—'

'It was an accident, wasn't it? I thought he was just messing around by the river with Josh?' She squirms in her seat, glances towards the exit.

An accident. This is exactly what I've believed for three years. As difficult as it was to get my head around the fact that it was such a senseless, stupid, random mistake, at least I knew. Now everything is unfinished, and I need answers.

'It *was* an accident,' I say. 'It's just that I wondered if you could tell me anything about Ethan that I might not know. It all helps with grieving.'

Her eyes narrow again. She doesn't believe me. 'How come my name came up anyway? I wasn't exactly best friends with Ethan.'

'No, I understand that. Otherwise I would have heard of you before now. I suppose I'm just curious.'

Daisy leans back in her seat. 'Okay. What do you want to know exactly?' She picks up her phone and checks the screen. 'I haven't got long.'

I can't tell her that I want to know everything. Every detail of every time she came into contact with my son, every exchange that passed between them. 'Start with how you met,' I say, ignoring the barista, whose clanging around is getting louder and more purposeful.

She shrugs. 'We were in the same maths class and had to sit next to each other. Mr Faulkner insisted on us all sitting boy, girl, boy, girl, like something out of the eighteenth century.' She rolls her eyes.

I chuckle at this, despite the situation.

'And we just used to talk a bit. That's all.'

'So you never met up outside of school or anything like that? Never hung around together at break times or lunchtimes?'

'No. Nothing. Mrs Monaghan, I wasn't Ethan's girlfriend or anything, if that's what you think. I really didn't know him that well. Didn't know much about him, except that he didn't work that hard, did he?' Her eyes widen. 'Oh, sorry, I shouldn't have said that.'

I wave my hand. 'No, it's fine. Ethan wasn't the most studious of people.'

'He was still clever,' Daisy continues, 'in a kind of hidden way.'

I know what she means: he was too busy clowning around to let people see what lay beneath. 'I don't want to make you feel uncomfortable, but do you think Ethan liked you as more than just a friend?'

Daisy snorts. 'No way.'

'What about Josh Butler?'

'Josh? No, it was nothing like that. I barely even knew Josh. I mean, we talked sometimes when I bumped into him and Ethan – they were always together, weren't they? – but he definitely never told me he was interested or anything like that.' She rolls her eyes again. 'And I would never have been into Josh. He was just a bit... out of control?'

I nod. Yes, he was, although I have to remind myself once again that Josh wasn't responsible for them ending up at the river that night. Ethan had his own mind.

'I'm just not sure how I can help you,' Daisy continues.

'There's nothing that sticks in your mind about the last weeks before Ethan died? Nothing at all?'

She shakes her head and reaches down to grab her bags. 'No. Sorry. Nothing weird at all. Anyway, I'd better go, they're about to close up.'

I stand up and get ready to walk out with Daisy but she seems to have other ideas. 'Actually, I just need to make a quick call, so I'll hang around here for a minute.'

I reach for her hand and shake it, a gesture she seems uncomfortable with. 'Thanks for your time, Daisy.'

As I walk away, I glance back, expecting to find her clasping her phone to her ear. Instead, she is watching me, and quickly looks down when she sees me turn back.

Why do I get the feeling she's been lying to me?

TEN

I follow him sometimes. It's got to the point where talking to him online just isn't satisfying me. I need much more of him. All of him.

I make sure he never sees me, of course, because that would ruin everything. The time has to be right for our first face-to-face meeting. He needs to be as desperate for me as I am for him. Soon. I feel it is nearly time.

It wasn't hard to find out his address. I just asked the right kind of questions and put the pieces together from the answers he provided. Getting the house number was trickier, but after walking up and down his road a few times I hit the jackpot and there he was, leaving his house, off to start his day. Following him allows me to be immersed in his life, and strangely it makes me even more attracted to him.

Seeing him interact with people – his fresh-faced smile and shy demeanour – is such a pull. I don't know how long I can stay in the background, getting to know him through only our written words. I need to act fast here, before there's any chance of him losing interest or getting suspicious that I don't actually exist.

Though I don't, in a way.

'Alissa,' he writes. 'Alissa, Alissa, Alissa. You're so beautiful and I think I'm really falling for you. I've never felt like this before.'

I'm getting closer now.

ELEVEN

Jake

Leanne opens her door, and for a moment she seems surprised to see him, even though she is the one who asked him here, urging him on the phone not to tell anyone – not even Zoe. Especially not Zoe. He can't remember how she put it.

She's still dressed in her smart work clothes – no surprise when she's probably only just made it home. She works as hard as he does – harder, even, because she's not got family commitments, no guilt about arriving home at midnight if necessary.

'Leanne? What's going on?'

'Just come in,' she says, pulling him inside and closing the door.

He doesn't take his shoes off, even though he always feels he should in here. Although he's not the most observant of people, he's well aware of how modern and spotless Leanne's flat is – not surprising when she's hardly ever at home, and also has a cleaner.

'Zoe doesn't know you're here, does she?' She looks nervous.

'No, but why didn't you want me to tell her? Has something happened, Lea? What's going on?'

Leanne sits on the sofa so Jake does the same.

'I met her for lunch yesterday and she told me about the email.'

Jake sighs. 'Oh, that. What about it? The police are looking into it and there's nothing more we can do for now.'

'That's just it. I'm really worried about her. She seems to be taking it upon herself to investigate and, well, where's it going to end up? She's just going to be reliving all the pain again when she's done so well to hold things together. I can't bear to think of her suffering all over again, especially for no reason. I've been thinking about this all day and it's just a sick joke, Jake, it has to be.'

'We don't know that for sure,' Jake says, wondering when he had this change of heart but knowing he has to defend his wife, even if it is against one of his closest friends.

'It won't come to anything,' Leanne says, so sure of herself that it puts him on edge. They've known each other since they were five and she has always been outspoken, never held back her thoughts, so this shouldn't surprise him. It's just strange that she's so adamant about it.

'Zoe just wants the truth,' Jake says. 'It's not doing any harm for her to look into it.' Again he defends Zoe, even if his heart is not entirely in it.

'No, but did you know she's running around talking to Ethan's friends?' Leanne stands up and folds her arms.

He sits up straighter. 'What are you talking about?'

'So she didn't tell you about rushing to Guildford to meet a girl Ethan knew at school?'

It takes him a moment to process this. 'When?'

'Today. She came to meet me for lunch but then rushed off to get there in time to meet her. I don't know what the girl's name is.'

Jake's confused. He knows about Zoe visiting the Butlers but she definitely didn't mention any girl. He searches for an excuse. 'She'll probably tell me about it tonight when I get home.' Will she? It's been a long time since they've told each other everything.

Leanne nods. 'Yes, course she will. She doesn't keep things from you, Jake. I just think you should tell her how crazy this all is. It won't do any of you any good. Just let the police do what they need to do.'

There is a long pause before he answers. 'How long have we known each other, Lea?'

'Too long. Makes me feel old.'

'And in all that time you've never been anything other than supportive, have you? So I'm actually a bit surprised you're being like this.'

She sits down again. 'All I care about is Zoe's happiness. Your happiness. This just won't end well, Jake.'

'Zoe knows what she's doing. She's too sensible to make stupid decisions.' Again, doubt fills his mind. He doesn't know anything for certain any more.

'But this is your son we're talking about,' Leanne says. 'It would be impossible for anyone not to be ruled by their emotions, wouldn't it? Zoe's not superwoman. She dealt with it all so well for Harley's sake, but who knows where her breaking point is? And believe me, we all have one.'

Jake stares at the woman before him, someone he's known for most of his life, and feels as though he's looking at a stranger. 'What's happened to you, Lea?' he says, shaking his head.

She turns away and stares at her shiny, pointed shoes.

'I'm not the problem,' she says.

TWELVE
Roberta

She's cooked Adrian a roast dinner tonight and it's not even Sunday. It's not a special occasion and he doesn't deserve it. He sits across from her, shoving forkfuls of food into his mouth like some sort of animal, chewing with his mouth wide open, not giving a damn how he looks.

This is the man she married. And that's not even the worst of it.

'Why are you staring at me like that?' he asks. 'What is it now?'

'Nothing.' She glances at her plate and cuts into a roast potato, her stomach squirming at the thought of swallowing it.

'Horse shit! Something's up with you and I don't have time for stupid games, Roberta. You've got something to say so just say it. Is this about Zoe turning up? She's really got to you, hasn't she?'

The past never stays buried. She must have known this all along, yet she's not prepared for it in any way. 'Do you think we were good parents to Josh, Adrian?'

He stares at her as if she's just spoken Mandarin. 'What? Why are you asking me that?'

'Please just answer.' Her voice is barely more than a whisper. It's always this way when she's in his presence, and she loathes herself for it.

Heavy silence hangs in the air and Roberta notices Adrian's face redden. Minutes seem to tick by before he responds. 'What does it matter now? Our boy is dead. Nothing will bring him back.'

She puts her fork down, still hasn't put any food in her mouth. No, it won't, she thinks, but we should both be suffering and you're not. The words crash around her head, desperate to be spoken but dying a death inside her.

'We're not good people, are we, Adrian?'

He stares at her, probably wondering where this has come from, how she's daring to say it. Usually she is reluctant to say anything that might push his buttons. But something has changed; seeing Zoe Monaghan the other day has caused an overwhelming waterfall of emotions to flood over her, and she no longer cares about trying to keep Adrian calm, about staying on the right side of his sanity. She's ready to take what comes to her.

'You're talking nonsense,' he spits, his mouth filled with food. 'You should probably just be quiet now.' His eyes glare a warning at her.

She does as he suggests and the rest of the meal is spent in their usual silence. But this time it's not because she's too afraid to speak out. No, it's not that. She's too numb, her head too filled with thoughts of Josh, of Zoe and Ethan. Darkness weighs heavily in the pit of her stomach, clouding her every waking moment.

Later, as Roberta clears away the dinner plates and tidies the kitchen, Adrian pokes his head round the door and tells her he's going out.

She nods and says nothing, carries on loading the dishwasher. He hasn't told her what his plans are and there's no point asking where he's going; he will only feed her a lie.

It's the slam of the front door that propels her into an action she's never taken before, never even contemplated. Abandoning the messy kitchen, she hurries out into the hall and throws on her jacket, checking her car keys are in the pockets.

And once she's outside, she jumps in her car and follows her husband.

Just as she knew he would, Adrian drives past his regular pub and heads towards the A3. She has no idea where he's going now, but she focuses on staying close enough behind him to keep him in sight without him noticing her car. She knows he is always a lazy driver, barely glancing in his rear-view mirror, too arrogant to care if there's anything behind him, or how close that vehicle might be.

A few minutes later they are on the A3. Why is she following him when she knows exactly what he's doing? Perhaps she needs to be a witness to it – one more nail in the coffin that is their marriage. And she's curious how far Adrian is willing to travel.

It's not long before she gets her answer as he pulls into a street in Farnham. The road is a cul-de-sac and far too quiet for her to risk driving into, so she parks on the main road and runs to catch up with his car, grateful she's wearing trainers that don't make a sound.

By the time she catches sight of him again he is knocking on someone's door, smoothing down his hair while he waits for an answer. It almost makes her laugh, Adrian caring about his appearance.

The door opens and Roberta sees her: a tall, attractive woman with long, dark hair falling across her shoulders, bouncing in waves that seem impossible to maintain. She's wearing a long, pink, silky dressing gown, even though it's not that late, and reaches forward to pull Adrian towards her.

It is the kiss that sends sharp, shooting pains through Roberta's body, the way he gently strokes her head and starts pulling at the cord on her dressing gown, even before the door shuts and all Roberta has left is her imagination.

She types the house number and name of the road into her phone and heads back to the car.

Something has shifted in her universe. Adrian has just made a huge mistake.

THIRTEEN

Zoe

'Shouldn't you be at work?'

Jake stares at me as I put my make-up on. It's past 9 a.m. and I was shocked to find him still at home when I got out of the shower.

'I need to talk to you,' he says, 'and you were asleep when I got home last night. Work can wait.'

'Wow, I don't think I've ever heard you say that before.' I smile to show I'm not having a dig at him.

'I'm worried about you, Zoe. All this email stuff, it's… I just think we need to put it behind us.'

My eyes widen. Something's happened to cause such a change of heart in Jake. 'Put it behind us? What exactly is that supposed to mean?'

'Calm down, that came out wrong. What I'm trying to say is that we need to put this in perspective and realise it won't do any good. We know what happened to Ethan, don't we? We lost him. Nothing else is important.' He pauses, takes a deep breath. 'I know you went to see one of his school friends yesterday and, well, I'm just being honest, but I don't think this can lead anywhere good.'

My first thought is that Leanne has let me down, but I quickly understand that she wouldn't have done this without good reason. 'I would have told you, I just didn't have a chance. What did Leanne say?'

'She's just worried about you, Zoe, and so am I. She seemed to think you weren't yourself when the two of you had lunch yesterday and—'

'Of course I'm not myself!' I try to keep my voice low; Harley is still in his room, getting ready for his exam. 'How can you expect me to just ignore that email?'

Jake sits on the bed and pulls on his shoes. 'I know it's hard but we just have to take a step back from this and try to be rational. There haven't been any more messages of any kind, have there? Nobody's approached you? It just doesn't make any sense to me. If this person is concerned about us, and really wants us to know the truth, then why are they making it into some sort of mystery? Making us try to piece together clues?'

It's been several days since I received the email, but only now am I considering this. There could be two things going on here. 'Because they want us to suffer? Or at least they want *me* to. It's funny that the email was sent just to me and makes no mention of you. What does that mean? Someone is deliberately targeting me. Even if none of it's true and there is no sinister explanation for what happened to Ethan, that's not all that matters here. I've been sent this message by someone and I need to know why, whatever that reason is.'

Jake takes a moment to assess my words, staring at me until he's finally ready to speak. 'I understand that, Zoe, but unless the police can trace the email then there's nothing you can do. And hounding Ethan's old school friends won't do any good. It was three years ago – they won't even remember anything now. Look, all I'm asking is that you take a step back. Don't let this control our lives. We're finally in a place where we have some kind of family life. I just don't want to lose that.'

He's wrong. We don't have a family life, we just have a *life*. I walk over to where Jake sits on the bed and put my arm around him. 'I promise you I won't let that happen, but you need to promise me something too.'

Jake sighs. He already knows what I'm about to ask.

'Please let me do what I need to do. I can't let this lie, whatever happens with it. If it turns out to be nothing then at least we'll know, and we'll find out who's targeting me and why.'

It takes him a few seconds to respond. 'Okay. But I don't like this.' He kisses the top of my head. 'You need to be careful. And don't keep things from me.'

I promise him I won't and go back to applying my foundation. Anyone witnessing me now would think I am a woman with a purpose, someone who knows exactly how her day will pan out. The truth is, I have hit a roadblock and have no idea what my next move should be.

Work is a welcome distraction, and just for a few hours I am able to put everything aside and focus only on the patients I am helping. This is especially easy to do when my first appointment is with a young couple who shouldn't have to be in this clinic. Juliet is only twenty-seven; she should have years of fertility ahead of her but instead suffers from unexplained infertility. She's been given every test available but nothing has shown up that might explain why she and her husband, Marcus, have been struggling to get pregnant for six years.

As I sit across from them, I want to reach out and take their hands, tell them that life is so cruel sometimes, preventing you from having something that comes so easily to most people, or taking someone away from you. The tears behind my eyes are seconds from falling and I can't let that happen in front of this brave couple.

'You're in the right place,' I say, trying to fill the room with hope. 'Dr Anderson is one of the best.'

They both smile and nod, even though inside they are probably shrivelling up.

I talk them through the protocol and my heart feels heavy in my chest. Juliet is too young to qualify for NHS treatment so they're probably using all their savings on this, or have borrowed from family. Perhaps they're even maxing out credit cards to pay for it. This isn't the first time I've wished I could pay for other people's treatment myself.

As they're leaving, I tell them it's all going to work out. It's something I know I can't guarantee in the lottery of IVF but I am compelled to say it to them.

Perhaps I am also speaking to myself.

Before I leave work, I text Harley to see how his exam went. His reply comes a few minutes later, telling me it went as well as it could have, and the smiley face at the end of his text reassures me he feels good about it. Seconds later he texts again, reminding me he'll be out with Mel this evening.

The happiness I feel, knowing things are going well between them, is tinged with sadness that Ethan never had the chance to have a girlfriend or sit his A levels, or have any kind of adult life. He would be seventeen now, and no matter how hard I try I cannot picture him at that age. He will forever be frozen in time as a fourteen-year-old boy.

When my phone beeps with another text, I assume it's Harley again, but it's not his name on the screen, just a mobile number I don't have in my phone. Intrigued and wary at the same time, I tap on the number and the message appears.

Hi Zoe, it's Roberta Butler. Can we meet this evening? I think there's a lot we need to talk about. Happy to come to London.

I knew there was more she had to say. My fingers can't move fast enough as I type my reply. Of course I will meet her.

*

Roberta is already standing outside Putney station when I arrive, and she doesn't smile as she spots me and walks to the car. Come to think of it, I'm not sure I've ever seen her smile – even before.

She opens the car door and lets out a deep sigh once she's buckled her seatbelt. 'Thank you for meeting me,' she says, staring straight ahead. She's dressed more smartly then I've ever seen her, in a fitted navy blazer, jeans and ballerina pumps, all of which look brand new.

'Have you eaten?' I ask, aware of how hungry I am myself. 'I could park up and we could get some food somewhere on the high street?'

'Thanks, but I'm not really hungry. Could we just… go back to your house?' She looks around her, scanning people walking past.

I didn't have this in mind when I agreed to meet, but it does seem like the easiest solution, and if I refuse then I'll never find out why she wanted to meet up.

Back at my house, Roberta shuffles nervously through the door, as if she's expecting an ambush or something. It's not hard to work out that she's always on edge because of Adrian, but surely she doesn't think he could have followed her here.

I urge her to come in and assure her that nobody else is at home. 'Harley's with his girlfriend and Jake won't be home from work until much later. We can talk in private.'

This seems to put her at ease and she moves through the hallway and follows me into the kitchen.

'This is a lovely house,' she says. 'Very different from your old one.'

She's right; different is what I wanted. Our old house was over a hundred years old and had heaps of character, whereas this one is a new build, minimalist with neat, clean lines.

'I remember Harley,' she says, gazing around the kitchen. 'He was always very quiet, I think. So different to Ethan and Josh.'

I flick the switch on the kettle without even asking if she wants anything. I am too desperate to hear what she's got to say to be bothered with a drink myself, although the formality of having steaming mugs in front of us is probably necessary.

'I loved that the boys were so different,' I tell her. 'They kind of complemented each other, and there was never any rivalry between them because they were such different people and wanted completely different things.'

Roberta sits at the table. 'Yes, I can see how that would work.' She glances up at me and her eyes look as if they are about to fill with tears. 'I wish I'd had the chance to give Josh a brother or sister. Even if it just meant someone to fight with – which, knowing Josh, it would have.' She wipes a tear from her eye. 'I know it's been so hard for both of us, but I imagine having another child to focus on helped to get you through those dark days, even just a tiny bit.'

I reach across the table and take her hand. 'Yes, you're right. If I didn't have Harley, I don't know how I would have coped.' Perhaps Roberta is stronger than I imagined. She is married to such a poor excuse of a man, who I imagine offered her little support.

'Even now, I can't really say that I'm coping,' she says, 'it's more like I'm just existing. I go to work, come home, cook dinner then go to bed. Every day. There's never any variation. Weekends are the worst. They leave me with too much time on my hands.'

I tell her that my work, and having a purpose, is what gets me through my own days. 'Don't you ever see any friends?'

Roberta snorts. 'What friends? The ones I did have pretty much disappeared after Josh died. They just didn't know what to say to me. I have colleagues at school who I'm friendly with, and they often invite me out to things, but I have no interest in socialising. I just want to be left alone.'

I tell her I understand, that even after two years in London I haven't made any proper effort to make friends, other than a couple of people at work. This is the second thing Roberta Butler and I have in common, even though in most ways we couldn't be more different.

The kettle boils and I ask her if she'd like some tea or coffee. 'Then we can talk about whatever you wanted to tell me.'

She waits until I've made us both a cup of tea before she speaks again. 'I'm sorry about the other night when you came to the house. Adrian was... out of order.'

'He definitely didn't seem pleased that I was there. But I understand the shock might have affected him.'

Roberta nods and reaches for her mug, holding onto the handle but making no move to lift it to her mouth. 'I'd like to say you're right and it was just the shock of it. I mean, I'm sure some of it was that, but, well, Adrian's just...'

'Rude?' The word leaves my mouth before I realise what I'm saying.

Thankfully, Roberta doesn't seem to mind. 'Yeah, I can't deny it. He is. I'm sorry.'

'Is that why you came here? To apologise for him? Because there's really no need. His behaviour didn't affect me one way or the other and it's not you who should be apologising for it. But I am concerned about you. I just hope he's different when the two of you are alone?' I don't know how we have got to this point, talking about Roberta's marriage. I was sure she was here to discuss Josh and Ethan. But I sense in her a desperate need to offload and I don't turn my back on people who might need help.

'He wasn't always like this,' she explains. 'Not really. Before we had Josh, he was a different person. Kinder. Laughed more. It seems fatherhood didn't really agree with him.'

'What do you mean?' My concern is increasing.

'Oh, Adrian didn't hit Josh or anything like that – he never would have done that. He just kind of ignored him, left me to deal with everything Josh got up to. Preferred it if he didn't even have to see his own son. That's why he was always out so much.'

I nod. 'I did notice that I hardly ever saw him. I just put it down to his work.' This is something I now find myself experiencing with Jake. 'Anyway, that's really sad; Josh was a good kid.' Am I lying? Just trying to comfort her? If I'd thought Josh was that bad, it would have bothered me that Ethan was hanging around with him all the time, yet nothing set off any alarm bells for me.

There are more tears in her eyes as she looks at me. 'Thank you for saying that, Zoe. I know he could be… difficult at times.'

'Ethan was so fond of him; that's all that matters to me.' I take a sip of tea. 'Speaking of which, I can't help wondering why you wanted to meet up tonight? You've come a long way and still have to get two trains back.'

'Actually, train journeys calm me down. And I've enjoyed the chance to visit London. The last time I came here was with my parents when I was a teenager. Probably Josh's age.' Roberta's lips curl into a hint of a smile and I feel sad that reminiscing about her childhood seems to be the only thing that can bring her any kind of joy.

I don't mention that this time she's hardly getting to take in the atmosphere of the city. She stepped straight off a train and into my car and now she's in my house, which could be anywhere in the country. 'So is this about Ethan and Josh?' I ask her.

'Yes. Kind of. I just… I've been thinking a lot about that email you got and I just wondered if you'd heard anything back from the police?'

My mouth hangs open. Surely Roberta hasn't come all this way to ask me something she could have found out with a phone call. Something doesn't feel right. 'They're still looking into it,' I say, playing along, despite my guard being up. 'These things take time, though. Especially when it's not a priority for them.'

'Will you… would you mind letting me know when you do hear from them?' She avoids looking at me as she asks this and stares into her untouched mug. It's clear that she's one of those people who find eye contact a challenge.

I give a small nod. 'Look, Roberta, are you sure there's nothing you can remember about that day or anything leading up to it? I know you said you possibly heard them arguing, but did Josh seem especially angry with Ethan?'

This gets her attention and she finally looks at me. 'No! Why would he have been? They were best friends. Even if they'd fallen out, it would never have got nasty.'

If she gets the gist of what I'm saying – that maybe Josh was angry enough with Ethan to do something stupid – she doesn't let on, doesn't confront me. 'I'm just looking for answers, Roberta. I'd made some sort of peace with the fact that Ethan died in a senseless accident, yet now I'm being forced to doubt everything I've ever believed. And if there's no truth to the email, then why is whoever sent it targeting me? Why didn't you get one too? Or why wasn't it sent to both Jake and me?'

Roberta shuffles in her seat. 'I can't answer that, Zoe. I have no idea. But perhaps…'

'Perhaps what?'

'Oh, nothing. I don't know what I'm trying to say.' She shifts in her chair.

I won't let this go. 'No, you do know, Roberta, so just tell me.'

She turns away and stares through the kitchen doors, out into the garden. 'Maybe someone's deliberately trying to upset you.'

Of course this has occurred to me, but no matter how much I would rather believe this is the case, there is nobody I can think of who would have it in for me that much. I try to treat people with kindness and respect and can't even think of anyone I've ever argued with. I explain this to Roberta.

She shrugs. 'I'm sorry, Zoe. I just don't know what to say. I know in my heart the boys drowned by accident, that there can't be any more to it. I just hope the police find out who sent the email. Then you'll have your answer.'

There is nothing more to say to her after this. She didn't come here to give me any useful information. There is only one thing she wanted.

We finish our drinks in silence and then she tells me she has to get back.

As I pull up to Putney station to drop her off, she reaches for the handle but doesn't open the door. 'Please promise you'll keep me updated,' she says, 'on the police investigation.'

And my suspicion is confirmed.

FOURTEEN

Harley

Mel's parents are so cool. They're laid-back and easy-going and he never feels any pressure from them, like maybe he's not good enough for their daughter. No, they just take him as he is and never comment on how quiet he can be. Harley loves being with all of them, more than being at his own house.

Sorry, Ethan. Believe me, it's nothing to do with Mum. She does her best for him and he knows she loves him, it's just that being in that house is stifling. Dad doesn't know what to say to him half the time. Oh, he makes small talk and all that, but he never goes any deeper. Never has the time.

'What are you thinking about?' Mel asks. They're in her living room, spread out on her sofa with Doritos and cans of Coke because her parents have left them to it and gone to their neighbours' house for drinks. They've both got work in the morning so it probably won't be a late one, and he can sense Mel is eager to make the most of this time alone.

'Nothing,' Harley says. 'My mind's blank – I'm just enjoying lying here with you.'

She rolls over onto him and he puts his arms around her slim frame, feeling the boniness of her shoulder blades. Mel definitely eats – he's seen her wolf down two Big Macs in one go – he just doesn't know where she puts it all.

'I know you're lying,' she says. 'You're thinking what I'm thinking, aren't you?'

Sex. That's what Mel's thinking about.

'Yeah,' he tells her, kissing her cheek.

'Let's go upstairs then.' She checks her phone. 'We've got some time.'

'Just how long are you expecting me to be?' he says, managing a laugh, even though he's terrified. Scared of letting her down, scared of letting himself down.

She laughs too, but hers doesn't seem to be hiding anything. Shouldn't she be nervous too? Maybe even more so?

'Come on,' she says, jumping off him and taking his hand to pull him up from the sofa.

He knew this day was coming but doesn't know if he's ready for it right at this moment. There's been no chance to get his head around it all and how it might change things between them. He doesn't want anything to be different. Everything's perfect, just as it is. Despite this, he lets Mel lead him upstairs and allows himself to just go with it.

Afterwards, Harley lies next to Mel, listening to the sound of his own heavy breathing. Mel's perfect body is draped across his and she's got the hugest grin on her face. He's made her happy. Thank God.

'Worth the wait?' she asks, nudging him playfully.

'Oh, yeah.'

'Do you feel different? I thought I would but I actually don't. Not really. I feel good, of course, but not different.'

He tries to work out whether he does or not. All that feels different is that he no longer has that weird heaviness inside him. That fear. It seems to have gone. 'I feel good,' he tells Mel. 'Really good.'

'Well, that's good to know.' She snuggles further into him.

For a moment she stops speaking, and he's actually relieved. The happiness he's just felt has become overshadowed by thoughts of Mum and how something weird is going on with her. He's convinced of it. She's not herself, despite her efforts to make him believe she is. It's unsettling.

He needs to find out what's going on.

FIFTEEN

Zoe

It's been a week since I received the email; seven days that have thrown my life into turmoil. I'm no closer to finding out the truth of anything, and I'm quickly learning that there are very few people I can trust. Although I understand her reasons for going to Jake, I can't help feeling that Leanne has let me down. She should have come to me first and been more honest at lunch about her worries.

I'm in the canteen at work this lunchtime; although it's not somewhere I usually go. Mostly I prefer to keep myself busy in the nurses' office while I eat, but today I need to see different scenery, be among the noise and hustle of this place and hope that somehow that will help me think. Being alone with my thoughts certainly hasn't so far.

'Hi, Zoe. Do you mind if I sit here?' I look up from my sandwich to see Doctor Anderson standing by my table. He's holding a tray with a plate of pasta and glass of orange juice. 'I don't want to interrupt you but this seems to be the only empty seat left.'

'Of course.' I move my sandwich and water closer to me, even though there is plenty of space on the table.

Despite being fairly new here, Leo Anderson and I have spoken many times and we get on well. Not many of the other doctors have much time for socialising with us, but he always makes an effort to talk and ask how we are.

'It's hot outside, isn't it?' he says. 'I can't believe we're having this heatwave so early in June.'

I smile. It's actually refreshing to discuss such a safe and normal topic as the weather amidst everything that's been going on.

'How are you finding it here compared to your last clinic?' I ask. Leo spent several years working for an international clinic in Spain, so this is probably a big adjustment for him.

'Love both places,' he says. 'It was just time for a change.'

Although I normally enjoy his company, I could do without having to make small talk right now. It's hard to take in his words or focus on what he's saying when I'm so desperate to find out who's been emailing me and why, especially when my lunch break is the only time I think about it. The rest of the time is for my patients and I need to give them all of my focus.

I smile at him. 'Yes, that's why we moved to London, so I know what you mean.' I grab my sandwich, suddenly feeling the weight behind my words. Ethan. Everything always comes back to his absence, and it always will. It's something I just have to get used to.

Opposite me, Leo begins talking about his old clinic and I let myself get lost in his words, nodding and smiling even though I'm taking in very little of what he's saying.

My phone beeps with a text and I apologise to him before grabbing my phone. The message is from a number that's not stored in my contacts.

People who do wrong deserve to be punished, don't they Zoe?
As Ethan's mother, why aren't you making sure that happens?

Without a word, I stand up and walk as fast as I can out of the crowded canteen, out of the building and into the fresh air, taking deep gulps of it before I sit on the steps outside the clinic and read the text again. I try to call the number but the phone's already been switched off. Of course it has.

There are only fifteen minutes left of my lunch break so there's little I can do now except call Jake and tell him what's happened.

'What? I don't believe it. What the hell is this person doing?'

I cover my left ear to try and block out the heavy thunder of traffic from the main road. 'I don't know, Jake, but the message doesn't feel threatening or nasty. That's what's weird about it. I don't know… It sort of feels like they really want me to find out the truth.'

Silence from Jake's end. He doesn't agree with me. 'Then why don't they just bloody tell you?' he shouts. I understand and forgive his frustration – it's not me he's angry with.

'I don't know.'

'It's a sick game, Zoe, I'm even more convinced of that now, and you're doing exactly what they want you to. You're falling for it.'

Does Jake think I haven't thought of this? That it hasn't plagued me every day for a week? 'I'm not falling for anything – I just need to know.'

The sound of Jake's breathing travels down the phone, but it gets lighter so he must be calming down. 'I do get that, Zoe. I don't like any of this but I do understand.' He sighs. 'So what now?'

I catch the sound of a woman's laughter in the background. It must be Cara, Jake's favourite person. 'I don't know, but I have to get back to work. I'll deal with this later.'

In the background, the laughter stops. 'Okay,' Jake says. 'Let's not do anything until we can talk again. You're still at work, aren't you?'

I sense Jake's relief that I'm at work and can't do anything for now. 'Yes, I'm here until six. Do you think you could finish a bit early tonight? It would be good to talk about this as soon as possible.'

I hear the same sigh I always get when I ask this of him. 'I really will try, Zoe, but it's tricky at the moment.' He lowers his voice. 'And Cara's just messed up a whole lot of accounts so I need to put all that right before I can leave.'

Again, the laughter in the background. She doesn't seem bothered by the mistake she's made, probably because her brother owns half the business so she feels her job is secure whatever she does.

Jake and I say goodbye and I trudge up the steps, the cool breeze of the air conditioning hitting me as soon as I step inside the clinic.

There is one thing I'm becoming more convinced of: despite Jake's assurance that we will talk about this, I am alone in whatever *this* is, and it's up to me to find out the truth.

SIXTEEN

My mother never wanted children; she's made no secret of that over the years. She was a career woman, working her way up the corporate ladder in an advertising firm, intent on getting to the top. The world was her oyster. And then I came along, taking both my father and her by surprise.

Despite this, though, she's done her best for me – at least the best that she was capable of – and she even managed to continue climbing that ladder, until the disease began eating away at her, slowly but surely sucking the life out of her until I became the parent and she the child. Now I can't even remember the woman that she was, can't picture her doing anything but lying on the sofa in agony.

I sit across from her now, feeding her minestrone soup because today the pain in her arms is too severe for her to manage. I force a smile and try not to show my resentment, try to cling to the love I have for her to get me through this.

'I wish you'd meet someone nice,' she says. 'You need to get out more, see your friends, have a chance to find love. Looking after me shouldn't stop you living your life.'

That's not it, though. If anything, it's me who is preventing any life being lived. But that's the way it has to be. Mum doesn't know about my secret life upstairs in my bedroom, doesn't know that the Internet has opened up the world to me, that perhaps this is the closest to happy I will ever be.

She will never meet him, and that fills me with sadness and emptiness. It shouldn't have to be this way. Still, thinking of him waiting for me, wanting me, erases the pain.

'I'm fine, Mum. I don't need anyone else to make me happy.' A lie. A complete lie. Sometimes I wish she could see through me, know that I'm not real, that nothing is real. How can she not see this when she's my mother?

'Well, that's admirable, of course, but you're only human. You need company, and not just from some grumpy old woman.'

'You're sixty-five, Mum. That's not old.'

She shakes her head then winces. 'Oh, it's all relative, isn't it? But you're young; you shouldn't be stuck at home all the time, looking after me.'

'You looked after me for years, didn't you? So now I'm just repaying the favour.'

She opens her mouth to argue but quickly closes it again. There's not much she can say to this. Fair is fair.

I need to get away. Spending too much time talking to her makes me anxious, as if my lies and deceit will leak out of me, flood across the room and drown her. I quickly finish feeding her and make my excuses to go upstairs.

'But it's still early,' Mum protests. 'It's only seven. Stay down here and keep me company for a while.'

'I've got work in the morning,' I say, knowing this will not be enough to pacify her. I work in a job centre, after all – not the kind of job where I'd need an early night. It's the kind of job where once I walk out of the doors at the end of the day, I don't have to think about the place again until I walk back through them in the morning. But I'm not complaining. I'm lucky to have a job and it gives me plenty of time for my online life.

Upstairs, I switch on my laptop and send him a message. A dirty one. One that will blow his young, inexperienced mind.

The reply comes quickly. 'I'd do anything with you. When can we meet? I'm beginning to think you're not real!'

Oh, but I am only too real, I think. I tell him to meet me on Saturday, at Westfield shopping centre in White City, the busiest place I can think of. Plus, it's far from anyone who might know me.

'Really? We're actually going to meet? I wish I could kiss you right now.'

There'll be plenty of time for that, *I think, growing excited even though I know this is like trying to catch the wind in your hands. I tell him I've got something to send him. 'I was thinking about you the other day,' I write, 'and I want you to know more about me, so I just wrote down my thoughts and feelings. Bit corny but I wanted you to read it.'*

'Send it now,' he begs.

In the middle of the night, he replies to my email, telling me he feels like we're connected somehow, that he can't explain it but we're meant to be together. How he can't wait until Saturday and won't be able to focus on anything until he's seen me, touched me.

Job done. So far so good.

SEVENTEEN

Zoe

The weekend passed too slowly, every minute feeling like an hour. The police have now seen the new message, yet it still doesn't seem to have swayed them from their initial belief. I'm up against it trying to persuade them; that's okay, though – I will persevere and see this through to the end.

Trying to focus on something positive, I take Harley shopping to pick up some holiday things. Jake and I both agreed that we would treat him to a week abroad for working so hard in his exams, so he's planning to go to Ibiza with Mel in a couple of weeks. When he's gone I will try not to let anxiety about him being so far away overwhelm me. He's nineteen, I remind myself. He's independent and sensible and he will be fine. Besides, he's going off to medical school in a few months, so I've got to get used to him not being in the house.

Now it's finally Monday and I can start finding out what the hell is going on. I've taken the day off work – the first one I've ever taken at such short notice. I hate letting people down, but I'm doing this for my son, for all of us.

When I call Ethan's old school, the woman I speak to informs me that his old head of year, Mr Keats, is teaching at the moment but she'll pass on my message. I reinforce how urgent it is and I'm not surprised when her tone becomes cold. She wasn't there when Ethan was a student, so she won't know anything about what happened, but Mr Keats will definitely remember. Although I barely registered his presence, he was at Ethan's funeral. I just hope there is useful information he can give me now.

After an hour and still no phone call from him, I decide to make my way to Guildford; the closer I am to the school when he calls, the better. For two years I couldn't bring myself to go back there, and this will be my third visit in a week.

By the time I arrive in Guildford, Mr Keats still hasn't called so I need to take drastic action. The school building looms in front of me as I park up and it feels larger than it did before. Ignoring the heaviness in my stomach, I head inside, prepared to wait all day if I have to.

Everything inside looks different, and it doesn't even feel like the same place. The walls and floors are now blue instead of grey and the curved reception desk looks brand new. This makes it easier, and I remind myself that Ethan would have finished here by now, and if he'd wanted to do his A levels might have chosen to go to college instead, like Daisy Carter.

I approach the receptionist, assuming she is the woman I spoke to earlier. Her eyes widen when I explain who I am and say that it's extremely urgent that I see Mr Keats today.

She frowns, clearly annoyed. 'I did pass on your message, Mrs Monaghan, so if he hasn't called back yet it must be because he's very busy.' Even when her frown disappears she doesn't replace it with anything like a smile.

I check my watch. 'It's nearly lunchtime, isn't it? I'm sure I can catch him briefly. I'll just go to his office.' I start to walk off.

'Wait! I'm afraid you'll have to stay here. You can't just go wandering around the school when you don't have an appointment. And you're not a parent of any student here.'

She has a fair point. I could be anyone, so she's right not to let me venture any further than the reception area. 'Fine. Then could you please call him again and tell him I'm waiting in reception?

I would really appreciate that, thank you.' I smile at her, just to prove it doesn't take any effort to be kind to someone.

Without waiting for a reply, I head over to the seating area and prepare myself for what will probably be a long wait.

'Mrs Monaghan, it's nice to see you again.'

Although he's kept me waiting long into the lunch hour, I'm relieved to finally be shaking hands with Mr Keats. His grip is firm and comforting, and I'm relieved that he's not immediately making me feel as though I'm wasting his time. He hasn't changed much in three years, and even back then I couldn't begin to guess his age. He's one of those ageless people, and could be anything from thirty to fifty, although judging from the grey hairs around his temple, I would say he's nearer to fifty.

'I'm so sorry it's taken me so long to get to you – it's been one of those days. Shall we go to my office? I don't have long as I'm teaching again next period, but hopefully I can help you with whatever it is you need.'

His office is much like I remember it; I have sat in this seat a handful of times before, listening to his concerns about Ethan's grades and effort. I would do anything to be having one of those conversations again, rather than discussing the death of my son.

'So how is it I can help you?' the teacher says, crossing his hands together. 'You moved to London, didn't you? This must be urgent if you came all this way to speak to me in person. I would have called you back, Mrs Monaghan, I hope you know that.'

'Thank you, but I would have asked to come in and see you anyway,' I tell him. 'This has just saved some time.'

I've had the whole drive to think about how to put things, how much information I should share, and I've come to the conclusion that I need to be honest if I want to be taken seriously. Leaning forward, I deliver the speech I've already prepared. 'As you know, it was ruled that Ethan and Josh drowned in the river that night by accident.'

He places his palms together. 'Yes, I'm so sorry. And I feel terrible that I never got a chance to talk to you in person afterwards, other than our brief exchange at the funeral. Such a tragedy, and I imagine that even three years on it hasn't got any easier.'

I shake my head. 'I'm here because the Friday before last I got an anonymous email from someone. It's best if I show it to you rather than try to explain.' I tap on my phone and hand it across to him, watching his expression.

'Oh,' he says, once he's read the message. 'What an awful thing to say. I assume the name M. Cole means nothing to you?'

'No. And then I got this text on Friday, when I was at work.' I gesture for him to pass my phone back and then I pull up the message.

He studies it for a moment. 'What does it mean? Do you have any idea who's sent these? I'm assuming it's the same person.'

'I have no idea who sent it. I wish I did. That's what I'm trying to find out. And before you ask, yes, I've told the police in London and they're looking into it.' I don't add that they're also not taking it very seriously, that they probably think I'm a nuisance for digging things up when they have already been neatly put to rest by police in a different county.

'Well, that's good,' Mr Keats says. 'So how can I help? Do you think someone at the school sent them?'

'Like I said, I have no idea. It could just be a prank, someone trying to mess with me, but I wondered if you could help fill in some of the details of Ethan's last days at school?'

He leans back in his chair. 'I see. Um, it was a long time ago. I can barely remember what I had for dinner last night, to be honest. All these changes to the curriculum are eating away at any time I've got, and my headspace.'

I expected him to have difficulty recalling anything. 'But you'd remember if there was anything strange or unusual at the time? With his behaviour. I mean, you would have let me know, wouldn't you?'

He taps his fingers on his desk, suddenly seeming anxious. 'I don't remember thinking anything at the time. You and I had a few conversations about Ethan's lack of effort, didn't we? I can't say it got any worse in the days leading up to… the accident. His behaviour was more or less fine, I just didn't really approve of him hanging around with Josh so much.' He shakes his head. 'I know I shouldn't say that, but I just used to think Ethan might have progressed more if it weren't for Josh.'

It always comes back to this, yet I'm still not convinced. Ethan was too strong-willed to be brainwashed by anyone. 'They were best friends, that's the trouble. And actually, Ethan had his own mind; I don't think Josh influenced him that much. My son certainly wasn't a pushover.'

'Well, you knew him far better than I did, so I'm sure you're right. But kids are greatly influenced by the peers they hang around with. I've seen the brightest, most studious kids go off the rails because of the people they're associating with. Happens all the time. Anyway, what happened to Ethan is such a tragedy. I'm so sorry.'

I'm not here for a lecture or for sympathy; I need something that will help me get to the truth.

'I don't know what to tell you, Mrs Monaghan,' he continues. 'Nothing sticks in my mind.'

'Can you tell me anything about Daisy Carter?'

'Daisy? I haven't heard that name for a while. She was a good student. Worked hard, did quite well in her GCSEs, if I remember right. She was Josh's girlfriend, wasn't she?'

His words stun me. He must be confused. 'No. She was just a friend to both the boys.'

He frowns. 'I'm quite sure she was Josh's girlfriend. I'd caught them, um, well, together a few times in the corridors. Told them to leave that kind of thing for outside of school, of course.'

So Daisy lied to me. I knew it. And did Roberta know about this?

'You're sure?' I ask. 'It was definitely Daisy and Josh?'

'Positive. This might surprise you, but it's not often I've caught kids together like that. It was a bit of a shock.'

'And as far as you know, was Daisy ever with any other boys in the school? I mean, did she make a habit of this or was it just Josh?'

'Not that I know of, and I really don't think she was that type of person, but I can't claim to be an expert on any of the kids' relationships, I'm afraid.'

He begins shuffling some papers together and I take it as a sign that he needs to get on and wants me to leave. At least I've now got something to go on.

I thank him and make my way out of his office, out of a building I wish I'd never had to set foot in.

Daisy Carter, you've lied to me and I'm coming to find out why.

EIGHTEEN

Jake

He's at work, staring at his computer screen, unable to move his hands. He's distracted today; everything feels wrong, out of place, as if the whole universe has been disturbed. In fact, it's as though he's been plummeted right back to three years ago and the moment they first lost Ethan. He doesn't want to be back there, but he has no choice. In a way, Zoe is forcing them to relive everything.

It's not her fault, Jake tries to tell himself. She's only doing what any mother would do, but why can't she just let it lie? Nothing can bring Ethan back, so they need to just get on with things.

Their marriage nearly didn't survive three years ago, and he's not going to let it fall apart now. No, Zoe needs to let this go, concentrate on Harley. He'll be living away from them soon so this time they have with him is limited. Ha, he should take a leaf out of his own book and practise what he preaches! He can't remember the last time he had any quality time with his son.

Thinking about three years ago makes him shudder. Zoe and he were like strangers, neither one of them knowing what to say to each other, and the terrible silences were far worse than any arguments or fights they could have had. At least that would have been some sort of communication. And Harley hated him; Jake knows this like he knows his own reflection in the mirror.

He really wasn't expecting there to be a second message. He thought one would be it, and that eventually Zoe would let it go.

Now there's no chance of that. Where's this going to end? He slams his fist down on the desk, grateful that nobody's here to see him.

Next to his computer, his mobile vibrates. He sees Zoe's picture and picks it up immediately. 'Hey, everything okay?' He hears the sound of traffic in the background. 'Where are you?'

'I'm in Guildford again,' she says, and Jake's head immediately begins to pound.

'Why? What's happened? Aren't you supposed to be at work?'

'I took the day off. Personal reasons.'

'Zoe, are you okay? You've never done that before.' Even when she's been sick with flu she's struggled in to the clinic.

'I've just been at Ethan's school, meeting with his old head of year – you remember Mr Keats, don't you?'

Jake knows the name but can't put a face to it. It was Zoe who dealt with most of the school issues. 'Go on,' he says, his heart sinking with every passing second. Zoe is never going to stop pursuing this.

'Well, I wanted to talk to him to see if he could tell me anything about Ethan's last days, but he couldn't think of anything.'

'That's because there is nothing, Zoe.'

'Wait, let me finish, there's more. When we were talking, he let it slip that Daisy Carter was Josh's girlfriend.'

Jake is confused, can't seem to get his head around what she's implying. 'But what does that have to do with anything?'

'Maybe a lot. When I spoke to Daisy, she said she was just friends with the boys – and not even great friends. She made out that she barely knew them. Now why would she lie, Jake? What possible reason could there be, other than she's hiding something?'

He pauses, tries to give his brain a moment to consider this. 'I don't know, Zoe. Maybe she didn't want to talk about it? Can't you remember what it was like, having a relationship with someone at school? More often than not, it's something you'd want to forget ever happened.' Jake had had his own fair share of disasters at that age.

'Maybe,' Zoe admits. 'I just got the sense that she was hiding something, and when I left she was on her phone the second my back was turned.'

'That doesn't mean anything. She's a teenager. They're always on their phones. Even Harley's is constantly glued to his hand.'

Zoe sighs down the phone.

Jake knows he's not being very supportive, but it's too difficult when so much is at stake. 'So you're coming home now?' Jake asks.

'No. Now I'm here I want to see if I can find Daisy again and ask her some more questions.'

'That is *not* a good idea, Zoe. Please just come home.' Even as he says this, Jake knows it's pointless, so he tries something else. 'It's harassment, Zoe. She's a seventeen-year-old and you're an adult. Just let this go. I'm sure she doesn't know anything about the messages you've been getting.'

Zoe ignores him. 'I'll see you tonight. I love you.'

The phone goes dead.

It should be even harder for Jake to focus after his phone call with Zoe, but somehow he switches off. He's had plenty of experience at that – forcing things out of his head and pretending they're not real.

He's designing a company logo for a new personal training business and is so engrossed in his work that he doesn't notice someone is standing behind him until he stands up to stretch his legs and get a coffee.

'What the hell, Cara? You scared the shit out of me!'

'Sorry, Jake. I was just watching you work. You really get lost in it, don't you?' That flirty smile again. The one that has no effect on him.

He glances at his watch. 'What are you doing here? It's nearly eight o'clock. And today's your day off.' It's also a day when Liam has been out at meetings since this morning and isn't due back in the office until tomorrow. This only makes him feel uneasy.

'I left something here,' she says, her eyes flicking towards her desk. 'Need it before the morning.'

He's not even going to bother asking what exactly she left here. No doubt it's a crock of shit. She just wanted to get him alone, he can sense it. 'Well, I was just about to leave so I'll wait until you've gone and then I'll lock up.'

But Cara won't be so easily brushed off. 'It didn't look like you were about to leave. Looks like you were about to get a drink.' She points to the mug in his hand.

'Nope. Just taking this to the kitchen to wash it up.' Anger boils inside him. Why should he explain himself to Cara? He makes up his mind to have a word with Liam in the morning about getting rid of her. He'd rather take care of all the admin stuff himself than put up with her presence any longer. If she was a man and he was a woman, he's sure he'd have grounds to make a sexual harassment case against her. *There's just something not right about her*, he thinks for the hundredth time.

'Don't let me stop you,' she says, fixing her intense stare on him. She really is unbelievable; thinking that just because she's attractive she can have any man she wants. Not this one. Not ever.

Ignoring her, he heads to the kitchen, silently cursing Cara because now he really will have to leave and he wasn't ready to go home yet. He half-heartedly washes his mug – it doesn't matter if it's still coffee-stained, he's the only one who drinks from it – and once again doesn't notice that he's got company until arms wrap themselves tightly around him.

'I know you want me,' Cara says, reaching down between his legs.

He spins around and pushes her away, too stunned to say anything.

She's not deterred. 'It isn't my imagination, Jake. I can see the way you look at me. I can read the signs.'

Now the words come hard and fast. 'Cara, I don't know what world you're living in but there is no way in hell anything's going to happen between us.'

'Oh, don't worry about your wife, she'll never find out. I know how to be discreet.'

Jake would laugh if he weren't so furious. 'You are joking, right? This is a wind-up?' He wonders for a second whether Liam's put her up to this to have a laugh with him, but knowing the state of their sibling relationship, it's very doubtful.

For a moment Cara actually looks hurt, but she quickly recovers. 'Oh, come on. Stop playing these games, Jake. We're alone here now – make the most of it.'

He stares at her – her shiny blonde hair cascading down her shoulders, her slim but toned body, the large eyes that seem to be begging for him. And Jake does something he knows he'll regret. He can almost see the next few days unfolding before him, the trouble it will cause, but he can't help himself.

Grabbing Cara by the arm he drags her from the kitchen, through the office and to the front door, ignoring her pleas for him to stop, that he's hurting her arm. He shoves her outside. 'Don't fucking disrespect me or my wife again,' he says, slamming the door on her and not caring if it smacks into her face.

*

We sit on the grass by the castle grounds, the sun shining down on us, bathing us in warmth. Daisy doesn't seem to appreciate it, though, and wraps her faded denim jacket tighter around her body. I peeled my lightweight jacket off the moment we stepped outside.

I'm waiting for her to talk and she knows this, although all she's doing is picking invisible mud from her trainers. I try to put myself in her position and remind myself she's only seventeen – it must be strange for her to be talking to me.

'So you and Josh…' I prompt.

'Yeah. We were together – if you can call it that. And actually, I really liked him to start with.'

'What changed?'

'The more time I spent with him, the more I got to see who he really was. And he wasn't a decent person.'

Although I knew Josh's behaviour was challenging at times, he didn't strike me as being that bad. And Ethan was clearly fond of him. 'Can you explain that a bit more? Did he do anything specific to make you feel that way?'

She turns away, staring across the road at the photography shop opposite. 'Josh only cared about himself. End of story. It's like he had no… what's that word when you can understand people's feelings?'

'Empathy?' I suggest.

'Yeah, that's it. Well, he had none of that. Josh wanted what he wanted and he didn't care how anyone else felt.'

'Okay. But Ethan considered him a friend. That has to count for something.'

She shrugs. 'Yeah, he was okay to Ethan. They'd known each other a long time, hadn't they?'

'Since primary school,' I say, trying to force away memories of picking Ethan up, Josh tagging along. It seemed, in the beginning, that Ethan was more of the leader and Josh the follower. Something changed, though, and I wonder what it was. It might have its roots in Josh's childhood, in Roberta and Adrian's parenting.

'Well, Ethan was much more decent,' Daisy is saying. 'I liked him a lot.'

'You told me last time that you didn't know him that well. What exactly happened between the three of you, Daisy?'

She lets out a heavy sigh and finally turns to face me again. 'Josh and I broke up because he was putting pressure on me.' There is a pause as she waits for my response.

Instantly I know what she must mean, but I need clarification. 'Pressure to do what, Daisy?' I can't come right out with it – after all, she's still only seventeen so I need to be careful what I say to her.

'He wanted sex. Ugh. It makes me cringe to think about it. We were only fourteen! There was no way I was ready for that and I told him straight.'

'So what did he do? He didn't try to—'

'No, not really. The pressure he put on me was all verbal – he never tried to physically force me.' She looks away. 'I don't think he would have known how. We were just kids.'

Pain swells in my stomach. Kids shouldn't be thinking about sex or adult issues; they should be enjoying their childhoods. What were Ethan's thoughts on it all? Did he feel ready at fourteen? I shudder as I consider this; it's something I'll never know, and in some ways I'm grateful for that.

'So is that why you left him?'

She looks away again, flicking her fringe out of her eyes. 'Actually, he left me.'

'Oh. I see.'

'He said he wanted to be with someone who didn't act like a child, and that was that. Next thing I know he's parading around the school with Rhia Johnson.' She snorts. 'I bet she didn't *act like a child*!'

'I'm sorry,' I say. Even though this happened three years ago, it's bound to have affected Daisy, her view of men, maybe even how she views herself. She appears confident, but who knows whether that's all a mask, hiding what's deeper inside her.

'My reputation at school was ruined after that. Josh spread such lies about me and I never lived it down. Everyone was nasty to me and it made me hate school. That's why I made sure I went to college for A levels – I had to get away from that place.'

'That's awful. Nobody should have to go through that.'

'I'm okay now, though. I've put all that stuff behind me. It's a different world once you leave school, isn't it?'

'Daisy, I want you to know that you can be totally honest with me. Was Ethan ever nasty to you?' I hold my breath and wait for her answer.

'No. He wasn't. He never said anything, even when Josh was trying to get him to join in taunting me.'

'And nothing ever happened between you and Ethan?'

She shakes her head. 'No. He wouldn't have done that to Josh.'

I remember Harley mentioning that both Ethan and Josh might have liked Daisy. 'So as far as you know, the two boys never fought over you?'

'No. What was there to fight over? Josh dumped me and Ethan never liked me in that way, so there was no problem.'

I think about all this for a moment, about what it means. Despite my initial hopes, it seems unlikely that Daisy can shed any light on what happened. And if the boys did fall out about her then they'd certainly worked it out by the time of the accident. Otherwise why would Josh have stayed the night at our house? I'd made them dinner that evening and nothing had been out of the ordinary.

'Just one last thing,' I say, 'and then I promise you'll never hear from me again.'

Daisy looks wary but nods anyway.

'Did Josh's mum know about the two of you?'

'I never met her. In fact, I never went to Josh's house – he only ever came to mine. I lived closer to school so never questioned it, but now I think about it, it is a bit strange.'

'It's hard to understand boys sometimes, Daisy. And it doesn't get much easier as you get older. Mind you, I'm sure they feel the same way about us.'

She laughs at this and then gives me a hug. 'I hope you find out whatever it is you need to.'

As I make my way back to the car, something niggles at my mind but I can't place what it is. I'm missing something here; nothing about it feels right.

There must be something else. There has to be.

TWENTY

Roberta

'I'm leaving you.'

There. She's said it now, and even in her quiet voice the words fill up the room, expanding, almost tangible.

Adrian doesn't flinch. 'Really? I doubt it.' He doesn't bother to look at her, can't take her seriously – never has been able to. She wonders if he has more respect for his other woman. The dark-haired one with the fancy dressing gown. Is she the only one he's messing around with, or are there others? Nothing would shock her; not when she's seen what the man's capable of.

Thinking of all this incites anger in her – anger she never she possessed – and forces her to see this through. 'Watch me,' she says, raising her voice to hide how much her insides are trembling, how scared she is. She'll feel better once she's out of this house and away from him, surely?

Adrian doesn't follow her upstairs when she walks off, which only makes her more uneasy. Shouldn't he be coming after her? He'll never just let her walk out of here; there's no way. Bit on the side or not, he will not suffer the humiliation of his wife leaving him.

Roberta's possessions – the ones she cares about at least – fit in a large suitcase and her weekend bag. She doesn't want wedding photos, or any mementos from her marriage; all she needs are clothes, toiletries and her photos of Josh. And, of course, the grey and orange hoodie he always loved to wear. It no longer smells of her son but it's still a comfort to her, even if it does fill her with deep grief every time she dares to get it out from her wardrobe and press it against her cheek. There's no way she'll leave it here, though. Adrian would get rid of it in seconds if he knew she was in possession of it. She remembers him clearing out Josh's room – stating that it would make things easier for them. He'd ignored her tears as she watched him strip away every last trace of their son. It was better that way, he'd said, the only way they could move on. Even though it had ripped her apart, she could see the pain in Adrian's eyes as he filled up bags to take to the charity shop, and in that moment she'd seen a flash of the old Adrian.

She's zipping the weekend bag up when she sees him in the bedroom doorway, staring at her. 'Why are you bothering with this charade?' he says, leaning against the doorframe. 'We both know you're not going anywhere. You can't, can you? Ever.' He is so sure of himself.

'Watch me,' she says again, annoyed at her feeble attempt at strength. But she must see this through.

'Do you think for one second I'm going to let you walk out that door? That's not going to happen, is it? It can't, and we both know it.'

Roberta tries her best to maintain eye contact. It's important she does this. That he knows and begins to fear what she might do. 'I'll go to the police. Tell them everything.' The words sound good, comforting.

'No, I don't think you will. Because where would that leave *you*? This isn't just about me, is it, Roberta? We're in this together.'

She's thought about this and knew he would play on it. 'Maybe I don't care what happens to me any more. Maybe it's worth the sacrifice.'

A frown appears on his face. He hasn't considered that she'd do this, that she'd have the guts. She hopes he's questioning everything he ever thought he knew about her. His weak and feeble wife, the one he could so easily push around. 'You wouldn't.'

'What have I got to lose, Adrian? My son is dead and he was the only thing I had to live for.' She wants to add that she doesn't even know whether she can still call herself a mother. Does that title get stripped the second your only child dies? Or are you always a mum? This plagues Roberta on a daily basis, but she will never give Adrian the satisfaction of knowing these thoughts.

'He was the only thing you had to live for because you *made* him your whole life, and that's why you're devoid now. It's like you don't exist. But I'm still not letting you walk out.'

She sits on the bed, fearing her legs will give way if she keeps standing, determined not to let her husband see her fear. 'Why do you want me here, Adrian? Really? We don't have a marriage; we don't love each other. In fact, I'd even go so far as to say we detest each other. So what's it all for? Show? You can tell people you threw me out if your ego is all you're worried about. I just don't care. Go and be with your little tart.'

Silence fills the room. While she was speaking, although the voice didn't seem like hers, she enjoyed being able to get the words out. Would even have said she was proud of herself. Perhaps she's gone a step too far, though. Now Adrian will question how she knows what he's been up to.

He steps into the bedroom, and as he heads towards her she tries not to cower like she usually would. Standing up, she lifts herself to her full height, even though she is far shorter than her husband.

Now he's right up against her, grabbing her arm, twisting it, reminding her of the Chinese burns her brother used to give her as a child. But that was in jest, just kid's play; this is not.

A million jumbled thoughts swarm around her head: is he going to hurt her? Or worse? Has she even left him an option? Closing her eyes, she braces herself for what's to come and is shocked when, just as suddenly as he grabbed her, Adrian lets her arm drop and stands back.

'D'you know what, Roberta? Leave. It's okay. In fact, I quite like the idea of you living in fear every single second of your life, not knowing what I'm going to do, because I'll tell you this much: going to the police will be the last thing you do.'

She looks up at him and this time what she sees in his face is not malice, not hatred. No, it's something far worse.

Grabbing her bags, she leaves their bedroom, and their house, as quickly as she can.

TWENTY-ONE

Today couldn't come soon enough. I've been counting down the days, hours and minutes until I can be close enough to touch him, to smell the scent of him. It's not all I want, not by a long shot, but for now it will have to do. One thing I've learned, being the person I am, is patience.

The shopping centre is even busier than I'd anticipated – of course it is, it's a Saturday – and I begin to feel anxious. There are so many young people around, people more suited to him than I. What if he meets someone else? I can't let that happen. I won't.

I'm an hour early and there's a seating area just across from Gap, where I told him to meet me. He won't notice me here, I'll blend into the background, just another shopper.

While I'm waiting, I eat a sandwich – no breakfast this morning, as it took me too long to help Mum with hers. I think about how a future with him will pan out. Just how will I make this work when everything is stacked against me? Connection or not, this is going to be the hardest thing I've ever done. He is the one I'm meant to be with; I know this like I know the sun will rise tomorrow.

Of course there have been other men – too many of them, if I'm honest – but none have given me the feeling he gives me, just with his words. What's that if it's not because he's the one I'm supposed to be with?

That's not to say I haven't liked people before, even fallen for them a bit. Take Billy Jackson, for example. He was my first, a lot older than I was, and he taught me things I'd never even heard of. I was in awe of him for his knowledge and experience – and then he left me. Told me I was too young, that he needed someone on the same life level as him. It took me years to understand what he meant by that, and getting over him was hideous and painful.

One thing all my relationships have had in common is that they've all been physical and have never lasted more than a matter of weeks. Not this time, though, not with him. It will be more than that, I feel it in every inch of my body, and my mind.

Yes, I'm older than him, but he'll soon come to see that age doesn't matter. Nothing matters except that we are connected. He has to know this.

I'm so consumed with my thoughts, and the excitement of seeing him, that I haven't noticed he's late. It's half past ten now, and we agreed to meet at ten. Still, trekking around London on public transport isn't always straightforward, so I won't worry yet.

Then it gets to eleven. Five past. Twenty past.

He's not coming. After everything – all our emails, sharing our deepest thoughts with each other, our fears and hopes – he's let me down. I should be hurt, upset, devastated, but instead I'm angry. I feel the rage in the pit of my stomach and it makes me want to throw up. I look around me and of course the toilets are miles away.

I don't give much thought to what I do next, it's more like a compulsion; I'm acting on instinct. Something forces me to take my phone from my pocket and text him.

'Sorry, can't make it today.'

I leave it at that; no explanation, no further apology for the late notice. Nothing to show him that my body feels like it's being ripped open.

Slowly, I get up to leave, and that's when I see him. He's walking towards our meeting place, not even hurrying, wearing a loose navy T-shirt and jeans. Trainers that look new. I'm so captivated by him, I don't notice at first that he's not alone, until he turns to someone and starts laughing. It's the friend I've seen him with before, several times, when I've followed him.

What the hell is he playing at? This was supposed to be a day for us and he's brought someone else along. Why? First, he's nearly an hour and a half late, with no explanation, and then he's got company with him.

Keeping my distance, I walk right past him, close enough that I could reach out and touch him if I wanted to. Of course he doesn't notice me; he's engrossed in whatever it is the two of them are talking about, and I am lost in the crowd of people swarming around.

I make my way out of the shopping centre, to the Tube station, feeling like I'm walking in slow motion, like everything has slowed down. Numb. Angry.

How dare he do this to me when I've got so much riding on it? Riding on him. Have I made a mistake in choosing him? I want to believe this, to know it, but when I scroll through the photos I've taken of him without his knowledge, I know I will have to fight harder. To make this happen one way or another.

TWENTY-TWO

Zoe

Harley's at home, eating a sandwich in the kitchen, when I get back from seeing Daisy Carter, and I rush to hug and congratulate him for finishing his last exam. 'It's over,' I say. 'Now you can enjoy the summer and get ready for university. Enjoy time with Mel.'

He feels tense in my arms when he should be jubilant. 'Well, it's better late than never, I guess,' he says into my shoulder.

I pull away and look at him. 'Don't think like that. It's only important that you've done it. Is something wrong? You don't seem happy.'

He puts down his half-eaten sandwich. 'I'm fine. Everything's fine.'

'Harley, I'm your mum – I know when you're lying.' I say this, but how well do I really know my kids? Apparently I didn't know half of what was going on in Ethan's life, and I'm starting to think that maybe if I'd been more observant, less consumed with work and my patients, he'd still be alive. But you can't force them to talk to you, can you? They know their own minds. I still the voice in my head and focus on Harley.

'I don't know,' he says. 'Something just feels weird. Like there's something going on – with you and Dad, maybe? Look, I'm nineteen, you don't have to protect me from anything.' He stands up and opens the fridge, rooting around before he pulls out a carton of orange juice. 'Do you want some?'

I shake my head. 'Harley, there's nothing wrong; your Dad and I are fine.'

'Really? Because the atmosphere around here's a bit weird. Kind of like it was after Ethan.'

Sometimes I forget how perceptive Harley is, how his quiet demeanour means his mind is usually working overtime. I open my mouth to spill the truth, but just as quickly change my mind. It's not fair to drag him into this; it's for me to sort out. He's leaving for his holiday with Mel soon and I don't want this hanging over him when he should be relaxing and enjoying himself.

'Perhaps I just wish your dad and I could spend more time together,' I offer instead. This isn't a lie, although it's not a major issue for me at the moment after receiving those messages about Ethan.

Harley walks across to me and puts his arm around my shoulder. 'I knew there was something, Mum. You should have talked to me. Dad can be so selfish sometimes.'

'He's trying his best. I'm not just saying that to defend him; he really is doing his best for us, to help us have a good life. I think he just struggles with juggling work and home life.'

Harley's not convinced. 'Hmmm. I suppose. But sometimes that's not good enough, is it?'

I don't feel comfortable talking about this with Harley, knowing how he feels about his dad, so I need to change the subject. 'Are you all packed? Mel must be really excited.'

He smiles; I'm finally getting used to calling her Mel. 'Not packed yet – there's still loads of time. But yeah, Mel's excited and can't stop talking about it, making all these plans for when we get there. It's nice to see her so happy, and it's a distraction from me moving away at the end of summer. She wanted to come with me but didn't get a place nearby so has to stay in London.'

'Oh.' This is the first I've heard of it, even though I knew it could happen. Young love often doesn't survive university days.

'It's okay,' Harley says. 'We'll deal with it.'

'I'm proud of you,' I say. 'You always handle things so well. You're so mature.' Maybe losing his brother has forced him to grow up too quickly, although I can't remember a time when he hasn't been sensible.

Harley smiles. 'Just doing the best I can.'

'How does Mel feel about it all? She'll be studying psychology, won't she? I would have thought there'd be plenty of universities offering that degree. Isn't there somewhere nearer to where you'll be?'

'It's too late now; she just has to accept the place in London. Don't worry, Mum, we'll be okay. Aren't you always saying if it's meant to be, it will be?'

I smile. 'Yes, that's my mantra.' As hard as it was to believe when Ethan died.

'Anyway,' Harley continues, 'I'm meeting Mel in half an hour so don't make dinner for me, will you? I'm treating her to Nando's this evening.'

'Okay,' I say, trying to hide my disappointment that I'll be eating alone again. I could do with a distraction from everything, especially when I have no idea what my next move will be.

After everything that's occurred lately, I should expect what happens, but it's a shock nonetheless. I'm eating pasta for dinner when a text message appears on my phone, once again from a number I don't recognise, and even though it's a different number from the one before, I immediately know it's the same person. This time I don't rush to open it. Instead, I sit staring at the digits, my breathing heavy and fast, wondering if there is any way I can just ignore it, pretend it never came and forget the other two messages as well. Then I think of Ethan, picture his infectious laugh and the way his face lit up when he was excited about something, and I know I can't let this go.

Maybe your son deserved to die.

Six words that have me struggling for breath, trying to convince myself that the words say something different, that I am somehow mistaken. This message is unlike the others. Sinister. And for the first time, I consider the fact that the person sending them may have had something to do with Ethan drowning.

When I can gather myself together, I take a screenshot of the message and send it to Jake. Seconds tick by, then minutes, and no reply comes. Deciding he must be caught up at work and hasn't had a chance to look at his phone, I grab my coat and bag and leave the house.

DC Palmer sits across from me, looking at me as if I've come in to complain about litter on the streets. She informs me that they were able to trace the first message to an Internet café in France, but there is no way to know who sent it and the account has now been deleted. 'And as for the text message,' she explains, 'it came from a pay-as-you-go SIM card which is unregistered so, once again, there's no way to know who sent it.' Her eyes flick to my phone. 'I can only assume it will be the same with the one you've just received.'

This is what I expected. 'So you're telling me there's nothing I can do? I just have to sit back and keep receiving these messages? Am I supposed to just ignore them, assume they don't mean anything?'

DC Palmer crosses her palms together. 'Mrs Monaghan, I can understand your frustration, and I want to know immediately if you receive any more, but at the moment, while there's no threat being made to you, there really isn't much more I can do.'

I shake my head. 'Do you have any idea how it feels to lose a son? And now I'm reliving it all again with these messages.'

To my surprise, she actually reaches forward and grabs my hand. 'I have two teenage boys, Mrs Monaghan, aged fifteen and seventeen, so while I haven't experienced your pain, I am a mother myself so I understand. It's just that there really isn't anything further I can do right now. Please keep me informed, though.'

'Can you reopen the investigation? See if anything was missed?' My eyes must be begging her, even though I try to keep my voice stable and rational.

'I'm afraid that wouldn't be up to me. And Surrey Police won't reopen anything without compelling new evidence.'

I knew this would be the case even as I asked the question. Well, if this is how it has to be, then it's up to me to find that evidence, and an idea is already forming in my head.

With assurances to let DC Palmer know if – or rather when – I receive another message, I leave the room and walk out of the police station, into the muggy summer air.

As soon as I'm in my car, I slam the door shut and reach for my phone. The anonymous number has probably been discarded by now but I begin typing a reply anyway.

Tell me who you are. I believe what you're saying but need more information.

For five minutes I sit in the car, sipping water from a bottle that's been in here for days, just so I look like I have a reason to still be in the police station car park. My heart sinks as it dawns on me that I'm not going to get a reply, at least not this soon.

The words in the message seem to echo through the car. *Maybe your son deserved to die.* How can that possibly be true? Ethan was no angel, I'm not in denial about that, but he would never hurt anyone, never do anything malicious. Yet, how can I just dismiss it, especially when his biggest influence was Josh Butler, about whom the same cannot be said? How do I know what the boys were up to when I was out of sight and out of mind? They could have been doing anything. And nobody has ever been able to understand why they went to the river that night.

I had always trusted Ethan, unless given a reason otherwise, so I wasn't breathing down his neck all the time. Now I'm beginning to think that was the wrong thing to do. I should have been more inquisitive, demanded more answers and explanations for things. Then he might still be alive today. But I cannot think what he could have done to make someone say he deserved to die. Surely only murderers and the worst criminals deserve that?

More than ever, I need to talk to Jake, but he still hasn't responded to my text. I start the engine and begin the drive to his work.

'What are you doing here? Has something happened?'

The look on Jake's face is more than just shock; he looks uncomfortable. I've turned up at his work unannounced several times before and never been greeted by these wide, nervous eyes before.

'Can I come in?' I say, ignoring my misgivings; all of that can wait. I look past him into the office and see that he's alone.

'Yeah, but what's going on?'

I follow him to his desk, where there are papers and pens scattered all over. I've interrupted his creative flow; this must be why he seemed uncomfortable to see me. Jake is not good with interruptions when he's in the middle of designing; once he's been distracted, he's never able to slip back easily into what he was doing. 'His flow', he calls it.

'I did text you but you didn't reply. That's why I had to come here.'

'Sorry, I was in the middle of something. Liam's out all day, meeting with clients, so I've got a pile of things to do before I can even think about going home.'

There is nothing new in this so I don't respond. Instead, it takes me less than a minute to fill him in on what's happened, including my visit with DC Palmer, and show him the text.

He stares at it for a long minute before saying anything. 'You need to delete it, Zoe. I'm now even more convinced that this is just some bastard trying to torment you, and you can't let him. Ethan didn't do anything wrong.'

Although I expected Jake to say something like this, it is still a blow to hear him so easily dismiss any other possibility. 'So that's it? We should just ignore it? Pretend it's not happening? The messages aren't going away, Jake – they're getting worse.'

'Zoe, please sit down, you're getting worked up.' He tries to guide me to his computer chair but I shrug him off.

'Of course I am! Someone's just told me that Ethan deserved to die! How am I supposed to feel?'

'I know, but just try not to think with your heart.' Be rational, he means; he's trying not to patronise me. 'Any sane person would have gone to the police if they had any information about what happened. Why would they want to do this to you? And what could Ethan have possibly done?'

That's what I need to find out. That's exactly the key to all this. There is no point arguing with Jake about it; I need to sort this out on my own, in my own way.

Paying another visit to Roberta Butler is what I need to do next.

TWENTY-THREE
Roberta

The bed and breakfast is shabby and doesn't feel clean. Roberta is sure it must be, and she has seen a cleaning lady in the corridor, yet every surface of her room feels as though it's contaminated. Yet it's all she could afford and it's what she deserves – so this is her home until she can sort out her future.

What future? She's not sure she's got one, doesn't know who she is without being Adrian's wife. She might have been a subservient doormat but at least she knew who she was.

Adrian. That piece of shit led her here, led her to do things she didn't think she was capable of. Lies and deceit are one thing, but what they've both done is far worse.

It's dark outside now and the only light in the room comes from the bedside lamp. It's enough, though; somehow it makes her feel safer. She sits on the bed and reaches into her purse, pulling out the photo of Josh she always keeps close to her. She doesn't often look at it now, and can't actually remember the last time she did. It's enough just to know it's there. Not like in the beginning, when she would clutch it as she fell asleep crying, salty tears soaking her pillow. How she had wanted those tears to drown her.

In the photo, Josh is wearing a red hooded top, his hair in desperate need of a cut and his eyes narrowed, like they always were when he was up to something. She'd like to think it was just innocent cheekiness, that deep down he had a kind heart and the ability to empathise, but that wasn't the case. Josh could be heartless sometimes. *Most* times. He lacked the ability to put himself in someone else's shoes, to understand what they were feeling.

It's when she has these thoughts that her mothering instinct, the urge to defend her son at all costs, kicks in, and she ends up justifying his character. He was a teenager, all sorts of hormones whizzing around his body, causing him conflict. It's so difficult being that age. That's all it was. He just needed to find himself. She should have helped him do that, but no, she turned a blind eye to his behaviour, would have done anything to keep the peace, to prevent him kicking off. Was she scared of him? No, of course not. Josh wasn't his father. And she's damn sure she never would have let him turn into Adrian, no matter what effort that took.

She strokes Josh's cheeks on the smooth surface of the photo then buries it deep inside her purse again, wondering if there was any point at which she could have changed what happened, so that both the boys would still be alive. Maybe she could have disciplined Josh more, said no to him once in a while? That might have set him on a different path. But actually, what it comes down to is that he was too damn nosy.

It's as simple as that.

Outside, the noise of traffic from the busy road is starting to fade. Everyone's going home to their families. To their lives. She lifts her phone from the bedside table and stares at the screen. No missed calls, no text messages or emails. Nobody misses or needs her.

She would even welcome something – anything – from Adrian because at this moment it feels as though loneliness and isolation will kill her. Isn't that just what she deserves?

It's only a matter of time before he comes for her. There is no way he will just let her disappear from his life. He would rather see her dead.

Come on then, Adrian. I'm ready for you.

TWENTY-FOUR

Zoe

I can't believe I'm here again, standing outside Roberta Butler's house, especially this late at night. However, this time I'm armed with more ammunition. I know she's been lying – or, at the very least, has chosen to keep information from me. Information I know will shed some light on what happened to Ethan.

The two boys were often at this house, and because she works in a school, Roberta was always home when the boys were, so there's no way she doesn't know what they were up to. And this time I'm going to demand answers.

Her red Peugeot isn't outside the house, but there's no off-road parking on this street so she may have had to park further away. Or her car could be in for a service.

Striding to the door, I make up my mind to wait as long as it takes if she's not in. I'm not needed at home: Jake is working late and Harley is out with Mel tonight so nobody will miss me.

I ring the bell and don't hear it make a sound so I tap on the door as well. Despite being summer, it's a bit chilly tonight, and I wrap my cardigan tighter around me and fold my arms while I wait.

Several seconds pass before the door opens and Adrian appears, frowning. I haven't even considered the possibility of him answering the door, or how I will get to Roberta if he does, so I'm momentarily speechless.

'Hi,' I say eventually, flashing a huge smile. 'Nice to see you again, Adrian. I hope you're well. Sorry it's so late but is Roberta home? I just need a quick word.' I flash him a huge smile, hoping he will be forced to meet my pleasantness with some of his own.

He stares at me for a moment, then sighs. 'No, she's not. Sorry.' He begins to close the door but I shove my foot in the way.

This actually elicits a laugh from him, which changes his whole demeanour. He should do it more often instead of looking miserable and shifty most of the time. 'Stubborn, aren't you?' he says.

'Where is she?' I ask. 'It's really important. I just need to talk to her for a minute.'

'Look, is this about that stupid email you got? Because we don't want anything to do with it. Neither of us. It wasn't sent to us and it has nothing to do with Josh. I'm afraid you're wasting your time coming here all the way from London.'

'No, I'm not. And I think Roberta knows that.' I say. It's a bold statement and not likely to get me through the door but I've got nothing to lose. If he wants a fight then that's what he'll get.

Adrian stares at me, his brow creased. 'Okay, have it your way. Come in.' As he steps aside, I begin to worry why he has all of a sudden made this so easy for me.

'Can I get you anything?' he asks, as we sit on the worn and faded grey sofa. His voice is much more pleasant now.

'Oh, thanks. Coffee's fine. Milk, no sugar.' His hospitality is another surprise; rather than making me feel comfortable, though, it puts me on edge. This is not the man I know, and not the husband Roberta spoke of the other day.

'I'll be back in a minute.' He goes off and I stare around the room, taking note of everything as if I'm a police detective. That's what I'm beginning to feel like.

I'm struck by the lack of family photos on the walls and above the fireplace. The blank spaces only seem to reflect loneliness. I'm sure Roberta used to have photos of Josh everywhere, and even though, after three years, I can understand her taking most of them down, I'm surprised there isn't at least one somewhere. I still have a framed family portrait of the four of us, a moment captured forever that I could never bring myself to take down from the living room wall. We're all different, I remind myself. It doesn't mean anything.

Adrian returns, holding a mug in each hand. 'Here you go,' he says. 'Hope it's not too strong.'

'That's fine, thank you.' I take the mug and place it on the floor by my feet. 'So do you know how long Roberta will be?'

'She's not coming back,' he says, taking a sip of coffee.

Uneasiness seeps through me. 'Oh? Has she gone away somewhere?'

'No, Zoe, not exactly.'

Even though he's being friendly enough, he's starting to creep me out; none of this makes sense. 'What's going on, Adrian?'

He shrugs. 'Well, I might as well tell you as I've got the feeling you won't let this go. As I said before, you're stubborn, aren't you? If you must know, Roberta's left me. Our marriage is over.'

It's hard to make sense of what he's saying; this is the last thing I expected to hear. When I met with Roberta last time, she didn't mention anything about an impending separation. Did she even know then? Or has something only just happened to trigger her decision?

Despite my feelings towards Adrian, I tell him I'm sorry to hear that. Besides, the man sitting before me seems different to the one I've drawn so many negative conclusions about. Perhaps her leaving him has been a wake-up call.

'I suppose I should have seen it coming,' he says. 'Roberta's... how can I put this? She's just not been right for a while.' He looks at me over his mug, waiting for my reaction.

'In what way? She didn't seem ill or anything. Exhausted, maybe.'

'I don't mean physically ill, Zoe.'

I hate the way he keeps using my name – coming from him, it feels creepy. But he's not being unpleasant. This is a side of him I've never known, and perhaps I should give him a chance. 'Go on,' I say.

He leans back on the sofa. 'For a long time now, Roberta's been acting strangely; it's almost like she's become a different person. Oh, I'm not being very clear, am I? What I'm trying to say is that I think Roberta has become mentally unstable. I just don't know what she might do next. That's why I let her leave, even though I really don't want my marriage to end. I suppose I'm still hoping she'll realise she's made a mistake and come back.' He pauses and lets out a deep breath. 'She's become erratic. One minute she's yelling at me and the next she's crying. I just don't know what to do. Weeks ago, I urged her to go to the doctor but she wouldn't listen, insisted she was fine.'

'I had no idea,' I say. I'm about to tell him that Roberta didn't seem erratic or unstable when I saw her at my house, but I think better of it. I'm quickly learning that I can't trust anyone. Not him. Not Roberta. 'Do you think it's to do with Josh?'

Adrian shrugs. 'To be honest, I have no idea. When it first happened, she seemed to keep it together. I mean, she cried a lot and didn't get out of bed for a long time, but that's normal, isn't it? She eventually went back to work and although she was quiet, well, that's what she's always been like, isn't it? I have to admit I was so wrapped up in my own grief that I barely noticed hers. That's terrible, isn't it? Maybe she's had some kind of delayed reaction to it?'

This doesn't seem likely but I'm no expert in this area. 'So what exactly has she been doing?'

Adrian places his mug on the floor. 'Where do I begin? Screaming at me, accusing me of having an affair when I barely even have time to eat. I work all hours so when she thinks I'd have time to fit another woman in, I don't know.'

I search his face, trying to determine any signs of deceit. Roberta and I are far from best friends but this doesn't sound like her at all. I want to question him further, ask him directly whether he *is* having an affair, but I need to keep him talking. Let him think I'm on his side. 'Well, I'm sorry to hear all this but what if she actually believes you *are* seeing someone else?'

He raises his eyebrows. 'With no proof? I'd say that's evidence she isn't being rational, isn't it? Which backs up everything I'm saying.'

I don't know how to respond to this so change tack. 'Where do you think Roberta's gone?'

He shrugs again, making me doubt how important this is to him. 'No idea. The only family she's got is her parents who live in Bath. I've called them, though, and they haven't heard from her for a few days.'

'Is she still going to work?'

'I assume so. They haven't called here looking for her or anything so unless she's called in sick then she must still be going in.'

Then that's where I'll find her. She mentioned before that she works at St Thomas's Catholic School, and there's only one school with that name in Guildford. It's too late now, but I'm not working until the afternoon tomorrow so I can stay in Guildford for the night then turn up at her school first thing in the morning. She won't be happy, but I need to talk to her.

'Aren't you worried about her?' I ask, although I shouldn't be surprised by his detached manner. 'Haven't you tried to find her?'

'Yes, of course I'm worried. I can't just turn up at her work, though, and I've got a job of my own. Plus, she made it clear when she walked out that she wants nothing more to do with me, so what am I supposed to do? Stalk her?'

There's more to this than Adrian is letting on; I feel it in the core of me. 'I'd better get going,' I say, standing up. 'Let me know if I can do anything.'

Adrian also stands, opens his mouth then quickly closes it again. 'What is it?' I ask.

He frowns. 'Look, I don't want to get Roberta into any trouble. She needs help, that's all. She's not a bad person.'

'What are you saying, Adrian?'

'I wasn't going to say anything, for my wife's sake, but now you're here it feels like the right thing to do. She's lost it, Zoe. I think Roberta is the one who sent you that email.'

TWENTY-FIVE

Jake

He reads Zoe's text again, hoping when he re-examines it that the words will say something different, not that she needs to speak to Roberta Butler first thing in the morning so she has to stay the night in Guildford.

Why can't she let this go? It will slowly destroy them; he's sure of that, while his wife is oblivious.

All the feelings he had when Ethan first died are flooding back, threatening to drown him if he doesn't find a way to stem the flood. Why couldn't he have saved his son? If he'd just woken up and seen the boys sneaking out of the house then Ethan would still be here today, and his marriage would be unscarred. He loves Zoe, he always has, even in their darkest moments, but he sometimes has to numb himself, make sure he is immune to her. It's his only way of dealing with things.

'Here you go,' Leanne says, handing him a glass of wine. 'You really look like you could do with it.'

'Thanks.' He takes the glass and places it to his mouth, his whole body feeling heavy as he takes a large sip.

'Wow,' Leanne says. 'Hard day at work?'

Jake probably shouldn't have come to Leanne's flat tonight, but she's his closest friend and he doesn't know what else to do. And there's nobody else who understands Zoe as well as she does. He was surprised to find her at home and, if he's honest with himself, part of him was hoping she wouldn't be.

So here they are, sitting on Leanne's sofa, both of them still in their work clothes. 'No, it's not that. Work's the least of my worries.'

'Then it must be Zoe. Is she okay? I know she must be angry with me for talking to you about her.'

'Actually, she didn't focus on that. She's too stressed about what's been going on.'

'Has something else happened, Jake – something to do with that email?' Her forehead creases as she asks this.

It's always so easy to talk to Leanne; she never judges him and he doesn't have to worry about upsetting her feelings or anything like that. He can just be himself. He can with Zoe too, of course, but every word between them is shrouded in other stuff. Ethan. And now these messages. He explains to Leanne that there have been two more, and it's unlikely the person will stop there. And the more messages Zoe gets, the more likely she is to pursue this.

Jake has some more wine then lets out all his concerns: how Zoe is staying in Guildford tonight, determined not to let this email nonsense go; how she's adamant that the messages are more than someone tormenting her.

'I've been worrying about this,' Leanne tells him, once he's finished. 'I saw what it did to her when Ethan died, and now it could be happening all over again.'

'Zoe's strong, though,' Jake says. 'I don't think she'll fall apart. She's already been through the worst.'

'But isn't that already happening? Just her pursuit of this is enough. We've got to help her – make her see she needs to stop. You know that as well as I do, Jake.'

She turns away and takes a sip of wine, shaking her head when she's finished.

'I can't stop her,' says Jake. 'I've tried, but she won't listen to me.' He admires Zoe's determination but it can be frustrating too.

Leanne chuckles. 'Isn't that what we both love about her? That she knows her own mind and won't let anyone change it?'

'Her stubbornness, you mean?'

'Yeah, that sounds about right. But this is serious, Jake. We need to do something.'

Jake feels like he's heading towards a cliff edge, unable to stop himself moving forward, and only one thing is certain: disaster. Ethan is gone; there's nothing they can do about that and they need to let it lie. He needs to convince himself that the guilt he feels is only causing him harm, along with everyone around him. He's not the same person he was before and he'll never be that man again, but he can try to make up for that.

'She needs to be reminded that it was an accident, doesn't she?' Leanne says, staring at him over her wine glass, which Jake notices is nearly empty. He hasn't even been aware of her drinking it.

He doesn't answer, and stands up, taking his wine over to the balcony doors. Leanne's flat overlooks the river and the view is breathtaking, especially when it's dark and the night is illuminated by street lights.

Jake is so caught up in the scene, he fails to notice Leanne has joined him at the window until she speaks.

'Jake, I know I'm changing the subject but I just have to ask you this. You'd never tell Zoe, would you? About what happened?'

He freezes, cannot bear to look at Leanne at this moment. He never thought he would hear these words or have anything like this discussion. He doesn't know what to say, but he's aware staying silent won't do any good. 'No, of course not. I would never hurt her like that.'

'It was a long time ago, wasn't it?'

He longs for her to stop talking about this, cannot bear to hear it. 'Yes,' he replies. 'And I've kept my mouth shut, never said a word, just like we agreed. What would she think of me – of both of us – if she found out now?'

He's often pondered this question, and it scares him, because ultimately their whole marriage is based on a lie. And as for Zoe's friendship with Leanne, well, he knows it would be over in a second if it all came out. He's spent three years ignoring this issue, pretending it never happened. He's good at that.

Now, though, standing next to Leanne, he remembers every detail clearly. It was six weeks after Ethan died and Jake had hit rock bottom. He hadn't wanted to burden Zoe with his own grief when she was struggling so much herself, so he'd borne the weight of it in silence and then turned to Leanne when it threatened to crush him and he could no longer keep it all in.

He'd gone round to the flat she'd had in Guildford, just as he'd done many times before, because she was his closest friend, and she'd listened to him, cried with him, shared his burden and understood why he felt so consumed with guilt.

They'd talked until the early hours of the morning, and somewhere along the way wine had been consumed, but he doesn't blame alcohol for what happened. No, he takes full responsibility.

He's ashamed of what he did. It started with him just holding her hand. He needed the warmth of human contact, to know that he still existed as a man, as a human being. That would have been fine, but then he was leaning into her, reaching for her face and pulling her towards him.

He expected her to push him away. Of course she wouldn't kiss him back – Leanne and Zoe were like sisters, and neither of them would ever hurt the other – and although she'd hesitated for a moment, pulled back slightly, within seconds they were frantically pulling each other's clothes off, discarding them on the carpet.

Afterwards, they'd both been horrified, shamefully covering themselves up, neither of them able to speak a word. Leanne had got up and shut herself in the bathroom, but before she'd left the room she'd turned to him and her eyes were filled with tears.

Neither of them said a word afterwards, and by not mentioning it, they somehow managed to maintain their friendship, so that eventually it was as if it had never happened. He can't even remember what the sex was like; his mind had been a fog of grief and guilt, even as his hands had been all over Leanne's body. All he knows is that it was a huge mistake, and not something he ever wants to relive or repeat. Leanne is his friend, not someone to sleep with. And even worse than that, she is Zoe's friend.

Why has she brought this up now?

'It's too late to even think about what she'd do if she found out,' Leanne says, staring through the window. 'The time to say something would have been right after it happened. But there was no way we could have when you'd both just lost Ethan. But if we had, maybe – just maybe – there might have been a small part of her that understood neither of us were in our right minds.' She pauses and he lets the brief silence wash over him. 'We're terrible people, Jake. I've hated myself every day since it happened.'

'Why did it even happen, Leanne? I know you've never been interested in me in that way.'

Leanne stares out of the balcony doors and seconds tick by before she answers. 'I'm so ashamed of myself. I know I'm the one who brought this up, but it's really hard to talk about. Maybe, though, it's about time we did.'

Jake almost doesn't want to hear what she's going to say next, but deep down he's always been curious. He knows his own reasons for his actions, but he has never been able to understand Leanne's.

'I felt your pain so much that I couldn't push you away, I couldn't stop what was happening. I knew how much you needed me in that moment and I couldn't let you down.'

Jake can't believe what he's hearing. 'Are you saying you felt sorry for me? That's why you slept with me?'

Leanne shakes her head. 'No, not at all. Oh, this is coming out all wrong. I meant, in that moment we both needed each other. You won't understand this but I needed you just as much.'

Jake is confused. 'In what way? I know you were close to both the boys, and still are to Harley. You almost treated them as your own, but—'

'I'd just split up with Seb, remember? He'd shattered my self-confidence and I was devastated but trying to cope, and then when Ethan died it just all overwhelmed me. I was there trying to support you, Zoe and Harley and inside I was a complete mess. Please don't think I'm making excuses – there are none – but, like you, I was not in a good place. I think we both just needed comfort from somewhere and we took it without thinking of the consequences.' There are tears in her eyes now as she continues staring out at the river, avoiding his gaze.

He doesn't know what to say to her and he feels as though his blood is heating up by the second. He wasn't expecting to have a conversation like this tonight. Eventually, though, he finds some words. 'I think it was better when we hadn't spoken about it. No good can come of going over it now. And to be honest, Leanne, I'm not in the best frame of mind to be addressing what we did.' He feels terrible for saying this when Leanne clearly needs to unburden herself. He reminds himself that she's always been there for him, so he needs to be there for her now, as uncomfortable as it makes him feel.

'Actually,' Leanne continues, ignoring him. 'There is something I've always wondered. Do you think I'm a terrible friend for what I did to Zoe?'

Jake has never felt so awkward around Leanne, not even in the days immediately following their night together, when he had to act as though everything was normal, pretend he hadn't seen Leanne naked, heard her groans in his ear. 'No. You've been a great friend to her, always. We just made a mistake, that's all. A huge one. At the worst possible time.'

'A mistake,' she mumbles. 'Yes.'

'And if you're a terrible friend then I'm an even worse husband.' He knows he hasn't been a great husband since Ethan died, and sleeping with Leanne played a pivotal part in this, but he has tried to block it out. He can't deal with the fact that Zoe deserves so much better than him.

Jake hesitates. 'So you've never... been interested in me in that way?' The question seems to come out of nowhere, but it's something he needs to make sure of.

'Stop with the interrogation, Jake!'

Jake's not sure why Leanne's suddenly so defensive, but he needs to defuse the situation. 'Look, sorry if I'm coming across all wrong. I don't mean anything by it, it's just something I've wondered since that night.'

Without a word, Leanne walks to the coffee table where she left the bottle of wine and refills both their glasses. 'The truth is, I had thought about it before it happened – long before I set you up with Zoe. I just didn't act on it. Don't ask me why, because I can't explain it.'

Can't or won't, he wonders.

'And then after we slept together, even though I felt so guilty and hated myself, like I said, it made me feel even closer to you, because I'd seen a different side to you. But I had to keep telling myself it was *you,* and at the end of the day you were my close friend. I just focused on that. My feelings about anything else didn't matter.'

She turns away and downs too much wine. This is the first hint Jake has had that Leanne might have wanted something more from him.

'Leanne, I'm sorry about what happened. It's all my fault – I should never have put you in that situation. I just—'

'I don't want to talk about this any more, Jake. I'm sorry I brought it all up. So, tell me, what are you going to do about

Zoe and these messages? That's why you're here, isn't it? Let's just focus on that.'

Now he's plummeting back to the present and he feels like shit all over again. 'I'm going to be honest with her about what a mistake she's making,' Jake says, only now deciding what he has to do. 'And then I'm going to stop her.'

Leanne searches his face, probably trying to determine whether he really means this. 'Good. I think we both know that's for the best, don't we, Jake?'

TWENTY-SIX

Harley

'My parents are going out in a few minutes.' Mel smiles at him, a cheeky, flirtatious glint in her eyes.

'Cool,' he says, yet now he feels a bit trapped, like he has no choice but to perform when a few minutes ago he had no idea they would be alone this evening. He'd had his mind set on listening to some tunes, maybe watching a bit of TV. They could catch up on *Dragons' Den* on iPlayer. He loves that programme, though he isn't sure Mel's a fan. She goes along with watching it, maybe just to please him, but she never seems particularly interested.

They're lying on her bed and she slides her hand up his leg and begins rubbing him. He feels himself stiffen beneath his jeans. 'D'you know what?' he blurts out, grabbing her hand and squeezing it in his. 'We haven't really celebrated the end of our exams. Shall we go to a bar and have a few drinks? It's been ages since we've been anywhere.'

Mel's smile disappears. 'Oh, okay, if you want to. I'll have to get changed, though. And put on some make-up.'

He thinks about pointing out that she doesn't need to wear that stuff, but he reconsiders. He can tell she loves wearing it, and he's already disappointed her once today.

When she begins removing her clothes right in front of him, even though her parents are still downstairs, Harley turns away and focuses on his phone, scrolling through Facebook, even though he hates social media. He would delete his account, but he feels damned if he does and damned if he doesn't.

He can feel Mel's eyes on him as she undresses, and he senses that she wants him to look at her, to forget going out and stay in her bedroom all evening instead.

Now he's mentioned it, though, he's becoming increasingly more desperate to get out, breathe in some fresh air and have a few drinks. He's still worried about his mum and isn't buying any of her protestations that everything's okay.

The next time he looks up, Mel's slipped into a navy blue dress that hugs every inch of her body. 'You look amazing,' he tells her.

'Thanks,' she says, but she seems anything but pleased at his compliment.

Harley wonders whether he will ever understand women.

They head into the West End and he picks the first bar they come to. It's just off Tottenham Court Road and seems lively enough, especially for a Monday night. It doesn't bother him that, at first glance, most of the people in there appear to be much older than he and Mel.

'Are you sure about this place?' Mel asks, as he leads her towards the door. 'I mean, we could go to Jewel? Aneeka went there last Friday and said it was amazing. She had such a good time.'

'That's in Piccadilly Circus, though, and we're here now.' It's not too far to walk but the time it's taken them to get here has already cut into their evening more than he'd like. He just wants to relax now that his exams are over.

'Okay,' Mel says, twisting her mouth. Harley is fully aware that this is the second time he's disappointed her this evening – or third, if you include him not watching her get dressed.

Inside the bar, Harley scans the room. Chart music plays from the speakers on the walls; it's not too loud and he's relieved that at least they'll be able to hear each other speak without constantly leaning into each other's ears.

'I feel like trying something different tonight,' Mel says, pointing to the bar. 'Not that I've tried loads of different drinks. Just bored of having the same old thing every time I go out.'

Harley likes her refreshing honesty. He knows lots of girls who would never admit that they aren't that experienced in anything. He grabs her hand, relishing the soft warmth of her skin. 'How about a B52? I've never tried one but they look interesting.'

'Never heard of it, but why not?' Mel snuggles into his arm as he gives the barman their order.

All the seats are occupied so they hover by the bar and discuss their upcoming holiday. Harley can't help but feel a rush of emotion towards this sweet girl; her excitement is infectious and he feels himself actually starting to look forward to it himself, even though up until now he's had reservations.

Someone slaps him on the arm and he spins around, ready to confront whoever's barged into him.

'Harley!'

It takes him a second to register that it's Isaac, his old school friend. Harley hasn't seen him since Isaac finished his A levels a year earlier and almost can't believe he's standing in front of him now. Isaac never posts on Facebook, and the last Harley had heard, he'd moved to Manchester for university.

'Isaac! What are you doing here? I thought you were in Manchester now?'

'Yeah, for uni, but I've come back for the summer. Mum and Dad have gone away on a cruise – God, they're so old – and I'm looking after the house for them.'

Harley laughs. 'Well, it's great to see you. Sorry we lost contact.'

'Ah, don't even worry about that.' Isaac glances at Mel.

'Isaac, this is Mel. She goes to our school but transferred this year so you won't have met.'

Isaac puts his glass of beer on the bar and offers his hand to Mel. 'Nice to meet you,' he says.

'You too.' She is polite and takes his hand, although she doesn't seem comfortable. Perhaps she's annoyed they're being disturbed.

'Well, I don't want to interrupt you guys so I'll get back to my mates – I'm with that lot over there.' Isaac points to four guys huddled in the corner. 'They're my footy friends. Just having a catch-up.' He turns back to Harley. 'Actually, we're going on to a club after this. Strawberry Moons off Regent Street. Heard it's pretty good, even on a Monday night. You two up for coming along?' He pats Harley's shoulder.

The invitation is tempting, but one look at Mel's face tells Harley he shouldn't accept it. 'Oh, I don't know, maybe another time.'

'No, you should go,' Mel says. 'I won't come – I'm really tired anyway. Go and have fun, Harley. Remember you're celebrating.' She smiles, but it's different from her usual one, too forced.

Harley wonders if this is some kind of test. 'No, I'm not leaving you to get home alone, Mel.'

'It's fine, honestly. I'll get a cab from right out the front. You can even wait with me, if you're worried.'

Harley takes a moment to think about all this. He's really fond of Isaac and would love to catch up, but how can he leave Mel? And her being so agreeable about it, practically pushing him to go, is a bit weird. 'No, another time, though.' He offers an apologetic smile to Isaac.

Mel straightens up, her tone firmer now. 'No, Harley, you're going. Like I said, I'm tired anyway so it's fine. Just go and have fun with your friends.'

Harley's never been into clubs, and he doesn't know any of Isaac's football friends, but it's so good to see Isaac again that he overlooks his uneasiness. 'Okay, if you're sure? I'm paying for your cab, though.'

As they stand outside and wait for Mel's cab, Harley can't help but feel anxious. All of a sudden, this feels like a big mistake.

TWENTY-SEVEN

Zoe

Adrian's words ring in my ears as I lie awake in bed, listening to the soft sound of Jake's breathing. I decided not to stay in Guildford last night, after all. As soon as I left the Butlers' house, I changed my mind about confronting Roberta at school in the morning. This is too serious an issue to address when she's about to start work, and I need her full attention. I've got the day off work today, so my new plan is to try and speak to her after she finishes at school, when she'll have more time and I might get a better response.

Is it really possible Roberta sent those messages? When I questioned Adrian further, he told me that Roberta's best friend in school was called Marianne Cole, and that as the email came from an M. Cole, wasn't it too much of a coincidence to ignore? It must have been the first name she could think of, he said, when she set up the email account. He's got a point, and it's something I will definitely confront Roberta with.

When I asked him why she would do it, all he could say was that she's always blamed me for not noticing that Josh and Ethan had left the house that night, which is completely at odds with Roberta's statement to my face that she doesn't hold me responsible for what happened.

Adrian made no mention of the other messages, but then there's no reason why he would know about them.

Thinking about all this makes my head ache. I wish I'd never read that first email. If only it had gone to my junk folder, then I never would have seen it. The texts would have come through load and clear, though. Whoever it is – Roberta or someone else – would have found a way to make me listen. Their determination would have overcome any obstacle.

It's 6 a.m. and no more sleep will come for me now, so I get up and leave the bedroom, quietly closing the door behind me. I'm sure Jake won't be asleep for much longer – always eager to get to the office – but I want him to have as much rest as possible.

He tried to talk to me last night, and I know he was relieved that I didn't stay in Guildford, but I was too tired to have any kind of conversation. Besides, I knew exactly what he would try and tell me. *Stop pursuing this, Zoe. Let it be.*

As I head past Harley's bedroom, I notice the door is slightly ajar. This is strange, given that he always shuts it tightly at night and he's never up this early, especially now he's got no more exams. Thinking he must have some other reason to be awake already, I knock on the door and wait for a response.

Nothing.

Gently pushing the door open, I peer inside, shocked to find the curtains open and daylight shining into the room. The bed is already made and everything else in the room is tidy.

I head downstairs to the kitchen, expecting Harley to be in there, but I find it empty. The same with the living room and downstairs toilet. Harley's not really the outdoorsy type, but I look into the garden where, again, there is no sign of him.

Starting to worry now, I open the front door and see that his car is still there, parked on the drive, just as it was when I got home. Stay calm, I tell myself, there has to be an explanation. He must have stayed at Mel's last night. But would her parents allow it? I'm not sure how liberal they are, even though Mel is eighteen and Harley nineteen.

I grab my mobile and call him, praying for him to answer and tell me off for overreacting, assuring me he's okay, that he's not a child. That history is not repeating itself.

Instead I get his voicemail.

Still I try to keep panic at bay. Mel's number is stored in my phone and I press her name, even though it's early and I'm sure she won't yet be awake.

'Hi, Mrs Monaghan.' Her voice is heavy with sleep.

'Hi, Mel, I'm sorry to call so early but I just wondered if Harley was with you?'

Her voice becomes more alert. 'No, he isn't. We went to a bar last night and bumped into a friend of his. Harley ended up going clubbing with him. I just got a cab home on my own.'

My stomach flips and churns, nausea rising in my throat. 'What friend was this? Do you know where they went?'

'I'd never met him before but his name's Isaac and I've heard Harley talk about him.'

I relax a little bit. 'Yes, I know Isaac. I'm guessing you don't have his number?'

'No, sorry. Harley must have crashed at his place. Have you tried calling him?'

'Just now and it went straight to voicemail. I'm a bit worried.' This is an understatement. Both my hands are shaking. It's because of what happened to Ethan. I'm terrified of losing Harley, too. 'Have you heard from him since you left the bar?'

'He texted me to check I'd got home okay and then I told him I was going to bed and I didn't hear any more.'

'And what club did they go to?' I need as much information as possible. I am already envisaging reporting all this to the police.

'Strawberry Moons, I think. At least that was their plan. I don't know, though, they could have easily changed their minds and gone somewhere different.' Mel falls silent for a moment. 'What shall we do?'

'Let's not panic,' I tell her, even though this is exactly what I'm doing on the inside. 'I'll try again and leave him a message this time, and I'll text as well.'

'Okay, I'll do the same,' Mel says. 'And Mrs Monaghan? I'm sure he's fine, don't worry.'

This is easier said than done when it's all so out of character for Harley. He always lets me know where he is, and it's worrying that he hasn't even texted or called Mel about whatever his plans were.

I leave a voicemail on his phone and text him to call me as soon as possible, all the time trying to be calm. Then I run upstairs and wake up Jake.

It takes him a moment to fully wake up, and when he does he pulls himself into a sitting position and stares at me as if I've gone mad. 'Calm down, Zoe, and tell me again what's happened.'

I repeat it all, hoping this time he is actually listening.

'So Harley didn't come home last night? Hmmm. Well, he is nineteen. He's an adult. He's probably just off with some friends somewhere.'

Anger rises inside me. 'Yes, but he's never done anything like this before. He always tells us where he is, doesn't he? Mel hasn't even heard from him!'

Jake slides his legs out of bed and grabs my hand. 'Let's just think about this. Maybe his battery died, so he can't contact us? You said it went straight to voicemail, so that means it's off, otherwise it would have rung, wouldn't it?'

He has a point, although I'm still not convinced. 'I know that, but he would have used someone else's phone to send a message, wouldn't he? You know Harley, he's too reliable for this. Especially after Ethan.'

Jake falls silent now, and I can tell he's trying to offer a rational explanation, like he usually does, but this time he comes up blank. 'I don't know, Zoe, it *is* a bit weird. Let's call the police and let them know he hasn't come home. I'll do it.'

While Jake makes the phone call, I go downstairs to make a strong coffee. It will help me function and I need to do something normal, to help me cling to a tiny glimmer of hope that I am simply overreacting.

A key turns in the front door and I drop my mug, shattering it into a hundred jigsaw pieces by my feet. Ignoring it, I rush into the hallway.

Harley is standing there, staring at me as if I'm a lunatic. 'Mum? What's going on? Are you okay?'

I rush towards him and pull him into a hug. 'Where have you been all night? I've been going crazy and Dad's calling the police.' I shout the words because right at this moment I'm as angry as I am relieved.

'I'm so sorry, Mum. I went clubbing last night with Isaac – do you remember him from school? – and I lost my phone. I didn't have your number. Or anyone's.'

That's the trouble with mobile phones – nobody knows anyone else's number by heart any longer. I'm quite sure I don't even know Jake's. 'Don't you ever do that to me again, Harley.' I hope he doesn't notice my tears soaking through his T-shirt.

'Harley's back!' I shout upstairs to Jake.

He rushes from the bedroom to the top of the stairs, relief on his face as he takes in the scene in the hallway below: me clinging on to Harley. 'See, Zoe, I told you he'd be fine. I'd better call the police back.'

Work call just after 8 a.m. and ask if I can fill in for a few hours for Jackie, one of the other IVF nurses, who's suddenly been taken ill. I'm grateful for the distraction, and leaving at 1 p.m. means I should still have time to catch Roberta after school.

As soon as I step into the clinic, I almost bump into Leo Anderson, who's engrossed in a patient's folder. 'Ah, just the person,' he says, suddenly looking up. 'Do you have time for a quick chat, Zoe?'

I've still got half an hour before I need to be on duty so I readily agree, welcoming the distraction from worrying about both of my sons. Once I'm in his office, I remember how I rushed off at lunchtime the other day and quickly apologise.

'Oh, don't worry about that,' he says. 'I hope everything's okay, though?'

I tell him it was just a family thing and he seems happy to hear this.

Sitting at his desk, Leo waves the folder as he offers me a seat and sits down at his desk. 'I think we need to change the protocol for Sarah Banks. This is her fifth cycle, and last time she had far fewer eggs collected. She's only thirty-five, but I recommend we try the shorter protocol this time. I've made notes on her file and she's coming in this morning.' He shakes his head. 'This is the hardest part of the job, when there's just no explanation for the constant failures. Both Sarah and her husband have had every test available and nothing's coming up to explain why it's just not working for them.'

'Because it's a horrible lottery and life's just not fair most of the time. For anyone.'

I slap my hand over my mouth, stunned by what I've said. How could these words have just left my mouth? What is wrong with me? I know Leo and I talk quite a bit, and he's always friendly with me, but I'm acting unprofessionally.

Leo stares at me for a moment, then, to my relief, slowly nods. 'Unfortunately, you're right. All we can do is the best we can for everyone, isn't it?'

'I'm so sorry, I should never have said that. I—'

He leans forward. 'Are you okay? I hope you don't mind me saying this, but you don't seem yourself. Is everything all right?'

I'm desperate to talk to someone about everything I've been bottling up, but this isn't the time or the place, so I nod, hoping this will be enough to stop his questions.

He lowers his voice, even though there's nobody else in here and his door is closed. 'You know, what you've just said is exactly how I feel about life. Nobody else here knows this but I lost my daughter five years ago. Leukaemia. She was only seven.'

His words pierce my heart. 'I had no idea – I'm so sorry. That's just awful.'

He looks down. 'I've never mentioned it before, even though we've talked a lot since I've been here, but it's difficult to bring up. It was the worst time of my life and I began to hate the world, to feel the weight of its unfairness. Why did it have to happen to us? Why not someone else? But that was such a selfish way to look at things, and I quickly snapped out of it. But Megan, my wife, wasn't able to do the same.'

I can understand this; I barely made it back from the brink myself. 'Well, it's hard, isn't it? Difficult to think rationally. Nothing makes sense once you've lost a child. Everything changes and nothing you do feels like what you would have done before, if that makes sense? You become a different person.'

He nods. 'That's true. And my marriage just couldn't survive it. Megan's bitterness drove us apart in the end, no matter how hard I fought to try and save us.'

I think of Jake, how this very nearly could have been our story, and I can't find any words to say.

'Anyway,' Leo continues, 'I'm sorry, you don't need to hear all this.' He hands me the Banks's file, and as I take it from him, I feel his eyes searching my face. It must be instinct, but somehow I know that he's aware of my situation, of what happened with Ethan – even though I've never mentioned it to him – and he's sought me out as some kind of kindred spirit, someone who knows exactly what's in his own heart.

'I lost my son too, Leo.' There, I've said it now, it's out in the open, floating around the room, ready to be picked up and handled by this kind-faced man I've come to think of as a friend.

He nods. 'I heard. I'm sorry. I never mentioned it because you didn't, and I guessed you weren't ready. What happened to your boy was in some ways even more senseless.'

And that's when I open up to him, and I find myself telling him everything that's been happening, up to the last text message.

'This isn't good,' he says, when I've finished speaking. This person knows something about Ethan's accident – they must do. Let me help you, Zoe.'

And finally there is someone who understands, who isn't trying to dismiss it all as a prank and doesn't think I'm going crazy. Someone who might just be able to help me get to the truth.

TWENTY-EIGHT

Ignoring him works wonders, just as I knew it would. He bombards me with texts and tries calling me all through the day. And even though I still long for him, I revel in his confusion and persistence. He won't understand what's happening, and it will drive him crazy that I can so suddenly switch off.

I don't answer any of his texts, of course. And he knows I don't like talking on the phone, that it's out of my comfort zone, so he must realise he's wasting his time there.

Most people would have given up by now, but not him. That must mean something, mustn't it? That we're fated to be together, that we are bound to one another. That nothing can stop it now.

'Why didn't you want to meet up?' This is what he asks, and what I've let him believe. What he doesn't know is that I was right there under his nose, ready to do this, to take us to the next level, to expose myself. It was like putting my neck in a noose and waiting to see if he would tighten it or remove it. I had high hopes, sure our bond was strong enough to combat whatever difficulties my age, or other things, might throw up.

'I love you,' he says in another message. 'I really believe I do. Look, if you're worried about anything, like how you look or anything, then I really don't care. I'm not superficial, it's you I've fallen for, nothing else. Just you. And everyone edits their profile pics, don't they? Everyone wants to look their best online. I get that, I really do. Don't hide from me.'

He's so young to have this outlook, and I wonder if he's just playing a game to get me to respond. No, I tell myself, I would know if this wasn't something real.

And that's when I know with certainty that this can work. He's young, able to be moulded and manipulated, like clay, by my experiences and knowledge. I can do this.

My mother is being taken into hospital. She's having difficulty breathing, but the paramedics assure me she will be okay. They ask if I want to come with her, but Mum frantically waves her hands around and tries to say 'no'. It will be because I've got work in the morning and she doesn't want me to be up all night in a hospital.

I begin to protest, until I see that this presents a perfect opportunity. I'm torn. My mother needs me, but so does he. What can I do at the hospital anyway? I'll just be hanging around, waiting for news. I can do that here.

'I'll come soon,' I tell Mum. 'Just let me sort something out with work.'

I watch as the ambulance drives off, my fingers already tapping away on my phone, giving him my address and telling him to meet me here as soon as he can, even though I know it will take him a while to organise getting here.

Here we go. It's now or never.

TWENTY-NINE

Jake

Things had to fall apart. It was inevitable, wasn't it, that if there were any loose threads in your marriage, they would eventually be pulled until you were left with nothing. That's how Jake was starting to feel.

The distance opening up between Zoe and him was widening by the minute, and the funny thing was, it wasn't something tangible; it was more of an atmosphere, something surrounding them. A thing he couldn't put into words but simply felt.

And Leanne was a loose thread, wasn't she? It had shocked him yesterday that she'd brought up what they'd done, and it made him nervous about what else she might throw into a conversation. That was the trouble with lifelong friends; they knew too much about you.

His morning started before 7 a.m. and now he is staring at his computer screen, unable to find the motivation to do anything, and angry at himself for not being able to block everything out as he usually does with ease.

'What's up with you?' Liam says, swivelling round in his chair to face Jake.

'Nothing. I'm just tired.'

'And I thought I was the one who'd had a late night. Didn't get to sleep until after 4 a.m. and here I am. Bright as a button!'

Jake ignores him. He doesn't want to picture what Liam might have been up to last night.

'And where the hell is Cara? She's got a shedload of filing to do and it's nearly eleven. This isn't on.' He reaches for his mobile and taps the screen. A few seconds pass before he puts it on the desk again. 'No bloody answer. I tell you, I could swing for her sometimes.'

Me too, Jake wants to say, remembering what she'd done only last night. He really doesn't care if she never turns up again. Watching Liam now, he wants to be honest and tell him what happened – he's sick of lies and deceit – but the words die before they even reach his mouth. He can't let anything affect their business, so instead he says, 'I'm sure she'll stroll in when she feels like it,' and turns away from Liam.

A few minutes later, Jake's phone beeps, just as he's found enough focus to begin work on the corporate logo he's designing for an accountancy firm. They were lucky to get this account – the company could have quite easily gone for a larger firm, but they'd seemed to like Jake and Liam's portfolio. *Something to be grateful for*, Jake thinks.

He wants to ignore his phone, but fears it might be Zoe, and that something else will have happened to send her into a panic – or worse, set her off on her mission again. He didn't get a chance to speak to her last night and advise her against pursuing this, then she'd been so caught up in worrying about Harley, and when he returned she was so relieved that Jake didn't want to bring anything up.

His heart almost stops when he sees Leanne's name on the screen. She's the last person he expected to hear from so soon, given their conversation last night.

Done a lot of thinking since last night and we need to talk. Urgently. Can you meet me for lunch? I'll come to you. 1 p.m. by the river near your office.

Jake checks his watch. It's only just gone twelve so he has a bit of time to prepare himself. He should have known this day was coming.

Leanne is half an hour late, adding to his anxiety. What's wrong with him? He's normally fairly laid-back, able to distance himself from his emotions, yet today he feels like a wreck. It's because he doesn't know what he's about to be confronted with. That, together with Zoe and these messages, is enough to drive anyone insane.

Finally, she hurries towards him as he sits on a bench overlooking the river. The pub is behind him but he has no desire to go there – he just wants this conversation over with as quickly as possible.

'Sorry I'm late,' Leanne says. 'A meeting overran and I couldn't get away any sooner.' She's out of breath, and for once her hair is out of place, slightly sweat-soaked. He's not used to seeing Leanne this way; she's normally so together.

'What's going on, Leanne? What's so urgent?'

She sits beside him. 'I couldn't sleep last night. It's just been haunting me – what a terrible friend I'm being to Zoe. And have been for three years. She's going through so much right now, practically reliving what happened to Ethan, but how can I truly be there for her after what I've done? It just feels all wrong.' Her words spurt out. This isn't the calm and measured way she usually speaks.

Jake needs to tread carefully here. Leanne seems volatile and he has no idea what she might do. 'I thought we agreed last night that it wouldn't do any good to bring this up now?'

Leanne shakes her head, stares towards the river. 'I know, but I've been lying to her and I know she'd never do that to me. Never.'

'Why is this all coming up now, Leanne? I don't understand.'

'I don't know, Jake. Maybe the guilt has finally caught up with me and it's all becoming too much. Seeing what she's going through might have something to do with it. It's just bringing it all home to me – how I wasn't really there for her when she needed me the most. She deserves to know the truth.'

'But you *were* there for her when Ethan died. What we did doesn't change that. You were always by her side, when you weren't helping me or Harley.'

'I didn't think about it then. I just focused on helping Zoe, trying to pretend nothing had happened between you and me. That was easy to do when Zoe needed my support.'

Jake can't fathom any of this. There's something Leanne's not telling him; there has to be. He tries to reason with her. 'But what good will telling her do? It will just cause her even more pain and, like you said, she's going through enough right now.'

'I know that, Jake. In the end, though, it comes down to this: would Zoe want to know? That's what I've been asking myself, and I really believe she would. Us sleeping together has tainted the relationship we all have, hasn't it? You can't deny that. And these messages are just bringing it all up again.'

He knows she's right, but he's got to talk her out of doing anything that will mess up all of their lives. 'To be honest, Leanne, I don't even think about it. Or I didn't, until you brought it up last night. I… put it all behind me.'

'Of course you did. You just want to live in your little bubble, pretend nothing else exists. That's what you always do, Jake.'

Jake is on the defensive now. 'Why are you attacking me? We made a mistake. Neither of us wanted to hurt Zoe – we weren't thinking straight – and mentioning it to her now will just rip her apart.'

Leanne ignores him. 'It's the lying that makes it worse, Jake. Don't you see that? With everything that's going on, maybe now is the right time to tell her, even though is seems like the worst time.'

And only now he does finally begin to see. Leanne isn't just talking about the fact that they slept together that night. It can't just be that; there is more to her sudden need for honesty.

He stares at her but she won't meet his eye. 'Leanne, I'm not saying anything to Zoe. Especially after what's been happening. Can't you see it would do more harm than good?'

She shakes her head. 'So you're asking me to keep this a secret for the rest of my life?'

'Yes, that's exactly what I'm asking. Let's all just live our lives like we have been for three years.'

Seconds tick by; he has no idea what Leanne's response will be.

She turns to him and looks him directly in the eye. 'Well, it won't be the first time I've had to keep your family secrets.'

THIRTY

Zoe

It's funny to think of Roberta working in a school, a meek figure surrounded by a classroom full of children. She might not be a teacher but I'm sure there will be times when, as a teaching assistant, she'll need to discipline the kids, and I just can't imagine her doing that. I never saw it in any of her interactions with Josh. All I could see was that her fourteen-year-old son controlled their relationship.

Parents are streaming into the building as I sit in my car and wait for Roberta to appear. I have no idea how long this might take; she could very well need to stay late, and once again I'm prepared to wait as long as it takes.

As it turns out, only fifteen minutes pass before she appears in the playground, her shoulder drooping from the weight of the large bag she's carrying along with her bulging handbag. Even though I only saw her days ago, she looks even thinner, waiflike, and I wonder if Adrian has been telling the truth and she really is troubled. Or is this all down to him?

The staff car park is on the other side of the road, and although I have no idea whether Roberta drove to work or not, if she did bring her car then I need to catch her before she can jump in it and race away from me. I'm working late tomorrow so I can't make the trip down here then. It's now or never.

Leaving my bag in my car, I get out and wait to see what direction she heads in when she reaches the school gates. She crosses the road, towards the car park, so I stride after her, only calling her name once we're away from the few parents still loitering around.

She turns around and her eyes widen when she sees it's me. With a quick glance towards her car, she keeps walking.

'Roberta, please. Can we talk?'

She doesn't turn around. 'I'm busy, Zoe, I need to go. Sorry.'

I run to catch up with her. 'I went to your house and I've spoken to Adrian. We really need to talk.'

She freezes and spins around, her face turns a shade paler. 'Why? Why did you talk to him? What… what did he say?'

So maybe there is some truth in Adrian's words. 'Can we go somewhere and talk properly? I think it's in your best interests, don't you?' I say this to play on her fears about what Adrian might have told me, though in fact our conversation really won't be in anyone's interests but my own.

'Fine,' she says, glaring at me. 'There's a coffee shop around the corner.' She lifts her bag from her shoulder. 'I just need to put this in the car. I'm not carting it around with me.'

In the coffee shop, Roberta accepts my offer of coffee and once we're seated, she lets out a strained sigh. 'What did Adrian say, then?'

'I'll get to that,' I tell her. I need something to hold over her. 'First I need to talk to you about Josh and Ethan.'

Another sigh, even heavier this time. 'Please, not this again, Zoe. How many times can I say that I just don't know anything.'

'I don't believe you, Roberta. There's more to this, I know it. I find it hard to believe someone would just randomly send emails and messages like this without there being something to it.'

Roberta stares at me. 'What do you mean? I thought it was just one email? Have you had more?'

If Adrian is right about Roberta being behind the messages then she's certainly doing a great job of hiding it. 'Yes, there have been more. The point is, something was going on with Josh and Ethan – you even said yourself that they'd had some kind of falling out.'

She shakes her head. 'That's not what I said. I just said I heard them having a disagreement. That doesn't mean anything. What are you trying to say, Zoe?'

'I think you know more than you're letting on, Roberta. Much more.'

Once again, her skin seems to pale. 'What has Adrian said? Tell me!'

I pause for a moment to let her stew. 'He thinks you're the one who's been sending me the messages.'

Silence folds over us and seems to last forever, until eventually Roberta breaks it. 'Why would he say that? Of course I didn't. Why would I? Can I see these other messages?'

Rather than give her my phone, this time I read them out to her and watch her expression as I repeat the words. Her face gives nothing away.

'How awful,' she says. 'This must be really hard to deal with.'

I ignore her. 'See, I've been trying to work it out, Roberta. And the only conclusion I can come to is that you think Ethan is responsible for what happened to them and now you're trying to punish me.' Now that I've said it out loud, it seems to be the only thing that makes sense.

Roberta looks horrified. 'But… but if I felt that way then why wouldn't I just come out and confront you? This is ridiculous! I need to know what Adrian has been telling you, Zoe.' Her eyes are desperate now, no longer angry.

I feel ready to tell her what Adrian said, even though I'm not convinced of his honesty. The two of them seem to want to get at each other, and it feels as though I'm stuck in the middle, a pawn in their twisted game. I recount my conversation with Adrian, informing Roberta of his claims that she's having some kind of breakdown and is acting irrationally.

Once I've finished, she seems – to my surprise – almost relieved, sinking back into her chair. 'He's saying this because I've finally had the strength to leave him. It's all lies, Zoe. I'm fine, and actually I've never been thinking with more clarity. For years he revelled in the fact that I was downtrodden and voiceless, and now that I've finally had the guts to walk away, he just can't take it.'

Looking at her now, my instinct is to believe her. Everything I've ever seen of Adrian screams at me not to trust him, not to like him, despite how amenable he was during our last encounter. And Roberta *does* seem different. Beneath her timidity, and behind the walls she puts up, I sense there is kindness, and something more human about her than Adrian could ever hope to have.

'What was your best friend's name in school?' I ask.

'What? Why are you asking me that?'

'Just tell me.'

'She was called Caroline, but we don't really keep in touch. I wouldn't even know where she lives now. What do you need to know that for?'

'Never mind. Look, if you want me to believe you, you're going to have to give me something, Roberta. If it's not you sending the messages, then surely you must want to help me in any way you can?'

She doesn't answer, and leaving her coffee untouched, she picks up her chunky handbag from the floor, sliding it over her shoulder.

'If you don't talk to me then I'll have no choice but to go to the police with Adrian's suspicions. I'm sure it's something they'd want to know.'

This seems to work and slowly she places her bag on the floor again. A young woman pushing a toddler in a buggy walks past us to the counter and Roberta waits a moment before speaking. 'Okay. The truth is, I don't think the boys were such good friends at the end. I don't think it was just a trivial argument they had.'

Her words stab at me, piercing my skin. I'm finally getting something out of her, getting closer to the truth. 'Go on.'

She pauses, appearing to gather her thoughts. 'I don't know if you can remember, but in the last few weeks before it happened, Ethan was mostly around our house. Can you even recall a time when Josh visited yours instead?'

I force my mind back, but so much has happened since then that it's impossible to remember. Even at the time I could barely remember what had happened in the days leading up to the boys drowning; every minute, hour and day blurred into one big empty hole. I allowed myself to be consumed with work, letting my patients' lives permeate into my blood so that I couldn't separate myself from their pain.

'I don't remember,' I tell Roberta. 'It's almost as if the time before stopped existing once Ethan was gone.'

Roberta leans forward. 'I know exactly what you mean. It's strange, isn't it? I try to recall memories of when Josh was a baby, a little boy, but they just don't come to me – not properly. Yet I remember every detail of the day we were told about the accident. And when I picture Josh now, it's at the hospital, when he was already…' She dabs at her eyes.

'We need to know exactly what happened, Roberta. Both of us do. There's more to this, and I won't rest until I've found out what it is.'

'I really don't know anything else – just that Josh didn't seem to want to be around Ethan as much after I heard their argument, but Ethan kept turning up at the house anyway.'

'Do you think Josh was angry with Ethan? Could Ethan have done something to him?' This idea fills me with horror, but I can't ignore that it's a possibility.

She shrugs, and once again I find myself wondering if this could be about Daisy Carter after all, even though she'd seemed adamant that it was nothing to do with her. I haven't wanted to bring up Josh's relationship with Daisy to Roberta but now I have no choice. I'll try to spare her the details, though.

'Did you know Josh was seeing a girl called Daisy Carter?'

Roberta frowns. 'Josh had several friends who were girls, but I don't think he had a girlfriend as such. They were a bit young for all that, weren't they?'

I know how secretive teenage boys can be, how their mums are often the last people they want to confide in about anything, let alone girls. 'You'd be surprised. So you never met anyone called Daisy?' Even though Daisy told me that she'd never been to Josh's house, I offer Roberta a description; I just want to be sure.

There's no flutter of recognition on Roberta's face. 'Josh sometimes had female friends over to the house, but nobody ever mentioned anything about being in any kind of relationship.'

'And when any of these girls were over did they hang out downstairs or were they allowed in Josh's room?'

Roberta seems surprised by my question. 'Josh was fourteen, not five. I didn't need to supervise him every second of the day.'

Perhaps you should have, then maybe both our sons would still be alive. Even as I think this, I feel like a hypocrite. Josh was staying at my house that night, he was my responsibility for those hours he was under my roof. Roberta would be quite within her rights to bring this up, to accuse me of being negligent. She never once has, though, despite Adrian's insistence that this is how she feels.

'I understand that, but you can't say with any certainty that Josh wasn't with someone called Daisy?'

She thinks about this for a moment. 'I suppose it's possible. But I really don't think the boys fell out over a girl.'

This backs up Daisy's story so I must be following the wrong path here.

'So you have no idea why the boys fell out or why Josh didn't seem to want Ethan around?'

'No. He didn't really tell me anything about his life, Zoe, and I didn't pry. I wanted to give him privacy. Don't we all deserve that?'

Some of us do, I think. 'So how do you know that Josh didn't want to be around Ethan?'

She leans back again, lets out a sigh. 'A few times, Ethan called him on his mobile and Josh just ignored it. Then Ethan would just turn up anyway.'

I struggle to work out what this means, what could possibly have been going on between the boys. 'And you didn't want to ask Josh what was happening with them?'

She shakes her head. 'Perhaps I should have. I'm sorry I can't tell you any more.'

'Do you think Adrian knows anything? Perhaps Josh found it easier to talk to him?'

Roberta's eyes narrow. 'No way. Adrian doesn't know a thing. I don't think he even knew what subjects Josh was planning to take at school the following year. And he's a nasty piece of work so I'd stay well away from him if I were you.'

Even though I'm aware Roberta has a newfound confidence, I'm still taken aback by this show of assertiveness. 'Is this it, then? You've left him for good? Divorce and everything?'

I notice her hand tremble as she answers, contradicting her earlier strength. 'Yes. I am never going back to that evil man.' She leans down to pick up her bag once again, signalling that my time is up.

'One thing I can't understand, though,' I say quickly, 'is why Josh stayed the night at our place? If he didn't want to be around Ethan, or was angry with him for some reason, why would he even come over, let alone stay for a sleepover?'

Roberta pulls her handbag over her shoulder. 'Maybe they were trying to sort things out?'

Or maybe Josh had other ideas.

THIRTY-ONE

Jake

He can't remember the last time he left work this early. It's 5 p.m., and it feels strange, far out of his comfort zone, even though he's stepping into his own home. It's not right that feels more comfortable at work than here.

It isn't Zoe, he thinks, peeling off his jacket. He still loves her. It's Ethan. Home – whether Guildford or London – hasn't been the same since the accident. How can anywhere be a home when one of them is absent? Gone forever. Ethan never even set foot in this place, yet his presence haunts them wherever they are; it's all around them, no matter what they do. And Jake's feeling it even more since these messages started.

He's being maudlin and he hates it. *Snap out of it. Focus on the task at hand.* That's what he needs to do. He's come home early for a reason: he's had a complete change of heart since talking to Leanne, and now that he's made up his mind to come clean to Zoe, he's determined to see it through. She doesn't deserve to be kept in the dark; she needs to know what happened between him and Leanne, and he needs to give her the chance to decide what to do. In his heart, he already knows that she will leave him and he doesn't blame her, but at least for once in his life he will be doing the right thing.

This is what has pushed him to finally tell the truth, when only earlier he was adamant that Zoe should never find out.

Plus, he senses that Leanne is on the edge of something, behaving unpredictably, talking about family secrets, and he can't let her tell Zoe first. It needs to come from him.

'Zoe?' he calls.

The house is silent, but then he hears footsteps on the stairs, too heavy to be Zoe's. She barely makes a sound around the place, almost as if she's floating instead of walking.

'She's not here,' Harley says, stopping on the stairs before he reaches the bottom.

'Oh. Do you happen to know where she is?' Jake already feels awkward; it's not often he finds himself alone with his son, having to search for things to say. It saddens him that they have nothing in common, and that every time he looks at Harley he sees anger in his son's eyes.

'At work?' Harley offers. 'Where else would she be?'

'No, she finished work a while ago. Should have been home by now.' Uneasiness creeps in. What is Zoe doing?

Jake tries calling her, disconnecting when it diverts to her voicemail. 'What is it with my family going missing?' he mumbles, more to himself than to Harley.

Harley catches every word, though. He never misses a thing. 'I wasn't missing, Dad, I was with a friend. And I'm sure Mum is fine. She'll be on her way home.'

'Yeah, you're right. Just ignore me.'

Harley finally descends the last few steps. 'Do you... want a coffee or something?'

Jake looks up, surprised by this offer. He can't think of any time when Harley's made him a drink. 'Um, yeah. That would be great.'

In the kitchen, he leans against the worktop and watches his son, wondering what's brought on this act of kindness. Harley seems tall as he stands at the kitchen counter, even though he's standing in bare feet, the bottom of his jeans dragging on the floor. He and his son are probably the same height now. When did that happen?

He's a handsome, intelligent boy and Jake is so proud of him, even though he's never said it to Harley's face. He needs to try harder. Especially now. He opens his mouth to say something but can't get the words out. Instead, he says, 'So how are you doing, then, son? Everything okay?'

Harley gives a half smile as he hands Jake a mug. He pulls out a chair at the kitchen table and slides into it, and Jake does the same.

'Fine. Mel and I have split up.'

Jake stares at his son; this is the last thing he expected to hear. Harley never shares personal details with him so he's momentarily at a loss for words.

'Actually,' Harley continues, 'split up isn't quite right. She's left me.'

Jake reaches across the table but then pulls his arm back. He should use this opportunity to help them bond, but it's a struggle. What is wrong with him? 'Sorry, son. That's tough.' Pointless words that won't help a bit.

'Yeah.' Harley nods. 'It's a bit out of the blue. One minute we're going on holiday together, the next she's telling me it's not working out. It's all booked and everything and I don't think we'll be able to get the money back.'

'Don't worry about that,' Jake assures him. He takes a sip of coffee. 'Did she say why? It's a bit vague to just say it's not working out.'

'Nope. Just said she doesn't think we're right for each other.'

'I'm sorry, Harley.' Jake should say more, but once again any useful words seem to escape him. Zoe would know exactly what to say. He wishes she was here, despite this opportunity to mend some bridges. 'Are you… How do you feel?'

Harley shrugs. 'I'm okay. Can we not talk about it any more?'

There it is; Jake is shut down in his attempt to reach his son. He understands, though. It must be strange for Harley to talk to him about his relationship when they barely even discuss the weather. 'Course. But I'm here if you need to talk.'

'I'm worried about Mum,' Harley blurts out.

Again, Jake is taken aback. 'Why? What's happened?'

'I just think… Don't you think she's been acting strangely lately? Kind of distracted? It's like she's not really here, even when she is. She told me she wasn't feeling well and had a cold, but she doesn't have one at all.'

Jake needs to be careful here. Even though Harley's exams are over now, he and Zoe have agreed not to trouble him with what's been going on.

'You know your mum,' Jake says. 'She just gets consumed with the patients at work, can't let their stories go when she walks out of the clinic. But that's why she's so good at her job. She really cares.'

'Harley's eyes narrow as he lifts his mug. 'Yeah, that must be it. There couldn't be anything else, could there?'

Jake feels uneasy. It's just lies on top of lies, never-ending. 'No, course not.'

'It couldn't be anything to do with you, could it?' Harley asks. 'I mean, you're hardly ever here. We moved here to have a fresh start for us all, but you're working even more than you did before.'

Jake is stunned, almost lost for words. 'I… Listen, Harley, it's hard starting up a business. You've got to put in the work to see the rewards. It won't be forever – as the business grows I'll be able to take on more staff and maybe take a bit of a step back myself. Your mum understands that.' He expects Harley will point out that it was exactly the same in Guildford, after Ethan died, when he worked for someone else, but he doesn't.

'*Does* she understand?' he says.

'Yes.' But suddenly Jake's not so sure. Although he knows exactly why Zoe is acting strangely at the moment, he also knows how perceptive his son is, and wonders if he's picked up on something he himself hasn't.

'Do you even love her?' Harley says.

'Of course I do.'

'Yeah, Dad, of course you do.' Harley stands up and tips the rest of his coffee into the sink. 'How could I think anything else?'

And then he is gone and Jake is left to wonder what the hell just happened.

THIRTY-TWO
Roberta

Zoe's visit has left her cold and empty, and as if she is covered in something she needs to shake off. It feels as though the world is closing in on her and it's only a matter of time before the inevitable happens. Secrets never stay buried for long. Sooner or later it all catches up with you and crushes you.

She sits in the dining room in the Bed and Breakfast, a plate of salmon and new potatoes growing cold in front of her and a glass of wine in her hand. She hasn't touched the food, but the glass of wine is her second in only half an hour. She doesn't usually care for alcohol so it's gone straight to her head, something she needs and wants in order to block out Zoe's visit.

There's only one other person in here: a man around her age, dressed in a suit, who's clearly on some sort of business trip. He's got a laptop and papers spread out on the table alongside his dinner – which is the same as hers – and every few minutes his phone rings.

At least he's got a reason to be sitting here alone, while she has no option. She should focus on the fact that she is finally free of Adrian – at least in one way. The tie that binds them will always be a noose around her neck, ready to be pulled tight at any moment.

By the time she's on her third drink, she doesn't notice the man get up and walk towards her.

'Excuse me,' he says, 'please feel free to say no, but I just wondered if I could sit with you to finish my drink? This place is dead and it feels a bit miserable sitting there on my own, but it's too early to go up to my room. Honestly, though, I won't take any offence if you just want to be by yourself.'

Roberta stares at him in disbelief. How do people have the confidence to go up to strangers and ask to share their table with them? She thought this kind of thing only happened in films, usually romantic comedies, which she loathes because they're so far removed from real life. Maybe it's the alcohol and she's imagined his whole speech. Perhaps he was only asking if he could borrow the salt and pepper from her table.

Fuelled by the alcohol, she plays along. 'Um, yeah, okay,' she says, not really caring one way or the other. He's right about it being too early to go up, though, and she'd only continue drinking anyway. There's nothing left to lose.

He sits opposite her and places his laptop bag to the side. 'Can I get you another drink?' He looks around. 'That's if I can even find anyone to take our order.'

Roberta laughs. 'Yeah, it is completely dead in here. I think they've all clocked off for the night. That's why I was smart enough to order a bottle.' She lifts it up and offers him some.

'Actually, I don't think there's enough left in there. Let me go and see who I can find. Same again?'

'Yes, please,' Roberta says, smiling at him. She has no idea what's going on but is happy to have a few minutes of escape from her life. This man doesn't know her; she can be anyone she wants to be. Happy, confident, together.

He comes back with a bottle of wine and he pours her another glass. 'I'm Lewis,' he says, reaching to shake her hand.

'Roberta.' So much for being someone else. She should have chosen Monica or Christina, used any name except her own.

'So what brings you to this fine establishment?' Lewis asks, gesturing around them.

Roberta chuckles again and it feels so good to laugh. 'Ha, yes, I've certainly got good taste, haven't I?' She has a choice now: she can reinvent herself and actually have some fun; or she can stick to the truth and not trip herself up with lies. How sick she is of deceit. She's torn between the two options, but then her mouth opens and the decision is made. 'I've just left my husband and this is the only place I could afford, plus it's near the school I work at as a teaching assistant. Not a teacher – even though that's my dream, I've never had the courage to follow it and get the qualifications I need.'

Lewis's eyes widen. 'Wow! You're certainly an honest and open lady. I respect that. Good for you. It's actually very refreshing.'

Roberta holds up her glass. 'This might have something to do with that,' she admits.

'Ah, yes. Perhaps we should have a coffee in a minute?'

'Oh, no. Not tonight. Tonight I just want to forget everything.' Did she say that out loud? Roberta can no longer tell what's in her head and what she's saying out loud to this man.

Lewis raises his glass. 'Cheers to that!'

'So what do you do, Lewis? How did *you* end up in this place?'

'I'm here on business, actually. I'm a sales rep for a pharmaceutical company, GlaxoSmithKline. I work in Brentford, so it's not that far, but I needed to be here for two days and I thought I might as well stay here to save myself that awful rush-hour commute.'

Roberta raises her eyebrows. 'And they put you up here?'

'Actually, I was booked into the Holiday Inn, but the reservation was cancelled for some reason and they didn't have any spare rooms. This was the only place I could get at such short notice.'

'That explains a lot,' Roberta says, feeling a chasm opening up between them. They're from different worlds; how can she hope to keep a conversation going between them?

Lewis frowns. 'What do you mean?'

'Oh, nothing.' Roberta focuses on downing some more wine. She's not usually a sociable person and, drunk or not, sooner or later she will mess up and Lewis will see that he's wasting his time in her company.

'So you're separated from your husband?' Lewis asks, lowering his voice and leaning closer towards her, even though there is nobody around to hear them.

'Yes, and good riddance to him.' Roberta raises her glass, taking a generous sip. She looks at Lewis's left hand, expecting to see a shiny ring on his finger, but there's nothing but naturally tanned flesh. She decides to ask anyway – after all, a lot of men don't like wearing wedding rings. Adrian never did. 'So how about you? Does your wife mind you travelling around the country for business?'

For the first time since he sat down with her, Lewis looks uncomfortable. 'Actually, I have no idea. We've been divorced for four years, and I wasn't a sales rep before that, so I have no idea how she would have handled it.'

'Oh, sorry,' Roberta says, secretly pleased that they might have something in common after all.

Lewis smiles. 'It's all right. We didn't have kids or anything, so it wasn't too messy. And we actually get on okay.'

His mention of kids sobers her up, like a thump to the chest, winding her. She doesn't reply.

'What about you, then?' Lewis asks. 'Any children?'

'Me? No. No kids.'

'Well, it's not so bad not having kids, is it? At least we get to do what we want, when we want.'

Roberta would give anything not to have that option. She should be with her son now, at home, clearing up after dinner, not sitting in a shabby B & B with a stranger. Again she says nothing, just swallows more wine and waits for the numbness to flood over her.

'Forgive me for saying this,' Lewis says, 'but you seemed a bit... troubled when I came in. Was it a messy separation? Do you want to talk about it? I'm a good listener, you know. And an expert in failed marriages, of course.'

And extremely nosy, Roberta thinks. At least someone is taking an interest in her, though; it's more than Adrian ever did. 'It's not my husband,' she says, 'not really.'

'Okay, well, I can still listen if you need someone to talk to.' Lewis's eyes are kind and warm, so unlike Adrian's.

Roberta flicks her fringe out of her eyes. She really needs to get it cut, but it seems too big an effort to make. Perhaps she will grow it out. Perhaps she'll never bother with herself ever again.

'I tell you what,' she says. 'How about you get us another bottle of wine?'

Her eyes slowly open, her eyelids stuck together from sleep. The curtains are drawn but they're too thin to shut out the sun and sharp light streams in, causing her to wince. She turns on her side, facing the tiny bathroom. Her head pounds, as if there is an orchestra inside it playing an out-of-tune symphony.

Memories come back to her in patches.

Lewis's smooth, dark skin, his hands all over her, his sweet breath in her ear, telling her things no man had ever said to her. The way he felt so different to Adrian. Firmer, more solid.

So she slept with him. Does she care? It was nice, as far as she remembers, but then she only has Adrian to compare him to. She can live with this. She'll just turn around, wake him up and tell him she's sorry, that she had a nice time but she's really not ready for anything more at the moment. Being divorced himself, he's bound to understand.

Then she remembers something else. Afterwards. Him holding her while she talked. Him listening, not saying much, just staring at her, hanging on her every word.

Oh God.

Fully awake now, she turns around, ready to make some excuse about talking nonsense when she's drunk. But the other side of the bed is empty. Doesn't even look slept in. The pillow is straight and the duvet neatly pulled across.

What the hell did she say to him?

THIRTY-THREE

Zoe

I walk through the door, prepared to confront Jake with my suspicions about Josh. All the way home, I thought about everything Roberta told me, and Josh wanting to get back at Ethan for something seems the only logical explanation. Was Josh the kind of boy who would lure his best friend to the river in order to teach him some kind of lesson, though? And if this is what happened, then how did they both end up dead? I'm not sure; it's a big leap from being disruptive in school to plotting something like this. Now, more than ever, my head pounds and my heart aches for the truth.

I stop short when I see Jake sitting on the stairs, staring at me.

'Where have you been?' he asks, his tone flat rather than worried.

'Sorry I didn't text or call you back. I wanted to speak to you once I got home, instead of on the phone. I'll explain everything.'

Now he looks concerned. 'What's happened, Zoe? Not another message?' He buries his head in his hands.

Again, I avoid answering. Something is going on with Jake. 'Where's Harley? Is he upstairs?'

'He went out about an hour ago. He and Mel have split up so I'm not sure where he went.'

'Split up? Are you sure? What happened?' I peel off my jacket and hang it over the banister, then sit beside him on the stairs.

Jake shrugs. 'That's all he told me. That she'd left him. You know Harley – he didn't tell me anything else. Actually, I'm surprised he even told me that much.'

So am I, but I don't say this to Jake. Perhaps he's mistaken and Harley just meant that he and Mel had argued or something. I'll have to find out as soon as I've spoken to Jake. 'I'll call him in a bit,' I say, 'check he's okay. Let's go in the kitchen – I really need some water.'

Jake follows me, his footsteps slow and heavy. He's acting really strangely tonight. 'You still haven't told me where you've been,' he says, sitting at the table.

I fill a glass from the tap and join him. 'Don't get angry but I went to see Roberta again.' I don't mention that I talked to Adrian last night; I need Jake to stay focused on what's important.

There are many responses I'm expecting, but Jake's reply isn't one of them. 'Right,' he says. 'I assume this time you have a good reason for doing that?'

'Yes, Jake, I do. I think Ethan and Josh fell out about something and Josh might have… tried to hurt him.' Now that I've said the words out loud, they seem impossible to believe, even though it's the only thing that makes sense.

Opposite me, Jake shakes his head. 'Oh, Zoe, how can that be true? They both died, didn't they? Where's this coming from?' His tone isn't angry or frustrated, just resigned.

'I don't have all the answers,' I explain. 'I only know what makes sense from the information I have.'

'But what about the last message you got? Didn't it say that Ethan deserved to die? Well, if Josh had wanted to hurt him then he'd be the one who deserved what he got, not Ethan.'

I tell Jake that he's looking at it the wrong way round, that the person sending the messages might think that because Ethan did something to Josh, he deserved what happened.

Jake thinks about this. 'Well, in that case, the person sending the messages would have to be someone on Josh's side of things. But other than Roberta and Adrian, who would that be?' He throws his head back against the chair. 'Don't you see how this all sounds?'

'Yes, I do. Look, I've already had my suspicions about Roberta, but I've been over everything and I'm no longer convinced it's her. Besides, why would she wait three years to start sending messages? And she never once blamed me, even though Josh was under our care at the time.'

Jake shakes his head. 'Unfortunately, I don't think it would have mattered whose care Josh was under or whose house he was staying at. Josh would have done what he wanted to do anyway. I think Roberta must know that.'

'I just want answers, Jake. What could the boys have been arguing about? I thought it might have been over that girl, Daisy Carter, but Josh was the one who ended things there. So even if Ethan had started a relationship with her afterwards, which Daisy claimed never happened, Josh probably wouldn't have cared. Besides, I believe Daisy was telling me the truth, eventually, that there was nothing going on between her and Ethan.'

'But there's no way to find out, is there? That's the trouble, Zoe. You've asked everyone who might know something – if there's more to the accident, that is – so what's the point of all this?'

I stare at my husband in disbelief. This is our son we're talking about, and Jake doesn't want to know. It's easier for him to ignore what's been happening. The man before me has fast become a stranger. Again.

And he's wrong: there *is* something I can try.

Jake leans forward. 'Zoe, I know now isn't the right time – in fact, it's the absolute worst time – but I need to talk to you about something. It's nothing to do with those messages, this is something else.' He pauses to take a deep breath. 'I was waiting for you to come home and I would have said it straight away but you started telling me all this stuff and, well, it's thrown me a bit.'

I'm on my guard now. It's not like Jake to instigate a serious conversation about anything. He normally does whatever it takes to avoid them. 'What is it?' As I ask this, I tell myself that it can't be worse than anything that's already happened. I've already lost Ethan, and as long as Jake and Harley are fine, then we can deal with everything else.

If Jake is fine.

I'm suddenly filled with fear. 'You're okay, aren't you? You're not ill or anything?'

He grabs my hand. 'No, sorry, it's nothing like that. I should have told you this a long time ago. I'm really sorry.' His eyes are watering, something I haven't seen since we lost Ethan.

This is not good. I pull my hand away, suddenly recoiling at his touch. 'Just say it.'

Jake shifts in his chair. 'I did something terrible, Zoe. I... I hate myself for it, and I know you'll never be able to forgive me, but I have to tell you.' Again, he pauses, this time letting out a deep breath. 'Not long after Ethan died, I... I slept with Leanne.'

His words bounce around the room and I'm unable to catch hold of them, to make sense of them. Surely this is a joke? It can't be true.

I stare at him, my mouth hanging open, my mind conjuring up all kinds of abhorrent images. My husband and my best friend. Somehow, I manage to speak. 'You and Leanne?'

Jake nods. He's staring at the floor, unable to meet my eyes. He doesn't want to see what he's done, to see the pain he's inflicting on me. 'I'm so sorry, Zoe. I was in such a bad place, I was a mess. My head was all over the place.'

Anger rises within me. 'How dare you use our son as an excuse?'

'No, no, I'm not. It was my fault, I just want you to know that I—'

'Never would have done it otherwise? Thanks, Jake, that's great to know.' My whole body feels numb, as if everything he's telling me is just bouncing off me. I can understand his words, but it's as if they're unable to penetrate my skin. Am I in shock? Denial? 'So all those times you were visiting her, it was to have a sordid little affair?' I shake my head. 'I thought you were better than that, Jake.'

'No, you've got it all wrong. It was just one time and never again. We never even spoke about it afterwards.'

'How did it happen?' I ask. I need information. All of it. I want to understand how it happened, how the two people closest to me, other than my children, could do this.

'I honestly can't explain how it happened. I'd gone to see her, as I often did, and I don't know, I just broke down and did something so reckless. I didn't plan it, didn't even know it was going to happen. I was just so overwhelmed with grief and… well, it felt as though you and I couldn't even bear to look at each other.' He holds up his hand. 'Not that it's your fault in any way. I just wasn't myself. Zoe, you have no idea how much I regret it and hate myself for what I did.'

Although Jake has the decency to look ashamed, this does nothing to soften the blows he's dealing me. The numbness has faded and it feels as though my insides are being ripped apart, organ by organ.

I can't speak. There are no words with which I can address this betrayal. My husband and my best friend. Thinking of what a cliché it is makes me want to laugh, even though inside I'm being torn apart.

'Zoe, I'm so sorry,' Jake repeats. 'It was a dreadful mistake. We both regret it.'

My jumbled thoughts turn to Leanne: the person who got Jake and me together in the first place. I feel sick. Even though I don't want to, my mind is forcing me to picture the two of them. Leanne is stunning and I've often wondered how she and Jake never ended up together, given that they're so close. 'We're just like brother and sister,' Leanne always joked, and this had been enough to reassure me. I'd not once worried about the two of them.

Now the memory of her words pierces my heart, shattering it into tiny fragments. 'Who started it? Who made the first move?' I ask – not that the answer will make any difference. Nothing he can say now will make a difference.

'I did,' Jake says, keeping his eyes fixed on the floor. 'She hesitated to start with and—'

'I've heard enough,' I say. I don't need to know any more details; nothing he can tell me will change the fact that everything I've ever felt for Jake has just died, and is as irretrievable to me as Ethan.

There are many things I could say to Jake in this moment. I could explain to him how the hardest thing to deal with is knowing he did this when our son had just died. Or that keeping it from me for three years, when we have been trying to rebuild our lives, has made our marriage even more of a sham. But I don't say a word. There's no point.

There's just one thing I need to know. 'Why are you telling me this now?'

Jake says nothing. He shuffles his foot and I want to stamp on it, dig my heel into it and draw blood. 'I know keeping it from you makes our betrayal even worse, but—'

'Why now?' I keep my voice measured, even though I want to scream at him. 'You've had three years to tell me, so why the hell now?'

'Because I'm finally doing the right thing,' Jake says.

Looking at the pitiful expression on his face, I stifle the urge to pummel my fists into him and inflict as much physical pain as the emotional pain he's causing me.

'Please, Zoe…' Jake tries to reach for my hand but I shove his arm away.

I ask him if Leanne knows he's telling me all this now, and he tells me that she doesn't.

'Get out of here, Jake. Now. You can go and pack up some stuff quickly, but I want you out of this house. Just get the hell out of here.'

Within half an hour he has gone, and I am alone in this silent and oppressive house, with no idea how to feel. All I know is that I'm angry, furious with Jake for his deceit, for betraying not just me but Harley and Ethan too. It wouldn't have made any difference if he'd told me when it first happened; there is no way I could ever have forgiven him, no matter how quickly he'd confessed the truth.

As for Leanne, I can't even think about her. My best friend. The one person, other than Jake, I truly believed I could trust. That is something I will have to deal with later; there's just no space in my head for it all.

As I'm lying on my bed, thinking these jumbled and painful thoughts, my phone beeps with a text message. Thinking it must be Jake, I ignore it and go downstairs to get myself another glass of water to soothe my dry throat.

When I get round to checking it, I immediately regret my decision not to have done so immediately.

You need to look closer to home. Your son was no victim.

THIRTY-FOUR

Harley

He feels like a stalker, standing here watching her head into her house, a pint of milk clutched in her hand. It wasn't his plan to follow her, but when he reached her road and spotted her leaving her house, he just wanted to know where she was going. He had to know.

Was she seeing someone else? It was possible. Likely, even, given the way she'd so suddenly ended it with him. At least this time she was only going to the shop around the corner, not meeting up with some guy. Harley has no idea what he would have done if Mel had turned around and seen him. There is no explanation he could have given her other than that he is quite possibly losing the plot. He hadn't realised just how much Mel had held him together, and now he is slowly unravelling.

It appears he is at a crossroads. He can turn around and go back home, and she'll never know he's been here, that he is having trouble accepting things, or he can just walk up to her front door and ask her if they can talk. Like he'd planned. They'll be alone; both her parents' cars are missing from the driveway, so this is the perfect opportunity.

With this thought in mind, he heads up to the front door, presses the doorbell and stands back.

He doesn't have long to wait before she answers. 'Harley? What are you doing here?'

'Can we talk, Mel? Just quickly.' He gives her what he hopes is an apologetic smile.

She bites her lip and he notices she's wearing deep red lipstick. It makes her look different; not the same Mel he'd been with, that he's kissed and held and shared an intimate part of himself with.

'I really don't think that's a good idea, Harley. What more is there to say?'

'I won't stay long, I promise.'

Seconds pass. 'Okay, come in. But not for long – I'm meeting the girls in an hour.'

It feels so different being in Mel's house now that he's no longer her boyfriend. He is out of place – if he'd ever been at home here to begin with. He doesn't seem to be at home anywhere. Still, he liked her parents and enjoyed coming here so he's grateful for that.

'What's going on, Harley?' Mel asks, as soon as they're sitting on the sofa. 'I thought we agreed we should have a clean break. None of that "let's be friends" stuff.'

That's what *she* agreed, at least. As far as he remembers, he said nothing of the sort. 'I just wanted to ask why,' he explains. 'I'm not trying to change your mind or anything, I promise, but you didn't really give me a reason for ending things.'

'Oh, Harley, could you really not work it out for yourself?' Her tone is patronising and again she seems like a different girl. How could she have changed so much in so little time?

'Are you seeing someone else?' he ventures.

Mel looks mortified. 'No! I'd never do anything like that. I thought you knew me, Harley.'

'Then what it is?' He thought about this all night, and he can't understand how her feelings went from hot to cold so quickly. He's torn right now: part of him thinks he should make the most of this, that freedom would be good; but part of him is terrified of life without her, what it will mean for him.

'You're not interested in me, Harley. Oh, I know you like me, but you don't feel that spark, do you? I think you've been trying to force it but it's just not there. You can't make yourself have feelings for someone. They have to be organic, come naturally.'

'That's not how it is,' he says. 'You've got it completely wrong.'

She shakes her head. 'I don't think I have. Face it, you had more fun with your friends that night you cut short our evening, didn't you?'

'No, not at all.' But he's lying, because he did have a good time with Isaac and his mates. He was more relaxed, not putting on an act or worrying about how he was coming across. It was just natural.

'You can't be yourself with me, Harley, and I don't deserve that. You'll meet someone at medical school, a girl you've got a lot more in common with. This wouldn't have worked in the long term anyway, would it?'

She's right. Whether it's two weeks, two years or two decades down the line, he's sure it would have all fallen apart eventually.

'My Dad's moved out,' Harley blurts out. He doesn't want to talk about his own relationship any more, and Mel is the only person he can talk to about his parents.

She reaches for his arm and gives it a pat. Condescension or genuine concern? He's not sure. 'Oh, Harley, I'm so sorry.' She doesn't ask why he has left, and this annoys Harley. Only a few days ago, she would have wanted to know every detail, to offer to help in any way she could. She really is cutting him off. There is no way he will ever be able to change her mind.

'I know it sounds awful, Mel, but I'm actually glad he's gone. I mean, I feel bad for Mum, even though she's putting on a brave face about it. It's just that I can tell they haven't been happy for years, so I suppose I've been expecting this. If anything, I'd thought it would happen sooner.'

'What's your mum said about it?'

'Not a lot. She said they just need time apart, that's all.' At least Mel's asking for more information now. Maybe this means there's a chance for them after all.

'And have you spoken to your dad?'

'No.' He's about to add that he finds it hard to talk to him at the best of times, and always has done, but Mel is looking at her watch and he knows he should leave. He can't burden her with all this anyway; he's already done enough to her.

'It's a shame about the holiday,' he says. 'Maybe we could—'

'I don't think that's a good idea, Harley, do you? Let's just draw a line under it all.'

That's it then. She's made up her mind and there's nothing he can do about it. 'I'll go now,' he says, standing up. 'You take care of yourself.'

He sees himself out and closes the door behind him. Everything is falling apart and he doesn't know how much longer he can hold it together.

It really is true what they say: what goes around comes around.

THIRTY-FIVE

Zoe

I sit clutching my phone, willing a text message or email to appear. Anything. It's been nearly a whole day since I replied to the last message, asking whoever it was to meet me, saying that I would listen to whatever they had to say and that I only wanted help getting to the truth. Even though what I wanted to do was curse them, I made sure my tone was kind, compliant and desperate.

There's been no reply and now I'm losing all hope. I can't allow myself to think about Jake or Leanne – not yet. This is more important.

'Sorry I'm late,' Leo says, sliding onto the bench next to me. We're lucky to have a beautiful park so close to work, but the river alongside it gives me chills. For me, it's not something wonderful to look at; instead, it is a sinister reminder of my son's death.

'Thanks for coming,' I say. 'I hope I haven't dragged you away from anything important.'

'Not at all. I was going to finish a bit earlier today anyway, so it's no trouble. I promised I'd help you and I meant it.'

I thank Leo and fill him in on the latest message. 'I don't think I'll get a reply – it's been too long now since I texted back. It's so frustrating, and I have no clue what to do next. It feels like I've hit a brick wall, and I'm really starting to worry that Ethan did something terrible. I just have no idea what it could be.'

'Do you think he might have done something to the other boy? Why do you think that?'

I tell him everything Roberta said about the two of them falling out, how Josh ignored Ethan when he phoned yet still wanted to stay the night at our house.

'That is a bit odd,' Leo agrees.

'It's just so difficult to get my head around. I know all parents say this, but Ethan was a good boy. Don't get me wrong, he was far from perfect and he got in trouble at times but I can't believe he would have hurt anyone. But Roberta was adamant that the boys had fallen out to the point where their friendship was practically over, and that had to be about something serious, hadn't it?'

Leo stares across the park. 'So do you think it's the other boy's mum tormenting you with these messages? Roberta, is it?'

'I haven't completely ruled it out, but I don't think it's her. She wouldn't need to do this; she could hurt me directly by just confronting me if she thought Ethan had done something. There'd be no need for her to keep anything secret.' As I say this, I remember how worried Roberta seemed about what Adrian might have said to me. But they're going through an acrimonious separation at the moment so of course she wouldn't be thrilled that I'd spoken to him. And Adrian is probably resentful because she's left him – that's got to be humiliating for a man like him – so he's just trying to get back at her.

'And there's no one else Ethan was close to at school? No other good friends?' Leo asks.

'No, not really. He was always with Josh. They did both have other people they hung around with but nobody else really came to the house. The only other person Ethan spent a lot of time with was Harley. They were very close. Completely different characters, but they had such a strong bond.'

I explain to Leo that I've kept Harley out of this because of how badly he fell apart when Ethan died. 'He blamed himself for not hearing the boys sneak out of the house. His bedroom was right next to Ethan's and he's normally a light sleeper, but that night he didn't hear a thing. It cut him up and he had to take time off from school. He's only just finished his A levels, a year behind everyone else his age. And this time, when I started getting the messages, he was taking his last exams so there was no way I could mention anything to him.'

'Could you say something now, though?' Leo asks. 'If he's finished his exams? He might be able to help. If the two of them were that close then Harley might be able to tell you something that could be important.'

Although I've thought of this, I'm still reluctant to discuss it with Harley, especially now that he and Mel have split up, but I'm being left with little choice. Maybe Leo's right. And if Harley knows what's going on he might be able to help. Last time I spoke to him he had no context for my vague questions. Knowing the truth might help him think of something.

'I think you're right,' I tell Leo. 'He's an adult now and it's probably not fair to keep him in the dark when it involves his brother. I'll speak to him tonight.'

'That's probably the right thing to do,' Leo says. 'Shall we walk for a bit? I don't think I've seen much more of the park than this spot we're sitting in.'

I keep forgetting that Leo is new to this area; it feels as though we've been colleagues for a lifetime.

'Yes, good idea.' I stand up. Anything to get away from the river.

'What does your husband think of all this?' Leo asks, as we make our way through the park, avoiding joggers who seem to be coming from all directions.

I'm not going to tell him about Jake's confession, or that I've just thrown him out of the house, that our marriage is over; I've already shared so much with Leo and it's not fair to burden him with even more. 'Jake's not convinced there's anything in it,' I say.

'In fact, he's discouraging me from pursuing this. Thinks it's just some sick prank.'

Leo stares at the ground. 'But you're a mum. You have to follow your instincts, explore every avenue, or you won't be able to rest.'

'That's exactly it.'

Leo smiles. 'I have to admit I used to be more of a "bury my head in the sand" kind of person, but my ex-wife changed me. She made me realise it's always better to confront what's happening, as painful as that might be, because it will always be there to bite you in the arse at any time.'

'I wish Jake would see it that way,' I say. But the truth is that everything's changed now and it's nothing to do with Ethan or these messages. I think of Leanne and wonder what she's doing at this moment. Does she know that Jake has told me the truth? If so, she's made no attempt to contact me.

'Talk to him,' Leo is saying. 'Just make him understand why you need to do this.'

'Yes, I will,' I say, knowing it will be futile, and that it no longer matters what Jake thinks anyway.

We turn the corner and head beneath some trees, and I feel my phone vibrate in my pocket.

It's another anonymous text message, from yet a different number.

Okay, if that's what it will take for you to do something about this. Meet me at the river at 9 p.m. Come alone and don't be late. I won't wait around.

My hands shake as I hand my phone to Leo and wait for him to read it.

'What river is this person talking about?'

I take a deep breath. There can only be one place they're referring to. 'The river in Guildford where Ethan drowned.'

Leo's eyes widen. 'Right,' he says. 'I'm coming with you.'

I've had the whole evening to think about why the meeting place is the river, and there's only one explanation I can come up with: this person wants to inflict as much pain on me as possible. They want me to suffer, to relive Ethan's death all over again. What choice do I have but to go along with it? This might be my only chance to get answers, even though it feels as if I'm heading straight into a trap.

After seeing Leo in the park, I went home for a few hours, hoping to talk to Harley, but the house was empty and I felt Jake's absence, despite it being usual for him not to be home in the early evening. Once again, I force myself not to think about him; I need to focus on Ethan and then I'll be able to deal with my feelings about Jake and Leanne.

Now, as I sit in the passenger seat beside Leo, letting the noise of the car engine and the motorway wash over me, I wonder how I will bring myself to walk up to the river, to stare out at it and try not to picture Ethan in there, flailing around, even though he could swim. I've often wondered why he couldn't save himself, and the only thing I can think of is that he panicked. It's only now I know that it could have been a completely different scenario.

Afterwards, I only went to the river once, and I was such a mess that Jake had to practically drag me back to the car. I didn't want to be there, but at the same time I couldn't bring myself to walk away. It almost felt as though Ethan was right there, that he still existed in that water. I have never let myself go back, scared that I will just keep walking straight into that river, just to be near my son. The pull of it is terrifying.

'How are you feeling?' Leo asks. 'Stupid question, I know.'

'Scared,' I admit. 'But so desperate for answers that I think I'd put myself through anything.'

'I don't feel good about parking further down the road and letting you walk up to the river by yourself. Let me come with you.'

I tell him it won't be dark and we have no choice; the person said to come alone, and I can't risk being seen with him in case it forces them to back off.

'I know,' Leo responds, 'but I don't like it. I'm worried about you – this doesn't feel right and I don't like that they want to meet you at the river.'

'They're doing it to get to me. That's what this is about. Probably all the messages too.'

He glances at me and shakes his head. 'It's awful that anyone would want to do that. You haven't done anything, so why punish you?'

'I don't know. Because they can't hurt Ethan any more? Oh God, what did he do?'

'Well, if he did anything at all, then hopefully you'll find out very soon.'

I glance at the clock on Leo's dashboard. It's eight thirty and we're only about ten minutes from Guildford. And the river. That place I vowed I would never go near again, and never thought I'd have cause to. Part of the reason we moved is that I couldn't bear to think of it being so close to us. Out of sight, yet right there, a looming presence on the edge of our lives.

Walnut Tree Close looks the same as it did three years ago, and my heart speeds up, pounding inside me. 'It's like nothing's changed.'

'Tell me where to stop,' Leo says.

For a second I'm tempted to tell him to just keep driving, to get us back onto the A3 and we can forget we ever came here. Then I picture Ethan's cheeky smile and large brown eyes, his

floppy hair that was always falling into his face, and I know I
have to keep going.

'Just pull over here,' I tell him. 'In the car park by those offices.
I don't have far to walk from here.'

He does as I say and swerves the car into an empty space outside
the building of a legal company. 'Are you sure about this? I still
think I should just come.'

I summon all my strength, will my legs to move and let me
get out of the car. 'I'll be fine. And I've got your number ready
to dial on my phone if anything happens. I'll be just across the
road, a bit further up.'

Leo grabs my arm. 'Be careful, Zoe.'

The fact that it's still not quite dark fills me with confidence,
even though there is nobody about. It's quarter to nine now so
I walk slowly, not wanting to get there too soon. I don't even
know if I'm going to the part I'm expected to; I've just assumed
the person means the exact location where the boys were seen by
witnesses. Witnesses who drove past because they didn't think
anything of two teenage boys messing around by a river in the
middle of the night.

Now I'm here and my body feels heavy with a sickening mixture
of fear and grief. It no longer feels as though Ethan is here; now
it's only the place he lost his life. I sit on a grass verge and look
up at the sky. It's too painful to even glance at the water. I don't
want to be here.

The minutes tick by slowly, and eventually it is 9 p.m. I look
around, but there's still no sign of anyone. It's okay, I think. They
will turn up. I wonder if I will know this person – I can almost
picture Roberta appearing from the shadows. She wouldn't come
here, though; it would be just as difficult for her.

Ten past nine. Still nobody here. I pull out my phone and open
the last text message, then start typing.

I'm here, by the river. Where are you?

There's no response. And still no footsteps, no sound around me from a human being, only the occasional hum of a passing car. This person isn't coming, I'm certain of that now. It's all just been another part of his or her sick game, and I fell for it and put myself through even more pain.

Even though I'm sure of this, I wait until nine forty-five and then slowly make my way back to Leo's car, checking behind me until the river is out of sight.

I check my phone, even though I haven't heard it ring or beep. There is a new message.

I told you to come alone. You've messed up big time. Now you'll never know the truth.

THIRTY-SIX

Mum is still in hospital, but her condition is stable. They're keeping her in as a precaution and I'm grateful for this. I have the house to myself and he'll be here in a few minutes.

I feel as if I'm going mad. How can I really hope to get through to him? To convince him that we're still right for each other after meeting face-to-face? I am not my photo, yet I don't look bad, and it's our personalities that have connected, at least on my part. I'm hoping that's enough.

Doubts plague my head, but the pull of him is too great to turn back now, and underneath the nerves is a strong sense of excitement. It's so virulent that it overpowers my fear. Perhaps we will laugh about this one day, far in the future, and share the story with our children.

Armed with a renewed sense of purpose and determination, I rush to the door when he rings the bell and open it wide, ready to explain things.

'Um, hi,' he says. 'Is Alissa home?'

And that's when words I haven't planned spew from my mouth. 'She's not here at the moment, but do you want to come in and wait? She told me you were coming so I'm sure she'll be back in a minute. She just went to the shop.'

He looks around and then shrugs. 'Sure. Thanks.'

And now he is in my house, and I feel like a nervous child, barely able to control the tremble in my legs.

'Has she been gone long?' he asks, stepping inside and scraping his shoes on the doormat. He's so trusting.

'No, she only just finished getting ready. It takes my sister forever to get ready for anything.'

He smiles at this, probably imagining how much effort she's made for him and how good she will look. Yes, Alissa certainly is a beauty.

I'm too nervous to drink anything but I offer him something, grateful when he declines.

My stomach churns, a constant reminder – as if I needed one – of the tricky situation I'm in. By inviting him in I have crossed even further over the line, and there's no way to turn back now. I am walking blind here, with no idea how long I will be able to keep up this charade. I might have an hour maximum before he gets suspicious or nervous. Somehow, I need to make him start falling for me all over again.

As it turns out, it's not as bad as I feared. We sit on the sofa, chatting away as if we've known each other forever, and several times I manage to make him laugh. He looks even more beautiful when he smiles, and his skin is smooth and looks soft like velvet. I want to touch it, but there's no way I will ruin anything now. This might actually work.

We're so engrossed in our conversation that forty minutes pass before he asks about Alissa again.

'Did she definitely remember I was coming?' he asks.

'That's what she told me. She wanted me to let you in and keep you company until she got back. She shouldn't be too long.'

'I don't understand what's happened. I hope she's okay?'

A flaw in the plan. I hadn't counted on him being worried that something might have happened to Alissa while she was out.

'I'll call her in a second. Just need the toilet.'

I lock myself in the bathroom and text him: 'Sorry I'm not at home. I got scared. Will make it up to you.'

When I join him again, he has a frown on his face and is staring at his phone.

'Everything okay?' I ask.

He shakes his head and his beautiful hair flops across his forehead. 'No. Alissa just texted that she got scared and isn't coming home.'

I sit beside him, desperately wanting to reach out and touch him. It's all I can do to restrain myself. 'I'm sorry about that. She's very shy – probably got scared that you'd met online. She's never done this before, you see. Just give her time and I'm sure she'll come around.'

'Do you think?' he says, his eyes widening with hope. 'I guess I was a bit freaked out too, coming here.' He stands up, ready to leave, and I know there's nothing I can do to keep him here. I've already been lucky that he's stayed this long.

'She'll probably get more confident when she gets old like me,' I say.

'You're not old,' he replies, flashing me his beautiful smile.

It is all I can do to stop my cheeks flaming. 'Why don't I give you my number and we can keep in touch?' I say. 'I'll talk to Alissa for you and see what's going on.'

'Really? Thank you.' There is no hesitation.

Once he's gone, I close my eyes and imagine he's still here in my house. In my bed. His soft skin blending into mine.

THIRTY-SEVEN

Roberta

'I know you're in there, Adrian. I need to talk to you.' She whispers the words through the letterbox, scared the neighbours will hear. She hates drawing attention to herself.

Eventually, he opens the door, his eyes wild. 'What the hell are you doing here? Can't keep away, can you? I knew you'd be back.'

Roberta tries to hold herself straight, to appear as tall as possible. She will not let him undermine her newfound confidence. 'That couldn't be further from the truth,' she says, as calmly as possible. 'I'm here because something's happened and I needed to tell you. I think someone might know.'

'Know what?' he laughs, and then realisation dawns and his face drops. 'Get the fuck inside.' He pulls her through the door, slamming it behind him.

'You'd better get talking, Roberta – and fast.'

She stares at his bare feet and shorts. His legs are a nice shape, she thinks, and don't suit his nasty personality at all.

'Well?' Adrian insists. 'What the hell is going on?'

'I need to sit down,' she says, already making her way to the living room. 'This conversation's too important to have standing in the hall.' She feels brave for saying this, and only hopes she can keep up this act of confidence.

Once they're sitting on the sofa, she begins, carefully constructing her story so it doesn't shed her in too negative a light. 'I… I

met someone yesterday. A nice man. We spent the night together.'
She forces herself to look at him.

Adrian stares at her; his mouth moves but the words take too
long to come out. 'You came here to tell me that you've screwed
some idiot?' A loud laugh erupts. 'Do you really think I give a
shit? Actually, I feel sorry for him. Must have been the worst night
of his life.'

Adrian's words stab into her chest – could this be why Lewis
left without a word? Was he repulsed by her and full of regret over
what they did? She recalls his touch, how excited he was, how
much they clicked. She didn't imagine that. No, there is a worse
reason why Lewis left, and that's what she came here to discuss.
She won't let Adrian put her down any more.

'Just shut up and listen, will you?' She forces herself to stare
him down, to show him she's changed, that she's stronger.

Adrian raises his eyebrows. 'Go on then. What happened?'

'I can't be certain, but I think I might have told him too much.
I'd been drinking and, well, I don't remember, but… the next
morning he was gone and I haven't heard from him since.'

Adrian jumps up. 'Ha, I told you. He doesn't want to know
you – you probably bored him to death. What's this got to do
with me?'

'Don't you get it? You're so fixated on putting me down that
you can't see what's important here. I think this man knows what
we did. I think I might have told him everything.'

She's never seen Adrian look so scared, and even though this
affects both of them, she takes satisfaction in knowing he is suffering. He sits down again, resting his head in his hands.

'How do you know you said anything?' he asks.

'I don't for sure, but I feel like I did, and I trust my instincts.'

'There are a million reasons he might have left without saying
anything. He's probably married and had to get back to his wife.
Bet you didn't think of that.'

'He's divorced.' How does she really know this, though? How does she even know his name is Lewis? Or that he works where he said he did.

'Yeah, that's what they all say.' Adrian smirks.

'You'd know all about that, wouldn't you? Is that the line you give to people?'

'Not people. Just one special lady. That probably hurts to hear, doesn't it? To know I actually love someone else, that I wasn't just screwing around.'

Roberta hates herself for it, but he's right. She much prefers to think of him as scum who would indiscriminately sleep with anyone. She doesn't want to know that he's actually capable of having feelings. He's probably lying, though; the only person Adrian loves is himself.

She's about to tell him that she doesn't care either way, but he interrupts her. 'So you can't remember what you said to this idiot?'

'No. But we're both in serious trouble if I did tell him anything.'

Adrian stands up again, towers over her. 'You stupid, careless bitch. Or have you done this on purpose? You threatened to go to the police, didn't you? Is this your way of screwing me over?'

She tries to convince him it's not. 'No. Just stop attacking me and listen. I threatened to go to the police if you didn't let me leave, but you did and I'm happy about that. I don't want to go to prison, Adrian, not if I can have any chance of a life.' But how can she, with this hanging over her forever, and the excruciating loneliness of seeing others living full lives while hers has ceased to exist. All she knows is that she has to fight for something, however little that might be.

'Who is this man? We have to find out what he knows.'

'All I know is that his name's Lewis and he's a sales rep for a pharmaceutical company. Divorced with no kids. That's it, Adrian, that's all I know about him.' *Other than what his body feels like*, she thinks.

'You mean that's what he told you, all of which could be a pack of lies, and probably is. You're so fucking stupid, Roberta. How could you do this? We've been careful for so long and all it takes is a few drinks and a man showing some interest in you to blow both our lives apart.'

Adrian is right about the last part. If Lewis knows anything at all then everything is about to change. The past has finally caught up with them both.

'I came here so we can sort out what to do. Attacking me won't solve anything, will it?'

He paces the room, letting out deep puffs of air, as if he's having trouble breathing. She doesn't bother asking if he's okay. She doesn't care one way or the other.

Adrian grunts. 'There's only one bloody thing we can do right now, and that's find this person.'

'How? I don't have his number or anything.' She'd also found out this morning that Lewis had already checked out.

'Where exactly did you meet this man?' Adrian asks.

She doesn't want to tell him but there's no choice now. 'At the place I'm staying. He was a guest there too, but he's checked out now.'

'Well, you'll just have to try and find out exactly who he is, get his address. You'll have to.'

She pictures the reception desk with its ancient computer and wonders if it would be possible to access it. It probably has a password or something, and she's no expert with technology. Adrian's right, though – she has to try, otherwise the police will be hunting them down. They probably already are.

'I'll try,' she tells Adrian.

'Don't try. Just do it. You need to sort out this mess you've made, Roberta.' He lunges forward and grabs her by the neck. 'And if you don't, I'll do whatever it takes to make sure your life isn't worth living.'

*

Adrian's words bombard her as she heads back to the B & B. He didn't just utter an idle threat – he's got nothing to lose by causing her harm, not after what he's already done. What they've both done.

The owner, Anna Cartwright, is seated at the reception desk this evening, a sight Roberta's not used to. During her brief time here, she has had to hunt her down if she needs anything; yet the one time she needs her to be absent, there she is, her head buried in a magazine.

'Hi,' Roberta says. 'I was just wondering if I could ask a quick question?'

Anna looks up from her magazine and shifts her glasses down her nose. 'Yes? Is everything okay?'

'Everything's fine. I just needed to ask about a guest who stayed with you and just checked out this morning. Lewis?'

Anna smiles. 'Oh, yes. Lovely man. What about him?'

'Well, we had dinner together yesterday evening and he was going to help me out with something, but I've lost his number. Is there any chance you could give it to me?'

Her smile disappears. 'I did notice you ate together, and I'm sure you're genuine, but I really can't give out guests' details. I'm sure you understand.'

Roberta had thought this would be the response. 'Of course. Perhaps you could call him for me, then, and just ask him to give me a call on this number?' She grabs an old receipt from her bag and scribbles her mobile number down, sliding it across the desk to Anna.

'I suppose I could. I don't like to get involved, though. It just doesn't seem very professional.'

Adrian's threat plays in her head once more. 'Please, Anna. It would really help me out.'

Anna glances at her magazine then back at Roberta, sighing heavily. 'Okay, I'll do it. Just let me finish my magazine. And perhaps you should be more careful next time.'

Yes, she should, Roberta thinks. If only Anna knew the full story.

Back in her room, she waits, pacing the floor with her arms folded in front of her. Anna stayed true to her word and passed on her message, but now, more than two hours later, Roberta knows there's no chance Lewis will call; if he'd wanted to keep in touch then he wouldn't have left like that in the first place. Even if he'd had some sort of emergency, he would have left a note.

Her hopes are raised when her phone beeps, but it's only Adrian, asking if she's sorted out the problem yet. She ignores him. He can wait. After all, it's ultimately his fault that there's anything to sort out.

By 10 p.m., Roberta is climbing the walls, her whole body drenched in a layer of nervous sweat. The absence of any response from Lewis means there's only one thing she can do.

Downstairs is dark, the B & B locked up for the night. Guests are given their own keys to the main door so she needs to be on alert for anyone coming in. She knows the computer will be password-protected, but at least she can tell Adrian that she tried everything she could.

She's right, of course, and now finds herself staring at a box asking for her password. She tries the name of the B & B and Anna's surname, but neither are correct. Not wanting to risk being completely locked out so that Anna has to reset her password, she gives up and goes back to her room.

It's another hour before she can bring herself to text Adrian.

No luck. We'll have to think of something else.

And then she flops down on the bed, turns on her side with her legs tucked under her and cries a flood of tears. For Josh. For what they did. For the life she should be living right now.

THIRTY-EIGHT

Zoe

'Are you okay, Mum?' Harley asks, as I walk into the kitchen. After not being able to sleep until around 4 a.m., I'm up later than usual. He's already had breakfast and is sitting at the table drinking coffee. It will always feel strange to see my son drinking coffee – Harley is still my little boy and I'm not quite sure when he grew up so much.

'I'm fine,' I tell him. It's a lie, but I won't have him worrying about me.

'Is it weird for you with Dad being gone, though?'

I haven't told Harley the exact reason for Jake moving out. I know he's not a child, and he's mature enough to understand adult relationships, but I want to spare him the details. Besides, their relationship is strained enough, and I don't want to add to it. Jake can tell him, if that's what he chooses to do.

For now, I have to focus on these messages and what really is behind them. I'm getting nowhere and I need Harley's help. 'It is strange without your dad,' I say, 'but to be honest, there's been something else on my mind and it's taken over a bit.' I sit down opposite him.

Harley puts down his mug. 'I thought there was something bothering you, Mum.'

Again, I wonder whether I'm doing the right thing. 'About two weeks ago, I got an anonymous email from someone. It was to do with Ethan.'

Harley stares at me. 'What do you mean? What did it say?'

For the next few minutes I fill him in on every detail, every visit I've made to people in pursuit of the truth, and finally the events of last night, when the person responsible for the messages didn't turn up at the river.

Harley listens in silence, never interrupting, and it's a testament to his maturity. 'Oh, Mum, I wish you'd told me this before. I could have helped you; we could have shared it all. I knew there was something wrong and that you didn't just have a cold. You've been going through all this by yourself, haven't you? I bet Dad's been no help.'

'Don't be hard on him. He just sees it in a different way to me. Thinks it's all a nasty prank. Speaking of which, do *you* think it's all just a hoax?'

Harley doesn't hesitate. 'No, I don't. Why would someone do that? It doesn't make sense. It would be pointless. Besides, you've never upset anyone, have you? Who would have it in for you?'

'That's exactly what I think. But if Ethan was up to something, then that might mean someone wants to retaliate.'

We both get lost in our thoughts for a moment. 'I can't imagine what he could have done,' Harley says. 'Ethan just wasn't like that.' His eyes are welling up, and I begin to regret bringing this up, making him relive it all.

'Harley, look, I know it's difficult for you to go over all this, but is there anything you can think of that might help us work out who's doing this and why?'

He takes a sip of coffee. 'I'm not sure. I'll have to think hard about it. Now I get why you were asking me about him the other day. I wish you'd just told me then.'

'Yes, and I'm sorry I couldn't. You still had exams and I didn't want anything interfering with that. Not after what happened last time.'

Harley raises his eyebrows. 'You mean my breakdown.'

I'm surprised Harley is speaking so bluntly about this – he's never really wanted to discuss it before, and has certainly never referred to that time in this way. Is this how he's come to think of it?

'Do you know what got me through it?' he asks. 'The thought of Ethan. I wanted him to be proud of me, and being a complete wreck wouldn't have achieved that. I had to sort myself out because that's what he would have done. He would never have fallen apart like I did.'

I reach for his hand across the table. 'He was always so proud of you. He really did look up to you.'

Harley looks away, his cheeks flushed. He's never been comfortable accepting compliments. 'Have you talked to any of his other friends? Apart from Daisy?' he asks.

'No. I wouldn't know how to track any of them down.'

'How about on Facebook?' Harley suggests. 'We could try that.'

Harley's mention of Facebook reminds me that Ethan used to have an account, but he deactivated it a couple of months before he died. I never thought to ask why, but now I wonder if this is something important.

'Do you remember that Ethan deleted his account? Do you know why?'

'I don't think it was a big deal to him. He told me it was boring and he'd rather be playing his Xbox or outside on his bike.'

Nothing sinister there, then. I'm also quite sure Harley doesn't use social media, but I check anyway.

'I've still got my Facebook account, but I hate it,' he says. 'Waste of life.'

I manage a smile then, despite the situation we're in; my two boys never followed the crowd. They always remained true to who they were.

'And I haven't been on it since Mel and I broke up,' Harley continues. 'I just don't want to see what she's been up to.'

'I'm sorry about you two breaking up – I know how painful it must be.'

'Not as bad as for you and Dad,' he says. 'You've been married forever.'

Forever – does anything ever last that long? 'I'm okay, love. I've got you, haven't I?'

Harley smiles, and it's such a huge, confident smile that for a second he reminds me of Ethan.

'So how can we track down Ethan's friends?' I say.

'It should be quite easy,' Harley explains. 'I can post something asking people who were friends with Ethan to contact me. I've still got a lot of people on my Facebook who I went to school with, so if they share it then word will soon get around and hopefully reach people in Ethan's year. I remember a few names, so I can send out some individual messages too.'

'Are you sure you don't mind?'

'No, course not. We have to do this – I'm not letting that person get away with tormenting you, Mum.'

I stand up and walk over to Harley, wrapping my arms around him. I know this will make him feel awkward, but I need to tell him anyway. 'I'm so blessed to have you,' I say. 'And I'm so proud of you.'

'Mum, I know,' he says, clearly uncomfortable. But he humours me and lets me get the hug out of my system.

'Harley, I know you probably don't want to talk about it, but are you sure you're okay about what happened with Mel?'

'I can't say it doesn't hurt, but I'll be okay. I was going away at the end of summer anyway, so who knows what would have happened? It's probably better this way.'

Even though his words are filled with positivity, I can sense his underlying sadness. *I wish I could take away your pain.*

Later that evening, while Harley is out with some friends, I grab my bag and head out of the door. There is something I need to do.

*

Leanne's mouth hangs open when she sees me standing at her door. I've never seen her caught off guard like this before. 'Zoe... um, hi. What are you doing here?'

Without waiting for an invitation, I step into her hallway. 'I'm the last person you expected to see, aren't I?'

She shuts the door behind us and looks even more anxious. 'I'm so sorry I haven't been in touch. We've got a lot to talk about, haven't we?'

'So he told you that I know, then?' This shouldn't surprise me; Jake has always depended on their friendship, and Leanne probably knows far more about him than I do. And now she knows him physically as well. I shudder at this thought, try to stop it overwhelming me.

'Let's sit down,' she says.

'No, I'm fine standing, thank you.' I walk into her spacious living room and cross to the huge balcony doors. There are a few seconds of silence before she follows me.

'It was a mistake, Zoe. A horrible, terrible mistake. I'm so sorry.'

'Of course you are – now that I know. But what about the three years you both kept it from me? Fooled me into thinking you were my closest friend, that I could trust you with my life?' I force myself to look at her, even though the pain is almost unbearable. 'You sat with me so many times while I was crying for my son, you comforted me, and all the time you'd slept with my husband.'

She steps forward and tries to take my arm, starting when I push her away.

'Don't.' I turn back to the window, and the stunning view that Leanne doesn't deserve. 'Do you know what I keep thinking about? What I can't get out of my head? When Ethan died, and Jake and I were falling apart, I was actually glad he had you to talk to. He spent so many evenings here with you, didn't he? When he couldn't bear to be at home with all the memories. With his wife and son. And I didn't for one second question anything, because it never occurred to me that either of you would do anything like that. How stupid was I?'

'Nothing ever happened after that one time,' Leanne says. 'Ever. I swear to you. It was just once.'

'That one time, when Jake and I were grieving for our son. How despicable can you get?'

She stares at the floor. 'I know. I'm so sorry, Zoe. There hasn't been a day when I haven't felt dreadful.'

'I find that hard to believe, considering you could look me in the eyes and hear my voice on the phone almost daily and never once let the façade drop.' This, I realise, is what hurts the most. 'Do you know something? Not that I'd ever forgive him, but I can almost – just a tiny bit – understand how Jake could have done it. He was a mess, a different person, and grief can make us do things that are out of character. But you, Leanne? What's your excuse?'

She crosses to the sofa and sits down. 'I have no excuse, Zoe. I know it wasn't the same as your grief, but I was devastated about Ethan. You know the boys have always been like sons to me.'

'Don't you dare—'

'Wait, just hear me out. I'm not making excuses; I already said I have none. I just want to explain myself. I was caught up in the moment and wanted to stop it, but it was weird, like Jake *needed* me. The thing is, I don't think it had anything to do with who I was, he just needed some comfort or release from his pain. I don't know, Zoe, I'm not a psychologist. But I hated myself afterwards, and I will never ever forgive myself.'

'That makes two of us,' I say. 'You should have told me. For three years, both my marriage and friendship with you have been lies.'

'I know you're right, but how could I tell you at that time? You were already going through hell; I couldn't add to that. And then it got harder and harder – you were making progress as a family and I just couldn't wreck that. Plus it didn't… it didn't seem like it had even happened.'

'I've heard enough!' I've kept my cool up until now, but my voice erupts.

Leanne stays silent; what more can she say?

'Did you ever want to be with Jake? Properly, I mean.' I don't know why I ask this; it's just something I need to know.

She looks at me for a moment, searching my face, and I can tell she's wrestling with whether to be honest or not. 'Not to start with,' she says, 'but I'm not going to lie to you any longer. After we… you know… it changed things for me. I'd honestly never seen Jake in that way before, but then suddenly all these feelings came flooding out, which I never even knew I had. But I ignored them, Zoe. I never once even considered acting on them – you have to know that.'

It's impossible to work out how I feel about this. 'And now? Are they still there?' Not that it matters. Jake and I are done now; there's nothing left to save.

'I don't know, Zoe. I hope not.'

'Is that why you've never settled down? Some crap about no man living up to Jake?' If this is the case, then I actually feel sorry for Leanne.

She shakes her head. 'No, it's not like that. I haven't been hankering after him all these years. I just haven't met anyone who… gets me.'

'And Jake "gets you", I suppose?'

A sheepish expression crosses her face. 'Yes, he does. But that comes from our friendship. You have to understand, though, Zoe, he doesn't feel the same way about me. He hasn't ever. He made a mistake while consumed with grief and he's regretted it ever since. I swear that's the truth.'

It makes no difference to me whether or not this is the case. Jake and I were probably over the second Ethan died, I just couldn't see it. Or maybe it was the moment he slept with Leanne. I will never know for certain.

'Please don't let this ruin your marriage,' she says. 'You've been through so much together already, and I know you can get through this.'

Disbelief courses through me. 'You just don't get it, do you? How can I ever trust either of you again? What it comes down to is that neither of you were truly there for me at the hardest time of my life. That's the point here. It means we all have nothing. The least you could have done is told me at the beginning.'

'That's what I wanted Jake to understand,' Leanne says.

'Wait – what do you mean? When?'

'When we talked about it the other day.'

So more lies on Jake's part. He specifically told me that he and Leanne had never discussed what they'd done. 'I'm done with both of you,' I say, heading towards the door.

Leanne is crying now, big, fat tears sliding down her cheeks, blurring her carefully applied make-up. I take satisfaction in seeing her this way.

'He loves you,' she says, swiping at her face. 'And Harley. He's lost without you both.'

'We barely saw him anyway, and he and Harley are hardly close, are they?'

She doesn't respond, because we both know the truth. Harley is so different from Jake in just about every way. The two of them have never been able to find any common ground.

'I'm going now. I've said what I came to say. Don't contact me, Leanne. Live your life and I'll live mine, but let's just stay away from each other.'

Again she is silent, and she doesn't follow me out when I leave. Closing the door behind me, I don't know whether I feel better or worse, but at least now I am free to focus on what happened to Ethan.

THIRTY-NINE

Jake

Nobody knows he's been sleeping in the office, hastily washing himself and brushing his teeth in the staff toilets before Liam gets in. His bed is the worn sofa in the kitchen area. What a disaster his life's become, and he has nobody to blame but himself.

He's thought about calling Zoe again, but she never answers and he knows how stubborn she is. He has zero chance of changing her mind. He knew it would be this way, and he can't blame her. In his heart he knows he doesn't deserve her, not after what happened with Leanne or how distant he became when Ethan died. She and Harley needed him and he was emotionally absent, unable to deal with their grief along with his own. It was all too much.

He misses Ethan every day, and knows if his son is somehow looking down on him now, he would be ashamed of him. Not just for what he did with Leanne, but because Jake knows things. Deep in his gut, he knows more than he's able to speak out loud. And it's time to put it right. Better late than never, he reasons. It won't make any difference to Zoe now, but he's got to do the right thing. Finally.

He's logged off for the night now, his brain no longer able to block out destructive thoughts, to avoid addressing the mess his life has become.

Jake lies on the sofa with an old coat he left here a while ago thrown over him – despite the summer warmth outside, the office is freezing – and tries to call Harley, but as he expected there is no answer and it eventually goes to voicemail. He disconnects the call without leaving a message.

He wishes he was better at communicating with his son, but there's a barrier between them that seems insurmountable. It's nothing he can pinpoint, but ever since he was young Harley has seemed to be wary of him and has kept a distance. He's not sure why. Ethan wasn't like that with him.

Just as he places his phone on the floor, he looks up and sees Leanne standing in the doorway, staring at him. He shifts himself up. 'What are you doing here? How did you get in?'

'You left the door unlocked and I knew you must be in here because your car's outside. I've been trying to call you.'

Damn it, he thinks. He's normally so fastidious about locking up. How could he have made such a mistake? 'I've been busy,' he says, knowing full well that Leanne will see through his excuse. She knows him too well.

She steps into the kitchen and sits on the end of the sofa, crossing her legs. She looks tired, and as if she's got no make-up on. 'Zoe came to see me this evening.'

Jake sits up straighter and pulls the old coat off his body. 'Why? What did she say?'

'I think she just wanted to confront me. Maybe she was wondering why I hadn't contacted her since she threw you out.'

Jake cringes at the words, even though they are the truth. 'What did you tell her?'

'Oh, Jake, don't you know by now I'm good at keeping secrets? I'm not going to hurt her any more. I just apologised to her. At least you'd warned me that she knew, so I was expecting a confrontation sooner or later.'

'She's never going to forgive us, is she?'

Leanne shakes her head. 'No, but do you blame her? I told you we should have told her when it first happened, didn't I? Secrets always come back to haunt you.'

Jake stares at her. He knows she is talking about more than just the night they spent together. He wants to say something but the words stick in his throat. 'You didn't do it either,' is all he manages to say.

'Yes, and I'll regret that for the rest of my life as well.' She looks around the tiny kitchen. 'You shouldn't be sleeping here like this. Why don't you stay at mine? I hate to think of you being here.'

It's a tempting offer. Jake's already got backache and it's only been two nights. 'No, thanks,' he says, deciding he'd rather put up with the back pain, or even waste some money on a hotel, than stay with Leanne and be forced to confront what they did.

'You're happy about this, aren't you?' he says. 'I know you, Leanne. You forget how well sometimes.'

'What do you mean? Of course I'm not. Zoe's my best friend. *Was* my best friend.'

Jake leans closer to her. 'Then tell me one thing. Why are you sending her those nasty messages?'

FORTY

Alissa has ended it with him. It had to be done, and now I can pursue our friendship safely and make it lead to something much more. He is under my skin and I believe I will soon be under his. The real me this time. I have an advantage: I know him through my correspondence as Alissa.

He doesn't take it well, and for days he bombards Alissa with texts, begging to meet up, to explain in person why she's no longer interested. I feel bad ignoring all his pleas, but it's for the greater good. He'll never know this, of course, though he will soon forget her. Time heals everything, Mum always says. Well, let's see how true that is.

After a few days he texts me, asking if I've had a chance to talk to my sister. Bingo!

'Shall we meet up?' I suggest. 'We can talk about it all.' He readily agrees.

It is liberating to be able to meet him with no fear. I am just me. We meet on Saturday afternoon in Green Park; I know it's a long way for him but he will travel any distance for Alissa. I'm not resentful about this because soon it will be all about me. Besides, I am Alissa, aren't I?

Rather than moping around, as I've expected, he's in quite good spirits, and I easily keep him entertained. The sound of his laugh seems to sink into my skin, and I soak him up.

He's surprised and touched that I've brought a picnic, and tells me nobody has ever done anything like that for him before. I reply that it's just a little gesture to cheer him up.

*

We meet up several times, and it's not long before Alissa barely enters the conversation. Today I let it slip that I think she might be seeing someone else, and a pained expression briefly crosses his face. But then he seems to straighten up, as if he has decided that if she's moving on, then so will he.

That's when I decide that tonight is the night I will make a move. He trusts me now, and I know he likes me, but I just need a bit of help.

He's all for it when I suggest going back to my place. Mum is in hospital again. She's developed pneumonia and needs to be under constant observation. I feel bad taking advantage of her ill health, but she wouldn't begrudge my happiness.

I tell him that Alissa is staying at a friend's house, just to make sure he's not coming in the hopes of seeing her.

'Have you ever drunk alcohol before?' I ask him, when we're sitting together on the sofa, even though I already know the answer.

'Not really. I mean, I've tried a sip of my mum's wine when she wasn't looking, but it was gross.'

'Try this,' I say, handing him a glass of gin and tonic.

He takes a sip and then starts coughing, his face flushed with embarrassment. I can't help but laugh, and this makes him pick up the glass and try again.

Easy.

It's not long before he's drinking as if it's water, and we sit together watching Game of Thrones *on TV. I slide closer to him every now and again, and he doesn't move away. In fact, he's laughing and enjoying himself so much that at times that he is the one sidling closer to me.*

Our legs touch and a frisson of excitement surges through my body. It's like electricity and I'm sure I let out a moan. I need more of him now, and I'm ready to take my chance. He's had so much to drink and his words are barely legible, but I will take what I can get.

I place my hand on his knee and wait to see what he'll do. His eyes remain fixed on the TV, and he doesn't flinch, so I keep going, moving my hand steadily further up his leg, until I can feel him in my hand.

'Woah, what… what are you doing?' he asks, but he doesn't push me away.

'Does it feel good?'

'I… um… no, I…'

'Just let me show you how good I can make you feel,' I say, stroking him until he is hard.

'We shouldn't… I don't…'

But I've got him. He is enjoying it and he doesn't want me to stop.

'Oh, no,' he groans, but when I lean forward and kiss him, he hesitantly lets me, and within seconds it no longer feels as though I am forcing him.

The next morning, I relive it over and over in my head. I can still feel his touch, the way every inch of him felt. I wanted him to stay the night but knew that would be impossible. He hadn't let anyone know where he was and he needed to get home, so I walked him to the station and told him I'd text him the next day. He was very quiet, though that didn't surprise me. This was the last thing he'd been expecting.

I knew I had to give him time, let him sort things in his head, but I couldn't help texting him that night: 'I do really care about you, just want you to know that.'

I should feel wracked with guilt that I manipulated and took advantage of him when he was vulnerable. But it's hard to dwell on that when I know how good I made him feel.

And now that I've had a taste of him, there's no way I can give him up.

FORTY-ONE
Roberta

This isn't her. She isn't some sort of stalker, and it's completely out of character for her to be standing here, outside GlaxoSmithKline in Brentford, about to go inside and ask to speak to Lewis, a man she knows nothing about.

She had finally remembered the name of the company he works for. She knew it was something to do with pharmaceuticals, but that had been all she'd been able to recall, otherwise she would have come straight here and not wasted her time waiting for him to phone.

Adrian has no idea she is here; she will wait and see what happens before she speaks to him. Anyway, he has turned her into this person – someone who would do anything to protect their lie. No, it was worse than a lie. A lie seems harmless in comparison. It feels odd that only days ago she was ready to go to the police herself, despite what that would mean for both of them. Could she really have done it? She thought that was the only way she could be rid of Adrian, yet now sees that she will never be free of him, even if she never lays eyes on him again.

And now she is standing outside this colossal pharmaceutical building, ready to confront a stranger who probably knows everything and could ruin her life within seconds by just making a phone call. Perhaps he already has.

Roberta is inside the huge lobby before she realises she doesn't even know Lewis's surname. Or if Lewis is indeed his actual name.

This could turn out to be bad. She takes a seat on one of the sofas that line the walls and pulls her phone from her bag. The company website may have employee names listed on it, and then she won't look like a complete crazy woman to the receptionist, who Roberta can already tell looks like she'll take no nonsense.

She's in luck: the sales team are listed in the 'About Us' section, and a quick scroll tells her his name is Lewis Hall. Looking at his smiling photograph, she feels a momentary wave of sadness. He was kind to her, and in a different life, if she'd been a different person, they might have had a chance of having something long-term. She's still sure they had a physical connection.

At the front desk, the young receptionist plasters a smile on her face when she sees Roberta. 'How can I help you?'

'I'm here to see Lewis Hall, one of the sales team, but I don't have an appointment.'

The smile disappears. 'Oh, well, I'll need to call up and check if it's okay. He might not even be in the building.'

She hadn't thought of this; his job will mean he spends a lot of time travelling.

'Can I have your name?' the receptionist asks, already picking up the phone. Her nails are bright red and immaculate. Roberta looks down at her own bitten ones. What had Lewis seen in her?

'Name?' the receptionist repeats.

There's no point lying. 'Roberta Butler.' She waits, her stomach churning, while the woman speaks softly into the phone. She couldn't manage any breakfast this morning, and if she had, she's sure she would have lost it all by now. She's not used to doing things like this – never will be, no matter how much she knows she's changed.

'He said he'll come down and see you,' the receptionist says, and Roberta instantly feels relieved. Perhaps she's got it wrong after all. She's even ready to accept that he feels he made a mistake by spending the night with her. Anything is preferable to the alternative.

'You can take a seat over there,' the receptionist says, pointing to the sofa Roberta sat on a moment ago. 'I don't know how long he'll be.' Her tone seems flat and almost rude now, making Roberta wonder what Lewis said to her. Oh well, at least he's agreed to see her.

It's another twenty minutes before the lift door opens and he appears, a frown on his face as he scans the lobby. He looks different to how she remembers him from Tuesday night. His suit is immaculate and he is professional and purposeful as he strides towards her. He was more relaxed and casual at the B & B.

She feels her cheeks flush and wishes the floor would swallow her up. She hasn't planned what to say and is way out of her comfort zone. Adrian's words ring in her head, a reminder that this needs to be sorted. She's got to pull it together.

'Roberta? What's going on? What are you doing here?' He's still frowning, and no part of him looks in any way pleased to see her.

'I'm sorry, but I had to come. Can we talk, please? It's really important.'

He glances around the lobby. 'I don't know if that's a good idea. I'm at work. Why don't I call you later?'

'Because you won't. And this can't wait.' The thought of her bleak future spurs her on. 'Surely you get a lunch break around now?'

He sighs and his whole body seems to sag. 'Okay. Five minutes. But not here. There's a park around the corner.' He walks off without another word and Roberta has little choice but to follow after him like an obedient puppy, all the while feeling the receptionist's eyes on her. She's sick of always being subservient to men, and once again she blames Adrian for everything.

Lewis is silent on the walk to the park, and he practically sprints there, obviously keen to get this over with, to get her away from him.

'Right, now you can tell me what's going on,' he says, when they reach the small, empty park. They're in the middle of London, and Roberta's surprised there's no one else around.

Here goes nothing – and everything. 'The other night, when we met, I'd had a lot to drink.'

'Yes, I did notice that, and I'm ashamed of myself. I'm sorry if I took advantage.' His features soften.

She shakes her head. 'No, it's not that at all. I just need to know what we talked about.'

There. She's said it now, and it can't be taken back.

Lewis frowns. 'What do you mean? I thought you were here because I left without saying anything. I'm really sorry for that. It's been a long time since I was with anyone, and I'm not used to it. I felt guilty and I thought maybe you'd regret it in the morning and want me to go, so I just left before either of us could feel awkward. Again, I'm sorry if I did the wrong thing.'

Roberta stares at him. 'That's it? That's why you left? It wasn't anything I said or did?'

Lewis leads her over to a bench and gestures for her to sit. 'Well, in a way. You talked about your husband a lot. Too much, I'd say, but I didn't mind. It seemed like you needed to get a lot of stuff out in the open. It's been four years since my divorce, but your separation is still recent, isn't it? So I do understand.'

So she talked about Adrian a lot. That's not good. 'What did I say about him?' The anxiety is back now, threatening to drown her.

'Can't you remember?'

'Not what we talked about. Just what we did.' She blushes.

He smiles for the first time. 'Well, that's a relief. At least I'm not forgettable.'

Why is he making a joke? This is too serious a matter for that kind of thing. 'So what did I say about Adrian?'

'I don't understand why this so important. Are you trying to tell me you're still together and you're worried he'll find out? Because I'm not that kind of person. Live and let live, I say. We're both adults, aren't we? I'm not going to say anything – to him or anyone else.'

'No, I didn't lie to you. We *are* separated. Everything I said was true.'

'That's what I'm afraid of,' Lewis says.

Roberta's heart thuds loudly in her chest. 'What do you mean?'

'From what you were saying, I got the feeling you were… I don't know… scared of him? Is that true? I still don't get why you came all this way to see me.'

'I know this is a bit weird, but I need to know exactly what I said to you.'

Lewis lets out a sigh. 'Well, for starters you shared way too much about the physical side of your married life.'

Roberta cringes. She almost doesn't want to hear any more. 'Like what?'

'You said you couldn't bear to have him touch you and you were grateful that most nights he'd fall asleep on the sofa with the TV on. And when you found out he was having an affair you were almost relieved. Hurt, of course, but still glad to not have to have him touching you.'

So far everything has been true. 'What else?'

'There wasn't much more than that, really. You just kept going on about what an awful and dangerous man he was.'

Dangerous. She shouldn't have used that word. But at least Lewis doesn't know any more. And she can't have mentioned Josh, as surely Lewis would have brought that up first. 'I'm sorry,' she says, 'for burdening you with all that. I don't even know you.'

'You're not the one who needs to apologise. I'm the one who left without a word. That was wrong of me. I've never done anything like that before.'

'Let's just forget it all.'

Lewis smiles. 'Well, I'd better get back to work. I'm off to Manchester this evening and I haven't even started preparing for the trip.' He stands up. 'I'd like to say let's keep in touch but you probably won't want to.'

This is the last thing Roberta has expected to hear. 'I, um, yeah, we should. That would be nice.'

'Just one thing, though,' Lewis says. 'Why don't you cut the act and tell me what's really going on? You've been lying to me from the second we met.'

FORTY-TWO

Zoe

It's Friday morning. Two weeks since I got the first message, yet I'm still no closer to finding anything out. At least Harley knows what's been going on. It's just the two of us now; I will keep Jake out of this as much as I can. No matter what he's done, he's still the boys' father, so I will update him when there's something concrete to tell him.

I'm desperate to speak to Harley and see if he's found out anything on Facebook; he was out last night so we didn't have a chance to catch up. It's only 7 a.m. and I have to leave for work in a moment, so I head to his room and ease open the door.

'Harley? Are you awake?'

'I am now,' he mumbles, rolling onto his back and sitting up in bed. 'Sorry, had a late night with Isaac.'

It's not like Harley to be partying so much, but I figure he's just trying to take his mind off Mel. 'Don't apologise for living your life. I'm just on my way to work and wondered if you'd heard anything on Facebook?'

'Actually, yes. Problem is, nobody seemed to know anything or else they couldn't really remember—'

'I didn't think it would come to anything.'

'Wait, Mum, I haven't finished. There is one person who said he'd be happy to meet up for a chat and go through it all, so I've arranged to meet him tonight.'

'That's great news. I hope he can tell us something.'

'Don't get your hopes up, but it does sound promising.'

'Who is it?'

'Kyle Andrews. Do you remember him?'

The name doesn't sound familiar, and once again I curse myself for not keeping a closer eye on who Ethan was associating with. I admit to Harley that I've never heard of this boy.

'Well, that's probably because he didn't go to our school, he just knew Ethan through some other people so you wouldn't have met him.'

'It's good news that he wants to talk,' I reply, feeling a little better about not knowing who he is. 'What time are you meeting?'

'Eight o'clock. He's working until seven.'

'Are you coming home after?'

Harley laughs. 'Don't worry, Mum, I'll make sure I fill you in as soon as I've finished talking to him.'

'And you'll make sure your phone battery's fully charged?'

Harley laughs. 'Yes, Mum.'

'Okay, well, I'll be here after work. All evening. Even if you just call or text.'

'No, I'll be home. I could do with an early night.'

At work, I find myself distracted. Usually I'm able to leave personal matters at home and focus on my patients, but today I'm struggling. I don't know if this Kyle will shed any light on the situation, but there is a lot riding on Harley's meeting with him tonight. And I'm counting the hours, desperate to be out of here but needing the distraction at the same time.

Just before lunch, I bump into Leo, and he pulls me aside. 'I've been worried about you,' he says. 'Is everything okay? We haven't had a chance to speak since the other night at the river.'

I assure him that I'm doing okay – I'm just in need of some answers.

'I'm so sorry about that night,' he says. 'I should have waited somewhere further away. It's just really creepy that this person was watching us.' He lowers his voice as he says this.

'I know. But one good thing's come out of it. I'm convinced now that I've been right all along. This isn't someone just trying to mess with me. It's one thing to send someone emails and texts, but quite another to actually follow them or watch them. That takes a lot more commitment.'

'You could be right,' Leo says. 'Look, I'm seeing a patient in a minute but can we meet later? For something to eat, maybe? I've had some ideas about everything and there's something I want to run by you.'

His suggestion takes me by surprise, but if there's anything useful he can offer than I have to take him up on it. Besides, I'd only be spending the evening alone, waiting for Harley to get back so he can fill me in on what happens with Kyle.

'Okay, that will work. Shall we just meet after work and go somewhere around here? I finish at six today.'

Leo smiles. 'I'll see you then.'

By the time I get home after dinner it's nearly 9 p.m. My whole body aches with fatigue and exhaustion so I make myself a strong black coffee while I wait for Harley. There's no way I will let myself fall asleep and miss any news. So far, I've held off from texting him, although my fingers itch to send him a message and see how it's going.

It was nice spending time with Leo. I could talk about Ethan freely, knowing he understands, having lost his daughter. I relived some memories of the things he got up to, but by the end of the meal I felt as though I hardly knew my own son. What exactly was he capable of? I'm now more convinced than ever that Ethan must have done something terrible – nothing else makes sense.

'I told you earlier that I think I can help you,' Leo had said when my chat about Ethan trailed off. 'A good friend of mine is an ex-police officer and although he's not officially a private detective or anything, he's good at finding things out. Would you like me to talk to him?'

This was unexpected but very promising. 'It's not anything illegal, is it?' I'd asked.

Leo had chuckled. 'No, of course not. He's totally above board. He has a lot of contacts and may be able to help in some way. I can't promise anything, but it's got to be worth a try, hasn't it?'

I couldn't argue with this. Although I'm holding out hope that Harley will bring home some vital information, it wouldn't hurt to have someone professional looking into things. 'That would be great. Thank you.'

'I'm so sorry you and your husband are going through all this,' he'd said.

I didn't mention that Jake is no longer around to be part of anything.

Now, as I sit at the kitchen table waiting for Harley, a sense of hopelessness threatens to overwhelm me, despite the possibility of having some help from Leo's friend. What does this person want from me? Ultimately, they must have a goal in mind, and if it's retaliation for something Ethan may have done, then they won't stop here, will they? Mentally torturing me won't be enough. So what's next?

My eyes pop open and I find myself slumped on the table. The coffee evidently did nothing to keep me awake. A glance at the oven clock tells me it's past midnight, so three hours have slipped by since I got home.

I check my phone but there are no messages from Harley, and a walk through the house shows he's not yet home. It's possible he's still out with Ethan's friend, although they didn't know each other so it's strange they'd spend so long together now.

Seconds away from a full-blown panic, I text him to ask when he might be home, forcing myself to remember my misplaced fears the other day when I thought Harley was missing. I can't overreact now.

This is easier said than done, so I put on some relaxing music and pace up and down the living room, desperate to hear the sound of a key in the front door.

1 a.m. comes and goes, and I can no longer curb my fear. Harley hasn't replied and the message I sent him remains unread. I call his phone but it immediately goes to voicemail. Surely he can't have forgotten to charge his phone before he went out, especially after I reminded him? No, this time feels different – more sinister, because he was meeting someone about Ethan.

What have I got my son involved in?

FORTY-THREE
Jake

Leanne had denied everything when he'd confronted her on Thursday night, but of course she would. She'd verbally attacked him and accused him of being a dreadful husband and father – words that cut like a knife, especially as they were coming from his closest friend.

Had he really been so blind? Misjudged Leanne so much that he thought he could trust her? He'd spent years believing she had no romantic feelings for him – just as he had none for her – but now it seems he'd got it very wrong. And she was out to make sure Zoe suffered. But why involve Ethan? It would have been enough just to tell Zoe that she'd slept with Jake; he can't fathom why she'd go to these elaborate lengths to mess with Zoe's mind, to make her doubt everything.

He needs to see Zoe and he needs to see her now, even though it's almost 2 a.m. He contemplates calling or texting to ask if he can come over, but it would be too easy for her to ignore him. No, turning up at the house is the only option. She needs to know what Leanne has been doing.

When he arrives at the house, he's surprised to find the hall and living room lights on. Zoe has always been an early night kind of person so perhaps it's Harley who's up. He strolls up to the front door, and even though he's still got his key, out of respect for Zoe he taps on the door.

Nothing but silence greets him, and he begins calling her mobile, but then the door is flung open and Zoe is standing there, her eyes red and raw.

'Zoe? Are you okay?'

'I thought… What are you doing here, Jake? It's the middle of the night.'

'I know, I'm sorry. Can I come in? We really need to talk.'

She doesn't say anything, but stares at him with her wide, dark eyes. She hates him; there's no way she'll let him in. He's half expecting her to slam the door in the face, and is stunned when she opens it wide and pulls him in.

As soon as she's shut the front door, Zoe hurls words at him. 'I'm worried about Harley. I think something might have happened.'

Not again, he thinks, but he's grateful she's talking to him when so far she's ignored every message he's sent her. 'What? Slow down. What's happened?'

That's when she tells him all about Harley using Facebook to try and track down Ethan's old friends. And how she hasn't been able to let this go and even went back to the river in the hope of meeting the person who's been sending the messages.

Leanne. Of course she wouldn't turn up.

'Last night, Harley was meeting a boy called Kyle Andrews who contacted him on Facebook. Apparently he knew Ethan. Do you remember Ethan ever mentioning him?'

The name's not familiar to Jake. 'No. And that's not a common name so I'm sure I'd remember it.'

'I don't remember him either. But Harley says he knew Ethan through some other friends.'

'Harley's probably just having a drink with him. He didn't drive, did he? So he must have intended to have a drink or two.'

'His phone's off, though. After he promised he'd keep it on in case I needed to get hold of him.'

'Remember last time, Zoe? His battery had just died, that was all. You can't panic about this. Let's just give him a chance to get home.' Jake can tell she's not listening to him.

'Harley knows how worried I was last time, and he promised it wouldn't happen again. This time is different.'

Jake is about to protest and point out that Harley's a young man and probably doesn't want to be tied to his mother, despite how close he and Zoe are, but he quickly thinks better of it. Things are already strained enough and he's lucky Zoe has even let him in the house. He needs to be on her side with this. 'Okay, so what are you thinking?'

'This is all connected to Ethan and the emailer. Harley's in trouble.'

Again, he holds in his thoughts. 'We need a plan, then. Let's start by calling everyone he knows to see if he's with them.'

He's relieved when Zoe perks up. 'I'll start with Melanie,' she says, already picking up her phone.

'Is it likely he's with her? They aren't together any more.'

'I know that!' Zoe snaps. 'But she still might have heard from him.'

'There's something I need to tell you first,' Jake says. It's now or never.

'Jake, I really don't want to talk about what you did. I've only let you in the house because this is about Harley. Don't think it means—'

'No, it's not that. I think Leanne might be the one sending you those messages.'

Zoe stares at him. 'What? Why do you say that? She wouldn't...'

'I've done a lot of thinking about it, Zoe, and I think she's harboured feelings for me for all these years and wants to get back at you.'

Zoe shakes her head. 'No. No matter what she's done, that doesn't sound like Leanne. She wouldn't do that to me.' There is a long pause. 'It's one thing that you slept with each other, but these messages are something else altogether.'

Jake sighs; he's not getting through to Zoe. 'I know that, but it makes perfect sense.'

'It made sense when I thought it might be Roberta. It's not Leanne; it can't be. And even if it is, I just want to find Harley right now, then I can worry about everything else.'

He knew she wouldn't listen to him. Now that he thinks about it, she never really has. 'Okay, you call Mel. I'll see if I can get any phone numbers or other contact details for friends from his computer.'

Upstairs, Jake can't help but feel like he's trespassing, invading his son's privacy in an appalling way. Harley's not missing. He'll turn up any moment now, just like he did the other day. Still, he needs to do this for Zoe's sake. To prove he still cares about his family.

As it turns out, he didn't need to worry about invading Harley's privacy – his computer is password protected and there's no way Jake can even begin to guess the password his son's chosen. He tries 'Mel' and 'Ethan' but neither work.

'Mel hasn't heard from him,' Zoe says, when Jake gets back downstairs. 'And she wasn't too happy to be woken up by me in the middle of the night.'

Jake can understand this. 'It's bound to be strange for her. They're not even together any more, and we don't really know why it ended.'

'I'm calling the police,' Zoe says.

'I think we should wait just a bit longer,' Jake insists. 'I'll stay here with you and if he's not back by morning, we'll call the station.'

'It's DC Palmer I need to speak to.'

'Then we'll call her. Just give him a chance to come home. Let's do it in the morning.'

Reluctantly, she agrees. 'It's funny you saying "we" when all along it's just been me, hasn't it, Jake?'

He lets this go. It's no more than he deserves.

'I'm going upstairs to wait,' Zoe says. 'You can stay down here.'

Jake must have fallen asleep, because the next thing he knows, he is being woken by sunlight streaming through the living room window. He slowly comes around and pulls himself off the sofa, sure that Harley has turned up while he was knocked out.

In the kitchen, Zoe is on the phone, thanking someone before she hangs up. When she looks across at him there are tears in her eyes.

'Harley's not home and I've had another text,' she says, handing Jake her phone. 'Look at it!'

He reads the words but can't make sense of them.

Two down, none to go. How does it feel to lose everything?

FORTY-FOUR

Zoe

'Is it okay if I take a look at Harley's room?' DC Palmer asks.

I nod. Even though I know Harley would hate anyone going through his things, I have no choice; I need to find my son.

I don't follow her upstairs, but hover in the hallway, avoiding Jake's eyes on me. 'I want you to go now,' I tell him, knowing full well he'll ignore my demand. With Harley missing, he's got the perfect excuse to hang around here, to try and make me regret my decision.

'No way. He's my son too, Zoe. I need to be here.'

For hours I've been thinking about Leanne, wondering if there's any possibility that Jake is right. She's not the person I thought she was, and I can't trust her. 'Are you really convinced it's Leanne?' I ask, sitting on the bottom stair, while from upstairs comes the clanging of drawers and wardrobes opening and closing. 'Why would she punish Harley like this? She's always liked him, always got on with him. It doesn't add up.' Just as Jake and I did, Harley also turned to Leanne a lot after Ethan died.

Jake sits beside me. 'Well, I'm evidence that people don't always make sense when emotions are involved. They do crazy things sometimes. Anyway, we've told DC Palmer our suspicions, so she'll follow it up. She's probably already sent someone to check on Leanne.'

Without telling Jake what I'm doing, I pull out my phone and text Leanne, asking her to meet me at my house in an hour. A few seconds later, she replies that she will, adding that she's sorry. If she knows anything about where Harley is then I am determined to get the truth out of her.

DC Palmer stays upstairs for another ten minutes, and each ticking second both makes me anxious and fills me with hope. She's taking this seriously. Finally. When she comes back down, I lead her into the kitchen.

'We've put out an alert, Zoe,' she says. 'You have to understand, though, we can't be certain that he's not missing of his own accord. He's an adult now and not classed as vulnerable—'

'But the message? It's clearly a threat!'

'It could be,' she says, 'and we'll do everything we can, but we need to keep an open mind.'

'This isn't just a coincidence,' I tell her. 'It can't be.'

'I have to say I agree with you, but just try to stay calm. We'll find him.'

I want to ask how I can possibly do that, and throw a barrage of questions at her about what exactly they're planning to do, but it won't help. She needs to be left to get on with her job. 'Thank you,' I say instead.

'Did you find anything in his room?' Jake asks.

DC Palmer looks up in surprise, as if she's forgotten Jake is here. Not surprising when he's barely said a word.

'Nothing of note,' she says. 'Do you have access to his laptop?'

'No. I've already tried to get on to it,' Jake tells her.

'Well, we can take it away and get our tech guys to have a look at it.'

She says this as if we have a choice, when the truth is we don't. Harley's privacy will need to be invaded if we're to have any chance of finding him.'

'And Leanne Clark?' I ask. 'Will you speak to her?'

DC Palmer frowns. 'I will, yes, but only in the context of whether she might have heard from your son. I can't accuse her of anything without evidence.'

'She's a good liar,' Jake warns, and I scowl at him. As well as being a hypocrite, he's doing nothing to help our cause.

As soon as DC Palmer leaves, I bustle Jake out of the door. Leanne will be here soon and I don't want him knowing I've asked her to come over.

'I'm here if you need me,' he says, his eyes full of sadness. I feel nothing, though, seeing him like this. He's destroyed any feelings I had for him and he's responsible for our family falling apart.

'I'll let you know if I hear from Harley,' I offer. It's the best I can do.

Standing on my doorstep, Leanne looks worse than I've ever seen her – smaller, almost, as if she's been diminished by the truth coming out, as if all the power she once held has gone.

'I'm so glad you asked me over,' she begins. 'I've been—'

'Save it, Leanne. That's not why I wanted you to come .' I step aside and let her in, even though every inch of me wants to push her way instead.

Once she's inside, I head into the living room and wait for her to follow. 'Harley's missing,' I say, before she's had a chance to sit down.

She gasps and her hand flies to her mouth. 'What? Oh my God. Since when?'

'He didn't come home last night. He was meeting up with someone in a bar and I haven't heard from his since yesterday morning.'

'That's awful. I can only imagine—'

'Can you, Leanne? Really? You've never wanted kids, have you? Never had that maternal instinct.'

'That doesn't mean I can't empathise. And you know how fond I am of Harley. Have you told the police?'

'Of course. They're taking it very seriously. Especially as I got another message – this time threatening. "Two down, none to go. How does it feel to lose everything?" That's what it said.'

'That's awful, Zoe.'

'I'm fed up of these games, Leanne. I've spoken to Jake and he told me he confronted you about the messages.'

Leanne sits down. 'Accused me, more like. It was awful – he's never spoken to me like that before, with such… hatred. But Zoe, you know I would never do anything like that.'

'Well, I didn't think you'd sleep with Jake after my son had just died.'

She stares at her feet, shaking her head. 'Why on earth would I send you those messages?'

'That's what I'm hoping you'll tell me – to make up for everything you've done. If you just admit it, then maybe we can find a way past this. I just want Harley back safely.'

'I can't admit it because it's not me, Zoe. Think about it – I'd have no reason to send those messages. Jake is delusional. He seems to have an inflated opinion of himself and thinks I've been after him for all these years. I bloody haven't. Not in the way he thinks.'

'Then in what way?'

'I told you this before. I can't deny I do have feelings for him. He's been in my life for a long time and we are – or were – so close, but I never wanted to ruin your marriage. I never wanted him for myself. I'm happy with my life; I focus on work and I don't need a man to fulfil me.'

I feel the truth in her words, but I need to be sure. 'We've told the police our suspicions. They'll want to talk to you. If you know anything about where Harley is then you need to tell me now.'

'Why would I know where he is?'

'Because the person who is sending the messages clearly had something to do with his disappearance. Just tell the truth for once in your life, Leanne.'

Silence fills the room, then slowly Leanne answers. 'You want me to tell you the truth? You've never wanted the truth, have you, Zoe? You just want to live in a little bubble, to pretend everything's perfect. Your husband, your marriage. Your sons.'

Despite being untrue, her words sting. 'That's low, even for you, Leanne. How dare you talk about my sons! And I'm the last person who would ever pretend anything's perfect. Name one time when I've done that!'

She falls silent for a moment. 'You're right. I'm sorry. Everything's a mess and I've just lost the two people closest to me in my life. I don't know what I'm saying.'

Is this evidence that perhaps she is a bit unstable at the moment? Could Jake be right about her? I do find it hard to believe she would do anything to Harley. 'So you don't know where Harley is?'

'No, I don't. I promise you.'

'Well, if you're innocent then you won't mind speaking to the police, will you?'

She shakes her head. 'Of course not. I miss Harley, you know. Before I moved to London, he used to always come round and see me and we had the best chats. Even after I moved, we were always talking on the phone, until you moved to London as well and he could visit me easily again.'

I remember this. I was always grateful he could talk to Leanne, although I won't give her the satisfaction of saying this now.

'He's a great kid, that one,' she says, almost to herself. 'You know, I…'

'What?'

'Never mind. I've actually got to go. I'm meeting someone for lunch.'

Normally I would have asked her who, and enquired whether there was a new man on the scene, but I no longer want to know anything about Leanne's personal life, now it has overlapped with mine in the worst way possible.

'If you're lying to me, Leanne, believe me – I will do whatever it takes to protect my son. I might not have been able to do that for Ethan, but I won't let anything happen to Harley. Do you understand me?'

'I'm not the person you need to say that to, Zoe.'

'Just be around for the police,' I say, standing up to show her out.

I watch her walk to her car, and feel as though I'm staring at a stranger, not the woman with whom I've shared everything for most of my adult life.

And all I can think is, who is there left to trust?

FORTY-FIVE
Roberta

She turns and runs, with speed she didn't know she was capable of. All she knows is that she has to get away from Lewis, and her body is doing everything to help her accomplish this.

It doesn't sound as if he is following her, though she daren't turn around and check. She just needs to get back to her car and away from the man who will ruin her life before the day is done.

An hour later she's pounding on Adrian's door – it's funny how quickly she's come to think of it as only his house – and she struggles for breath while she waits for him to answer.

'What the hell are you doing?' he says, dragging her into the house. 'Why are you drawing attention to us?'

'I found him. Lewis. He… I'm sure he knows. He told me he knew I'd been lying to him. I… I just ran and didn't wait to hear what he was going to confront me with.'

Adrian grabs the sides of his head, yanking at his hair, and paces the hallway. 'Fuck! This is all your fault, Roberta. We were okay. Nobody was ever going to find out, and now you've ruined everything. You and your big mouth. Do you realise what this means?'

She doesn't need to be told. The end of their lives. 'We need to tell Zoe,' Roberta says. 'She should know. It's over now for us anyway.'

'Are you crazy?' He clutches her throat, squeezing at it, and she almost wishes he would keep hold until she takes her last breath.

'She doesn't need to know anything and you will not say a word. Do you hear me?'

He loosens his grip and she manages a slight nod.

'Good. Look, let's not panic. There's still a chance to put this right. Where did you find him?'

'I remembered he'd told me where he works, and I went straight there. It's GlaxoSmithKline in Brentford.'

Adrian lets go of her. 'In that case maybe I'll just pay him a little visit, make sure he doesn't talk to anyone. In the meantime, you stay away from Zoe and anyone else. I can't trust your mouth. This is serious, Roberta – you do realise that, don't you?'

Roberta doubles over and vomits all over the hallway tiles. She used to love these deep red tiles, had spent hours browsing in the shops before she decided on them, yet now she wants to rip them up and hurl them through the window.

'Damn it, what is the matter with you?' Adrian snarls. 'Just go and sit down and try to calm yourself. I'll bring you some water.'

Roberta's almost touched by his gesture. Almost, but not quite, because she knows the monster that he is. She's seen it first-hand, and she will never forget that he's the reason for all of this. If only she'd had more guts, stood up to him right when it happened. She could have changed the outcome for all of them.

When Adrian joins her in the living room, his manner is calmer, his voice softer. He hands her a glass of water. 'Drink it all. I don't want you puking all over the floor again or collapsing or something.'

For a second she wonders if he's poisoned it, but that wouldn't be his style – it wouldn't allow her to feel enough pain. She laughs out loud; a hysterical noise which doesn't sound human.

Adrian just stares at her. 'You know, we really need to stick together in this. Whatever's gone on between us – none of that matters now. We'll be divorced soon enough but this will always tie us together. We can't be enemies, Roberta. Do you see that?'

But I hate you, she thinks. I despise you more than it should be possible to dislike anyone. The tie needs to be broken. 'Yes, you're right,' she says, forcing the words out, trying not to choke on them.

Adrian smiles, and just for a second he looks like the man she fell in love with, the man she believed in. 'Good. Now I need to leave to get to Brentford. It's still early enough that he should be there if I hurry. I'm just going to have a word with him.'

She shouldn't have told Adrian where Lewis works. Every inch of her body screams at her that this is a bad idea. But then she pictures Lewis picking up the phone, telling the police everything she revealed to him that night.

'You need to hurry. It's nearly rush hour, so it'll take you ages to get into West London. I'll text you the exact address.'

'Good girl,' he says, and the smile he flashes this time is like the one she remembers from the past.

They leave the house together and get into their own cars without another word.

She's just made a huge mistake, but there's nothing she can do to stop it.

FORTY-SIX

Two days pass before I hear from him. Two miserable days since we slept together. I stew over my actions. What if I've driven him away for good? Wouldn't it have been better to have him as a friend in my life, rather than this deep black hole?

No. I needed him. Need him. And I had to have him; it was almost as if I was powerless to control it. I know he enjoyed it — there was ecstasy on his face when I touched him, and that can't be faked.

But still, two wretched days where I'm watching my phone and waiting. Of course the worst-case scenario crosses my mind: he's had time to register what we did and now he's telling someone. Someone who could get me into serious trouble. This was a gamble I took, though, and I only hope the bond between us is strong enough that he wouldn't do that to me.

On day three he finally texts, just saying hello. What a relief! Everything's going to be okay now. I have been worrying needlessly. 'Let's meet up,' I suggest, and after a couple of hours he replies again, saying he will come over.

Mum is still in hospital, so this will work. That he wants to be alone again is a very good sign. I assure him that Alissa is staying at a friend's house again for the night, and that we will have plenty of time to talk.

When he arrives in the afternoon he looks nervous, and hovers on the doorstep for so long that I wonder if he'll run away. I gently take his hand and he flinches, but lets me lead him inside.

'I've… I've never done that before,' he says, when he's composed himself. 'I… don't know what to think.'

'In my experience, it's best not to overthink things, I reckon. Go with your feelings, your heart. Did it feel right to you? Did I feel right?'

He nods. It's barely perceptible, but there nonetheless.

'Sometimes we can't help who we fall for. Life isn't black and white, and nothing is ever straightforward. All I know is that I have feelings for you – deep ones – and I believe you feel the same. Why don't we just go with it?' I reach across and place my hand on his leg, and this time my touch doesn't cause him to recoil. A surge of heat courses through my body.

'Shall we watch a film?' I suggest, and he willingly agrees. This should put him at ease.

I deliberately give him some space, moving a few inches away on the sofa. I want him to feel like he has some control, that I am here if he wants me and we can take things at the speed he wants. It's the least I can do, despite how desperate I am to have him again.

It works, and after an hour he is moving towards me, cuddling up to me. I can feel his breath on my skin.

The second time is even better. He's more confident, and I can relax knowing that this time he is not intoxicated. This time he knows exactly what he's doing.

It's a while before we meet in public, but I understand. I'm far from his age and it might look odd to other people. But I want to teach him not to care, that nobody else's opinion matters. Only ours.

Sometimes he cries, and I let him – just hold him against me and tell him it will all be okay. 'Don't worry about the future,' I say. 'Just live in this moment.'

FORTY-SEVEN

Zoe

Leo's home is a beautiful townhouse in Chiswick, and inside it is neat and cared for. I know several doctors who are meticulous at work and yet their homes look like they've never been touched with a duster or vacuum cleaner.

'We could have come to you,' Leo says, leading me into a huge kitchen-diner. 'You didn't have to make the journey here.'

'It's fine. I needed to get out of the house, otherwise I might have gone insane. You know, staring at the front door, hoping that Harley would walk through it any second.'

'I'm so sorry this is happening to you, Zoe. I couldn't believe it when you told me this morning. Anyway, the friend I told you about, Tim Ellroy, will be here in a minute. He was happy to drop everything when I told him your situation and that Harley's gone missing.'

It doesn't feel real: Harley gone; me standing here in Leo's kitchen. I feel like I've lost all my senses. 'So he knows everything? About Ethan and all the messages?'

'Yes, I've filled him in, and he's already got some information for us. Don't worry, I'm sure he'll be able to help in some way. They were gutted to lose him from the police – he was all set for big things within the force.'

I feel uneasy that I'm depending on other people so much to help me; I'm usually so independent. 'Why did he leave, exactly?'

Leo shrugs. 'Think the job just ate away at him. Ripped out his soul, he likes to say. But hey, it's lucky for us, because he's free to help.'

'How much will he charge?' I think of my bank account. I've got a little money saved up, but who knows what this will cost me.

Leo smiles. 'Not a penny. He's my good friend and won't accept it.'

'Thank you,' I say, although I am willing to pay anything if it will find my son.

The doorbell chimes and Leo goes off to answer it.

'Zoe, this is Tim,' he says, as soon as he's back in the kitchen. Beside him is a tall, dark-haired man who looks around the same age as me. His jawline is stubbled and he's dressed casually in jeans and a T-shirt.

He steps forward and holds out his hand. His grip is firm and reassuring. 'Zoe, I'm so sorry about your son. Both of them. Let's see if we can work out what the hell is going on.'

We sit at the table and Leo makes coffee while Tim pulls a notebook and loose sheets of paper from a rucksack. 'So, first of all, I want you to know that the police will be doing everything they can to find Harley. I'm not a replacement for them in any way – I have to make that clear – but I do have the time and the contacts to be an extra resource.'

I thank him and tell him I'm lucky that DC Palmer is taking this seriously.

'What they might not have the resources for is to go back and reinvestigate what happened to Ethan. That's the trouble,' Tim explains.

I nod. 'They don't seem to think it was anything other than an accident.'

'Well, I don't believe in coincidences, and everything points to the fact that his death and Harley's disappearance are connected. I'll need a list of all Ethan's school friends, and I'd like to chat with them, just to see if anything's been missed. It doesn't hurt to start from the beginning.' He slides a piece of paper and a pen over to me. 'This morning, I hacked into Harley's Facebook account – I hope that's okay? – to see if we can work out who he was meeting. Now, this is the strange thing. Although there are messages backwards and forwards from someone called Kyle Andrews, when I dug a little deeper, I found out that Kyle is actually on holiday in New Zealand with his parents, and not due back until next Friday. Now I could be wrong, but I don't think he'd have been able to make a journey to London and back that quickly, do you?'

For seconds, I sit speechless, unable to make sense of what I'm hearing, unable to believe that within a few hours this man has already found out this information. 'I… What does that mean?'

'It means that Kyle Andrews did not send those messages – unless for some reason he was playing a prank. Doesn't sound likely, given that he's been sunning himself and surfing for the last few days. Someone must have hacked into his account and pretended to be him in order to get Harley to meet up.'

A sharp pain shoots through my stomach. 'In order to what? Abduct him?'

'That I don't know, Zoe. I've got a friend trying to see if they can find out who got access to his account, though it might take a while. There is some good news: according to the messages, they arranged to meet at The Piano Bar in Islington. Nice place; I've been there a few times.'

'I need to tell DC Palmer all this.'

'Yes, you should. Please don't mention that I'm helping you, though; the police don't take kindly to any outside interference, even if it might help them.'

I nod and reach for my mobile. When I get through to someone, I'm told that DC Palmer isn't available at the moment, but will call me back as soon as she can.

'I need to go to that bar right now,' I tell Leo and Tim. 'It could be hours before she gets back to me, and I need to know if Harley went there as planned.'

'I understand,' Tim says. 'I would come with you but it's best if I get on with chasing up Ethan's friends. I'm going to start with Daisy Carter. I know you've already spoken to her, but it's worth looking into a bit more.'

'I'll go with you, Zoe,' Leo says. 'I just need to cancel an appointment.'

'No, it's okay. I'll be fine.' I am already standing up and grabbing my bag.

'Keep us updated,' Leo says, and I feel two sets of eyes on me as I rush from the house, feeling as though this is not my real life, that I've somehow become an actor in a film. A film that won't have a happy ending.

By the time I reach The Piano Bar, it's nearly 8 p.m. I feel anxious stepping inside; I don't know what I'm going to find out – if anything – and to think that this was probably where Harley was just last night fills me with dread. Where is he? I need to know he's okay, and I've had enough of unanswered questions. Behind all of this – all the messages, Harley's disappearance, the strange behaviour of almost everyone close to me – is an explanation. And I need to find it.

It's Saturday night, so the place is busy. I make my way to the bar and order a lemonade, ignoring the barman's strange look, and when he hands me my drink I ask him if he was working last night.

He frowns at me, maybe trying to assess whether I'm some weird older woman trying to hit on him – he must be half my age – but then he seems to decide it's a harmless enough question. 'Um, no. Why?'

'I'm looking for someone. My son. I just wondered if he'd been in here last night. He was supposed to be meeting someone here.'

'Oh. Well, Karen was here.' He points to a tall, curly-haired woman serving at the other end of the bar.

'Thanks.' I take my drink and head over to Karen, who at this moment is engrossed in a conversation with the two young men she is serving.

It seems to take an eternity before the men head off, and as soon as they do I try to get Karen's attention. 'Hi, I was told you were working here last night – is that right?'

She frowns at me. 'Yeah? Why?'

I pull out my phone and find a picture of Harley. It's over a year old but he hasn't changed much in that time. 'My son's gone missing and I think he was here meeting someone last night. Do you happen to remember him?'

She immediately softens. 'I'm sorry. Let's have a look.' She takes the phone and studies Harley, handing it back so quickly that I'm sure she doesn't recognise him. 'Yeah, he was here. It was quiet for a Friday night because the football was on and I remember him sitting alone for a while.'

My spirits lift; this is a huge breakthrough. 'Did anyone come and meet him?'

She shakes her head. 'No, and he didn't stay long. He left after he finished his drink. He probably wasn't here more than half an hour.'

So Kyle Andrews never turned up. 'Okay, thanks.' I turn to leave.

'Wait, I did see him again. A few minutes later I went out the front for a cigarette and he was there on the pavement, leaning into the window of a red car, talking to the driver.'

Fear and hope intermingle within me. 'Did you see what car it was? Or what the driver looked like? Male? Female?'

She shrugs. 'No, sorry. I wasn't paying attention. Was just having my ciggy. I can't notice everything that goes on around here, you know.'

She has a fair point. 'Will you tell the police all this? They'll be coming to speak to people here soon.' I say this with certainty even though I have no idea how long it will take them to get around to it.

'No problem. But I can't be much help, other than telling them that he was here on his own.'

'Thank you,' I say. 'You've been very helpful.'

Outside, I lean against the wall and gather my thoughts. Harley was here last night to meet Kyle Andrews as planned, but the boy was never going to turn up. It was a set-up, and then someone in a red car approached Harley. Was it the person who's been sending the messages? Neither Roberta nor Leanne have a red car, so that rules them both out, although it could quite easily have been a hire car.

I study the buildings around me, checking for CCTV. There are no visible cameras, but on the opposite side of the street there is a yellow CCTV sign.

DC Palmer still hasn't returned my call, and when I call back this time I'm ready to insist on talking to someone, to kick up a big fuss if I have to. I know it's Saturday night, and she deserves time off, but this is an emergency.

'Can I talk to someone dealing with my son's case, then?' I ask the officer who answers the phone, when I'm once again told that DC Palmer is unavailable.

I'm told the hold the line and a minute later a man's voice greets me. 'PC Griffiths,' he says. Short and to the point.

I tell him about the bar and that Harley was talking to someone in a red car, but instead of being pleased with this development, he asks how I knew Harley had gone there.

'I just remembered him mention it,' I reply, the promise to Tim Ellroy to not say anything cemented in my head.

'Right, well, we'll definitely look into it. Thank you for this information.'

'There must be CCTV outside the bar somewhere. There's a sign for it.'

'Yes, of course we'll look into that. It could be, though, that the driver of the car just stopped and asked for directions or something like that. He may not have got in the vehicle.'

'I know.' This has occurred to me but I'm trying to be positive. 'Can you tell me where DC Palmer is?'

He sighs. 'She's having a family emergency so can't be reached today. She'll be back on Monday. In the meantime, I will chase this up. Okay?'

He sounds bored, as if a search for a missing nineteen-year-old is below him. 'Thank you,' I say, grateful that Tim Ellroy is helping me as well.

The next thing I do is call Leo to update him. He sounds out of breath, as if he's walking. I remember him mentioning an appointment but don't want to ask what it was about. Instead I just ask if he's okay.

'All fine here. I'm glad you've got something to go on now,' he says. 'I'll let Tim know. And Zoe? We'll find him.'

When I get home, I sink onto the sofa and curl up, grabbing my mobile to try Harley's number again. As before, it goes straight to his voicemail. 'Harley, I know you can't get this message but I just want to tell you that I'm doing everything to find you. And I will find you, Harley, wherever you are. Don't worry.'

I will not let another of my sons be taken from me.

FORTY-EIGHT

Roberta

For two days, she's been trying to call Adrian, and not once has he answered or returned her texts. This is bad. Really bad. Now it's Saturday and she can't wait any longer; she needs to know what he's done about Lewis, needs to be sure her suspicions are unwarranted.

Outside their old house – Adrian's house – she once again hammers on the door. His car's outside and it's too early for the pub, which is the only place he ever ventures to on foot.

He'll be avoiding her because he's done something terrible. All that talk about sticking together was just to mess with her head, and she's the gullible fool who fell for it.

Turning around, she's about to head back to her car, to wait out of view of the neighbours, when the door slowly opens.

'Roberta! I've told you before about making all this commotion. Why can't you just ring the bell and wait?' His voice is low, despite the force of his words.

'Because you never answer!' she hisses. 'What are you doing? I've been calling and texting you for days.'

'I've had a lot to sort out, haven't I? No thanks to you. Look, bloody well come inside, won't you? I don't want to have this conversation out here.'

A sense of déjà vu assaults her as she steps inside. She's going round in circles, always ending up here, no matter how much she wants to never see Adrian, or this house, again.

'What happened with Lewis?' she says, as soon as he's closed the door. 'Did you find him at his work? What did he say?'

Adrian shrugs. 'Yeah, I found him, and nothing happened. We just had a little chat, that's all.'

Roberta frowns. 'And he agreed not to say anything?'

'I can be very persuasive when I want to be.' He smiles. 'You should know that, Roberta.'

So can all the other evil men in the world, Roberta thinks. 'What exactly did you say?'

Adrian walks through to the kitchen and she trails behind him. 'I don't think you need to worry about that, do you? I've sorted it out.'

'Yes, I do. Worry is exactly what I need to do. What did you say to him? And what did he say? Why won't you just tell me?'

'Just drop it, Roberta. This was your mess to sort out but I've done it for you, haven't I? I've just saved both of us. Can't you just be grateful? Prison's no place for someone like you, is it? You wouldn't survive one second in there.'

'And you would?'

'Well, let's be grateful we'll never have to find that out, shall we?'

His patronising tone makes her want to smack him, to stab him with one of her kitchen knives. But she knows she could never do that, no matter how much she hates him. Too much blood has already been spilled.

Roberta shakes her head, begins pacing the kitchen. 'How can you be sure he won't go to the police? Especially now that you've threatened him? Why would he listen to you?' Fear is building. None of this feels right; it's all too easy.

'Oh, he won't – trust me. Now will you stop going on?'

But she can't, and won't, let this drop. 'That's just it – I don't trust you. Not one bit.'

Adrian throws his head back and laughs. 'Well, Roberta, that's your problem, isn't it?' He walks towards her. 'I think you should go now. The problem's been sorted and there's nothing else to do. Maybe from now on you'll keep your big mouth shut. And at least I know now that you'll never go to the police, or you would have let him do it for you.'

There is a loud crash from upstairs, and both of them swivel to stare at the door. 'What was that?' Roberta cries.

Adrian grabs her arm and she notices there is fear in his eyes – something she's not used to seeing. 'It was nothing. Just go.'

She is too quick for him and slips out of his grip, running for the stairs. She has no idea what she'll find, but if there's another woman in this house, she will drag her out by her hair. There is no way she will put up with living in that B & B while Adrian moves his whore into the house that she still half owns.

Although he's rapidly gaining on her, somehow Roberta is too quick for him and races to the bedroom, flinging the door open, only to be greeted by an empty room and an unmade bed. But she knows she heard something.

'I told you to leave,' Adrian says.

He's blocking her way now, preventing her from going anywhere. 'Who's here, Adrian? This is still my house and I won't let you have someone else here. You—'

There is another crash, louder this time, and it's coming from the bathroom. She dodges past Adrian and runs to the bathroom door. It's only when she's right outside it and grabbing the handle that she notices there are two bolts on the outside, both of them pulled across. What the hell?

Muffled sounds come from inside and Roberta wastes no time in sliding back the locks and throwing the door open. Behind her, she can hear Adrian's deep breaths.

She doesn't know what to expect, but her heart almost stops when she sees Lewis bound and gagged on the bathroom floor. He's lying on his side and thrashing about, banging his legs on the floor.

His eyes meet hers and they are wide with fear.

Roberta senses Adrian behind her, his heavy breath on her neck. 'What have you done?' she asks, her eyes fixed on Lewis.

'I had no choice, Roberta. This was the only thing I could do. I needed to keep him quiet.' His voice is unsure, as if he knows he's gone too far.

She spins round and pounds on his chest. 'You can't do this. Let him go. Now.'

'I can't do that. He'll go straight to the police and now he'll be able to add kidnapping to his statement. That's even more trouble for us. I had no choice, Roberta.'

'You're a monster,' she says, unable to turn back around and see Lewis in that state. 'And this is nothing to do with me. I never would have let you do this.'

'Let's talk about this downstairs, Roberta.' Adrian grabs her and forces her into the hall, locking the bathroom door behind them. He pushes her forward, forcing her to grab the banister to keep from toppling down the stairs.

'What… what are you going to do with him?' she asks, as soon as they're downstairs. 'You haven't thought this through, have you? You can't just keep him locked in the bathroom forever.'

'I need to think about that,' he says, pulling her into the kitchen. 'Look,' he hisses, 'I didn't have a choice. I didn't have time to come up with a plan. This man knows what we did and I need to keep him quiet. Do you know what he did when I threatened him? He laughed at me, told me I was crazy.'

You are, Roberta thinks. Even more than she realised. The image of Lewis writhing on the floor like a dying fish assaults her, and she can't prevent tears from forming. 'Please let him go, Adrian. I'm sure he won't say anything, not if he thinks you'd do this again, or worse.'

Adrian shakes his head. 'I can't do that. It's too late. What's done is done, Roberta. Just like before.'

'But this is completely different. You haven't hurt him, have you? You've got a choice now and you can do the right thing. We can make him promise to not say a word. Get some sort of guarantee. I'm sure he'd be so grateful that you've let him go that he wouldn't say a word.'

There is a long pause, and she becomes convinced Adrian will actually listen to her – until he finally speaks. 'You really do live in a fantasy world. There's no choice now. It's gone too far already. And this is your fault, not mine. I did what I had to do.'

Roberta thinks about the evening she spent with Lewis. He was kind to her and she knows he is a good person, even though he left without a word. She can't let Adrian do this. 'Please let him go. I'll deal with the consequences if he does go to the police. I'll tell them it was all me, that you had nothing to do with it.' Her voice is pleading; despite the strength she showed earlier in defying Adrian and investigating the loud crashes, she now seems to have reverted to the person she always is around him. She hates that this is happening.

Adrian leans in, shoving his face so close to hers that she can feel his stubble on her skin. 'Do you expect me to believe that? You said earlier that you don't trust me – well, that works both ways. In fact, you being a part of all this makes me nervous. You're unstable and I don't know what you're capable of. Look what you've already done. I won't let you ruin my life.'

The funny thing is, Roberta doesn't even know if she can trust herself. She was terrified when she worked out that she had told Lewis everything, yet not long before that, she'd been willing to go to the police herself, just to get Adrian out of her life. And now, as she stares at him, she knows there is only one option.

'I don't want to go to prison,' she says. 'You're right – I wouldn't survive.'

Adrian lets out a deep breath. 'That's better. There's no way out of this, Roberta. He knows too much.'

She stares out of the window, noticing the lawn is overgrown and all the flowers she took such care in planting have wilted. For the first time since walking out on Adrian, she feels sadness at leaving this house behind, and wishes there was a way for her to keep it, to get him out instead.

'Shall we have a drink?' she suggests, desperate for oblivion.

'What? Seriously? Things didn't go so well the last time you had one, did they?'

'I don't mean get drunk; I just want one. Anything will do.'

Adrian shrugs. 'I suppose.' He walks to the cupboards and pours two glasses of whisky. 'It's all I've got.'

She takes it, already knowing she will loathe the taste and will have to force it down her throat.

'Didn't you drive here?' Adrian asks.

'I'm only having one. Besides, I can get a cab back and pick the car up in the morning.'

He raises his eyebrows. 'You've changed. What's happened to you?'

'My son is dead. Of course I've changed.' She takes a sip of whisky, forcing it down as quickly as she can.

'No, I mean recently. I hardly recognise you.'

'Good.'

'Yeah, it is. You needed to change.'

She ignores him. There is no way she wants to discuss anything about herself with him. 'So what are you going to do with Lewis?'

He takes a long swig of his drink. 'Don't worry your little head about that. I'll take care of it, like I always do.'

'Good. And you're right – I don't need to know.'

FORTY-NINE

Mum is back home from hospital now, so inviting him over is out of the question. And his place is definitely off limits, forcing us to meet in public, choosing the quietest spots so that we can still touch each other. It is torture to be in his presence and not be able to feel his skin against mine.

This evening we are sitting by the river, and even though it's dark now, and there aren't many people about, we check carefully before we dare to kiss. He smells of shower gel and I nuzzle his neck, breathing him in.

'Maybe we shouldn't do this here,' he says, looking around us. 'Someone might see us.'

'I don't care. I really don't. And you shouldn't either.'

'But—'

I stop him talking by placing my hand down his trousers, and soon we both forget where we are.

'Someone's there,' he says, after a few moments. His body stiffens and he straightens up, pulling away from me. 'Can we just go for a walk or something?'

I'm disappointed, but agree to his request. And as we walk along the riverbank, I keep thinking that perhaps it's time I moved out of Mum's. She won't mind; she's always saying she wants me to have my own life. I could find somewhere nearby and still be there to look after her.

I tell him my idea but don't get the reaction I'd like.

'That's good,' is all he says, his eyes focused on anything but me.

*

It's later that night, when I'm in bed, that I get his text. He hasn't replied to me since I got home, and I've sent him over ten messages. His words are blunt. He can't see me any more and he doesn't want me to contact him, ever.

I throw my phone across the room and it crashes against my wardrobe, shattering the silence.

FIFTY

Zoe

It's early on Sunday morning when Tim knocks on my door. I look behind him for Leo, but soon see that he's come alone.

'I hope it's not too early?' he says, 'although I can see you're already up and about.' He gestures to my clothes: jeans and a loose T-shirt. Most people will probably still be in their pyjamas at this time.

'Not at all. Thanks for coming. Can I get you anything?'

'I'm fine, thanks. I picked up a Starbucks on the drive over. It was a drive-through one – unbelievable! How lazy have we all become?'

I smile, despite the reason Tim is here, despite my son still being missing and my marriage being over, but sure that Harley would find it amusing too.

I offer him a seat and he settles himself at the table. 'You must be here with some news?'

'Yep, I've been a busy man,' he says, pulling out his phone. 'Firstly, I managed to track down a few of Ethan's school friends. None of them could really tell me much, and they didn't think Ethan had acted differently around that time.' He pauses. 'Thing is, though, it's been three years and memories fade, especially as they've all gone through such changes in that time. They were fourteen when it happened, and now they're seventeen and living different lives.'

Daisy Carter is a good example of this; I remember how reluctant she was to revisit those school years. We become such altered people when we leave the school gates for the final time. 'So nothing useful?' I ask.

Tim smiles. 'I messaged Kyle in New Zealand but got no reply. Luckily, a contact of mine got an address for his parents, so I gave him a call. Now this is where it gets interesting. According to Kyle, he's never had a Facebook account.'

'So someone created a fake one using his name?' With the sole purpose of getting to Harley.

'Yes, it looks that way,' Tim says. 'I'd mentioned that might be the case, remember?' Anyway, he told me something interesting. He remembers someone telling him that Ethan and the other boy, Josh, had been arguing a lot at school. He didn't pay much attention to it at the time, as he didn't go to the same school and had never met Josh, but he's sure that's what he was told. He can't remember who said it, but this is something to go on, Zoe.'

'Roberta's already told me that, so it backs up what she's said. She knew they'd fallen out, but didn't know why.'

'Well, here's where we're further along, then. According to Kyle, it had something to do with a mobile phone. He doesn't know what, though.'

'A mobile? Whose? What could that mean?'

Tim shakes his head. 'Not sure yet. Perhaps one of them took the other one's phone?'

I try to imagine this scenario but can't. Ethan had a fairly new mobile, but then so did Josh, as I remember. Neither one appeared better than the other. And Ethan wasn't like that. He barely cared about his phone and half the time ended up leaving it at home by mistake. Plus, Josh was so spoilt that he would have got any phone he wanted to just by kicking off to his mum, even though I'm sure she and Adrian couldn't have afforded it.

I explain this to Tim and he cautions me to keep an open mind, not to rule anything out.

'Do you still have Ethan's phone?' he asks.

'Yes, but I haven't been able to get it working since he died. It was in his pocket when they found him and must have got water-damaged.'

Tim nods. 'Can I take a look anyway? There might be something a friend of mine can do, depending on the extent of the damage.' His smile fades and a frown appears. 'Do you mind me asking when the boys were found?'

And just like that I am reliving that morning. I'd woken up at around 9 a.m. – much later than normal, as it was a Saturday – to an unusually quiet house. Jake had left for work and I was surprised that I couldn't hear anything from Ethan and Josh. They'd been up listening to music quite late, so I assumed they were just tired, but when I went to check on them at around ten, I found Ethan's room empty. His bed was neatly made and the sleeping bag I'd left for Josh was still rolled up, unused.

Alarm bells should have rung immediately – Ethan only ever made his bed after I nagged him to do it – but I still thought they must be downstairs. I never expected what was to come; I had never been an overanxious mother.

It's only when I realised they weren't downstairs, or in the garden, that panic set in. But it was a controlled panic, something I could keep at bay while I tried to think rationally. They were fourteen-year-old boys and had probably decided to take themselves off somewhere. That was it. I'd long ago accepted that I had to give Ethan some space to grow up and be independent. I'd done that with Harley, too, and he'd always been fine, always let me know where he was.

Then the knock on the door came. The one most people can't even bring themselves to comprehend. Two uniformed police officers, sympathetic smiles on their faces, asked me if it was okay to come in. It was almost 11 a.m. by then, and all I could think was that Ethan and Josh must have got into some kind of trouble. And I hate to admit it but in my mind I was already blaming Josh.

The rest I cannot think about. All I remember is that a thick fog wrapped itself tightly around me and I was millimetres away from suffocation. I was doing things on autopilot, unable to grasp what had happened, convinced it must all be a huge mistake. This couldn't be happening to us.

But slowly it began to sink in, especially when the police said that, from initial findings, it appeared that the boys had both been in the river for several hours, most likely overnight. They'd been found by someone walking past at around 8 a.m. – while I was still asleep – and it had taken the police some time to trace the boys as they'd had no ID on them.

I'm crying as I finish recalling the events of that morning to Tim Ellroy.

'I'm sorry to make you go through all this,' he says. 'But anything you can remember will help, Zoe.'

'I'm okay,' I assure him, even though of course I'm not. 'I just want to find Harley and be sure about what happened to Ethan. That's all that matters now.' I swipe away my tears, angry at them for falling when I'm trying so hard to hold it together.

'Well, we might not be able to get into his phone,' Tim says, 'but that doesn't mean we won't work out what exactly the boys were arguing about. Do you know if Josh's phone was also damaged?'

'I'm not sure. I can check with his mum, Roberta. I assume he must have had his with him too.'

'Okay.' He pauses. 'Um, there's something else. I—'

My mobile rings, blaring out into the kitchen. It's on the worktop, and I rush to answer it before the person gives up.

'Hello, Mrs Monaghan, this is PC Griffiths.'

'Is there any news?' I don't bother with a greeting.

'Yes, actually. We were able to study the CCTV from Friday night outside The Piano Bar, and Harley was definitely there. It shows him going inside at 7.55 p.m. and then leaving at 8.40 p.m. He walks as if to cross the road and then a red car stops and he leans in to speak to someone.'

I hold my breath.

'The conversation lasts less than thirty seconds and then the car drives off and your son heads in the opposite direction, towards the Tube station.'

'So… the red car is irrelevant?'

'Probably just someone asking for directions. We lose track of him after that, as many of the CCTV cameras along that road aren't working. I'm sorry I don't have anything more, but we're still looking into it.'

'Thank you.'

'There's one other thing. We haven't been able to find anything significant on his laptop. I'm sorry about that.'

'Okay.' It's just one more dead end.

'DC Palmer will be back in tomorrow, so you can call her with any questions.'

After thanking him again, I end the call and turn back to Tim, filling him in, even though I'm sure he's got the gist of it already.

'While the police focus on finding Harley, I want to concentrate on Ethan and Josh. Can you give Josh's mum a call to see if she still has his phone?'

Without answering, I dial Roberta's number and wait for an answer. It's still quite early but I doubt she's the type to have a lie-in. There's no reply. 'Maybe I'll try again in half an hour,' I suggest, when there's no reply.

'How about I try next time?' Tim says. 'From what you've told me, she might be reluctant to speak to you about this again. With me, though, she will think you've taken this to official channels.

I won't lie to her, of course, but I don't need to tell her exactly who I am.'

'You mean you'll let her think you're the police?'

'Something like that. Whatever it takes to get some answers, eh?'

I can't help but like this man. He's doing this for nothing, giving up his time for me, just as a favour to Leo, yet he seems to be putting everything into it. I decide to ask him about this.

'I hate unanswered questions,' he says. 'And I want to help find your son. As well as that, working is good for me. It keeps me busy.' Although he has a small smile on his face, I sense sadness beneath it. There's something there.

'Do you miss being in the force?'

'I left because it was interfering with family life. Then my wife left me anyway and I no longer had my family. Kids went to live with her and I just got my weekends with them.'

'Sorry to hear that.'

'It's okay; I try to make the best of things. Anyway, I don't miss the force as much as I miss being busy. That's what I need.'

'Luckily for me,' I say. 'So what was it you were going to say when my phone rang?'

Tim looks uncomfortable. 'Ah, yes. This is a bit awkward, but it's essential that you know. I spoke to Daisy Carter. She was really friendly and happy to speak to me, at least at first. I think it helped that I told her Harley was missing and it might be tied up with Ethan's accident.'

He pauses and I urge him to go on.

'This is really difficult. She told me that she hadn't exactly been honest with you when you'd spoken to her the last time.'

I'm filled with dread at what I'm about to hear, and it's made worse by the fact that Tim Ellroy, a professional man, is struggling to come out with it. 'Go on. Please just say it, Tim.'

'She said that it wasn't Josh she'd been seeing. It was Ethan.'

FIFTY-ONE
Roberta

It happens quicker than she expects, but within a couple of hours, Adrian is asleep in his armchair, letting out loud grunts as he breathes out. He never could handle his alcohol, despite being a regular drinker. And it had been easy to keep him talking, keep him filling up his whisky glass; all she had to do was let him insult her and put her down. He was enjoying it so much he forgot his priority was to get her out of the house and then deal with Lewis.

Now, upstairs, she heads straight for the bathroom to put things right. Lewis is sitting up this time, his back against the bath. He looks crumpled, as if his blood has been sucked out of him. She steps inside, leaving the door open so she can listen out for any sign that Adrian is waking up.

Lewis's eyes widen, and she realises he fears her. He must think she and Adrian are in this together, despite hearing what she said to Adrian about letting him go. 'Let me take this off,' she whispers, ripping the masking tape from his mouth. He winces but doesn't make a sound.

'I'm so sorry he did this to you. Please believe me – I had no idea.'

'What the fuck?' he says, too loudly, as soon as he's able to speak.

'Shhh! We have to be quiet. He's asleep downstairs and could wake up any second. We need to be quick.'

'Please just get all this shit off me,' Lewis says, attempting to move his bound hands. 'Get it off!'

'I need scissors,' Roberta says, assessing the amount of masking tape Adrian has used. 'There should be some in the kitchen – just wait a second.'

She checks on Adrian on her way to the kitchen, relieved to find him still slumped in the same position in his chair. Luckily, the scissors are still in the cutlery drawer where she always kept them, and she grabs them and rushes back upstairs to Lewis.

As soon as he's free he tries to stand, but his legs are shaky and he stumbles against the bath. Roberta steadies him and leads him out onto the landing. 'I know I'm not your favourite person right now but you need to come with me. We need to get as far away from here as possible. Once he realises I've helped you he'll be after us both, and next time I'm sure he won't waste any time keeping us locked up.'

Lewis nods and lets her lead him downstairs and out of the house. Even though Roberta shuts the door as quietly as she can, it still makes a loud click. 'Come on, that's my car over there.'

Neither of them speaks until they've put some distance between them and the house, but then Lewis suddenly erupts. 'What the hell is going on, Roberta? He kept going on and on about what I knew, and I don't bloody know anything! What the hell is this all about?'

She ignores him; there will be time for that later. 'Do you want some water? There's a bottle in my bag on the back seat.'

He reaches over and pulls out the water, taking a long swig of it before replacing the lid.

'It's Saturday night and you must have been in there since Thursday evening,' Roberta says, horrified to even contemplate this.

'I don't know – I have no idea what the bloody day or even time is. All I know is he turned up at my house on Thursday evening and said he was your husband and needed to talk to me about you.

I assumed you weren't separated after all and I felt guilty. I stupidly let him in because he seemed reasonable – upset, even. I'm a fool! As soon as he got in the house he battered me over the head with something and knocked me out. The next thing I knew, I was in that bathroom, tied up.' He bangs his fist on the dashboard. 'You should have told me you were still together. I never would have done anything if I'd known – I'm not like that. And why did he keep going on about what I know, and having to shut me up?'

'It… complicated,' Roberta says, knowing that's an understatement. 'I can assure you that Adrian and I are not together any more. I left him, just like I told you.' Something occurs to her. 'Wait a minute – how did Adrian find your house? He only knew where you worked.'

'Maybe he followed me home from work? He did knock on the door pretty much as soon as I got back. Anyway, if you're separated, then what the hell is this all about?'

Adrian is devious; he must have wanted to avoid any CCTV cameras outside Lewis's office. 'Can we just decide what to do first? And then I'll fill you in on everything, I promise.'

'Do you know what? I don't care. Just let me out of this car now.'

'Please, Lewis. I know I've given you no reason whatsoever to trust me, but we need to talk about all this.'

He shakes his head. 'No. I don't need this in my life. I don't want anything to do with it.'

Roberta is desperate now. She wants to make sure Lewis is okay, to get him far away from Adrian, but she also needs to find out exactly what he knows. 'How about a compromise? You give me two hours of your time. Just a couple of hours to hear me out, and then you can go to the police and you'll never have to see me again.'

Silence fills the car. He'll never agree to it – he's too angry, too scarred by what Adrian has done.

To her surprise, though, when he finally speaks it's not to say what she expected. 'Okay, have it your way.'

So she's bought herself two extra hours of freedom. Perhaps it's just as well that the police will become involved, as there is no way Adrian will leave her alone once he finds out that she let Lewis go. No way in hell.

It's time for her to take control for once in her life. 'Look, we can't go back to your place because he knows where you live. The B & B seems the best option. He has no idea where I've been staying, so—'

'If he tracked me down – a total stranger – then I'm sure it won't be too hard for him to find out where you are.'

'But at least we can talk about everything. Plus, you need some food. We can't just keep driving around aimlessly.'

'It looks like I don't have much choice, do I?' Lewis shakes his head. 'Fine. Not for long, though.'

It's strange, being back in her room with Lewis, the place they slept together, but it's all overshadowed now by the threat of what Adrian will do to them both.

They stopped at a café on the way over and picked up some food to bring back, and Roberta watches while Lewis silently devours a cheese and ham sandwich. Although she's got one too, she makes no move to eat it; food is the last thing she wants.

'So are you going to tell me what this is all about, or do I go straight to the police?' Lewis says, once he's finished eating. He is calmer now and Roberta dares to hope that she can get through to him, perhaps keep him on her side.

She sits on the bed, avoiding his stare. 'I'm not a bad person,' she begins. There's a long pause before she can bring herself to continue. 'But something happened three years ago – something Adrian and I both did – and I've been running from it ever since.' She looks up. 'But you know that, don't you?'

'For the fiftieth time, Roberta, I have no idea what you and your husband are talking about! What is it I'm supposed to know?'

Roberta stares at him, incredulous. He seems genuinely perplexed. 'But when I came to see you at your work, you said you knew I'd been lying.'

He frowns. 'Yes, I was talking about your son. I'm so sorry, Roberta, but I googled you and found out you had a son. I'm so sorry about what happened to him. But why did you lie to me and tell me you had no children?'

Roberta doesn't know whether to laugh or cry. 'You mean I really didn't tell you anything awful when I was drunk?'

'No, I told you before, you were just going on about Adrian a lot. You never mentioned your son or anything else.'

Roberta digests this information. There's still a chance that she and Adrian can get away with this. All she needs to do is convince Lewis not to tell the police what Adrian did to him.

She imagines this possibility, can see herself saying the words out loud, but something stops her from doing it. It doesn't feel right. For three years she's been hiding from the truth, living in fear that it will catch up with her, and she can't do it any longer.

Looking at Lewis now, at the kindness in his eyes, despite the situation, she decides she's got nothing to lose. 'I'm sorry I lied to you about Josh, my boy. It's just so hard to talk about, and everything's all tied up together. You know, like the butterfly effect. If different decisions had been made then he'd still be alive now.'

Lewis moves over to the bed and sits beside her. 'I'm sorry about your son. I can't imagine what that must be like. But what exactly happened?' He grabs her hand. 'You need to talk to someone, don't you? Something tells me you've never had a chance to do that.'

She looks up at him, her eyes glassy with tears. 'Do you mean you? After everything Adrian did? After what I've done?' She gets it though: he feels sorry for her. That's why he agreed to talk to her now rather than going straight to the police. She decides to ask him about it.

'I'm here with you now, despite everything, because I believe you've suffered enough. I know I'm not a parent, but I come from a close family – I've got three siblings and loving parents – so I know what it would have done to my mother if she'd lost one of us.'

Roberta can't find any words; instead, a fountain of tears floods down her cheeks, soaking her top.

'Roberta, I don't know what you think about that night we spent here, but it wasn't just some game to me. Even though we'd only just met, I really did like you. I think we hit it off pretty well. It's just that you freaked me out, the way you kept talking about your husband. Ex-husband, I mean. I thought it would be better if I stayed away. I'm too old for games.' He's about to reach for her hand but seems to think better of it. 'But something serious has clearly happened and I can't help you if you won't tell me what it is. It sounds as though it won't be easy to hear, but I'm an open-minded person and I'm no angel myself. We all make mistakes. So please will you just trust me and tell me what this is all about? Then we can deal with Adrian together.'

Seconds tick by, and once again Roberta can't find the words to answer him. She's at a crossroads now, and whichever direction she takes, everything will irrevocably be changed.

'What you said earlier – about doing something terrible – does it have anything to do with your son's death?' Lewis asks, when she doesn't respond.

And now the tears come hard and fast and it's both soothing and painful at the same time.

It's time to purge herself of the devil inside her.

FIFTY-TWO

Zoe

Daisy Carter. It always comes back to her.

Tim has gone now, with the intention of contacting Roberta to find out about Josh's mobile phone, and I am left alone to struggle with this new information. Before he left he made me promise not to contact Daisy, that she had insisted she didn't want to talk to me any more, but how can I leave it at that? I need to know what happened between her and Ethan, and all she would say to Tim was that she had been seeing him. Things must have been bad for her to keep this to herself until now.

Lying on Harley's bed, it takes me almost half an hour to construct a message for Daisy, one which I feel will be heartfelt enough to have an impact on her.

> *I know it must have been hard for you to talk to me, Daisy, and I really admire your courage in doing so, but please – I only want the truth, no matter how bad it might be. You had your reasons for keeping your relationship with Ethan from me, but please know that, whatever happened, I will listen to you without any prejudice. Please just help me get to the truth so I can find my other son.*

Now, once again, it's just a waiting game and I am at the mercy of other people's actions.

To keep myself busy I sort through Harley's things, even though I know DC Palmer has already searched his room. She doesn't know my son, though, and might not have noticed something that could be important.

There is nothing out of the ordinary; Harley keeps no secret boxes or diaries and there was nothing on his laptop. Plus, it's not as if he's run away, planned his escape from a life he doesn't want. I know this wasn't his choice.

Five minutes later, as I've got all Harley's things back in order, Daisy replies.

Come to my house then. My parents are in and I think they'll want to hear what I've got to say too. Address is 68 Cumberland Avenue.

I'm relieved that she'll see me, but apprehensive that she wants her parents present too. *Ethan, what have you done?*

I rush from the house and try to push this from my thoughts on the drive to Guildford.

Standing in front of Daisy's parents makes me automatically feel guilty, as if I've done something terrible and am about to be cautioned or reprimanded. They're both tall and commanding, and although I'm used to standing up to people, I am entering unknown territory here, with no idea what their daughter is about to reveal.

Mrs Carter introduces herself as Helen, and tells me her husband is Tony. 'We're so sorry about what happened to Ethan,' she says, reaching for my hand. 'And we're sorry to drag you out here. Daisy hasn't told us a thing so we have no idea what this is about.' She glances at her daughter, who is sitting on the sofa with her legs crossed beneath her.

'Yes,' her dad says. 'Shall we get to it, Daisy? What's going on?'

Neither of them seems pleased about this situation and suddenly I feel sorry for Daisy.

'I'm sorry I lied to you, Mrs Monaghan. But I hope you'll understand that I had my reasons.'

A lump forms in my throat. 'It's okay, just tell me what happened.'

'It was never Josh I liked,' Daisy begin. 'It was Ethan I wanted to be with. I'd liked him since the beginning of secondary school but he never seemed interested. We were so young, but at the time it hurt like hell.' She takes a deep breath. 'Anyway, towards the end of year nine we started talking a lot more and I felt like there could be a chance for us. He invited me to this party one of Josh's friends was having and I went with another girl in my class.'

'So Ethan was there?' I interrupt. I don't remember him going to a party.

Daisy nods. 'Yes. And Josh, of course. Apparently they'd told you and Josh's mum that they were staying round each other's houses so neither of you would know about this party. It was meant to be a big secret – it was a year eleven student's party, but he liked Josh and didn't seem to care that the four of us were only in year nine. His parents had gone away and his older brother was supposed to be keeping an eye on him, but he'd gone off with his girlfriend for the night and didn't care what we were all doing.'

'So there were no parents around?' I glance at Helen and Tony, both of whom look as uncomfortable as I feel. I know things like this are a natural part of growing up but it turns me cold inside, especially as I know this story won't end well.

'No. Just a bunch of kids.' She stares at the floor, then looks up at her parents. 'I'm sorry, but I was drinking a bit. It was disgusting but everyone else was doing it so I just joined in.'

My head is throbbing; I need to ask her if Ethan was drinking too, but I don't want to interrupt her now that she's finally being so forthcoming.

'Somehow I ended up in a bedroom with Ethan, and—'

'You were fourteen!' Helen cries.

'Let me finish, Mum, please.'

Tony takes Helen's hand and urges Daisy to continue.

'We were talking for a bit, getting on really well, and I really felt as though we were about to get together, but then Josh burst in. He'd never given the impression that he liked me, but he plonked himself on the bed and then told Ethan to go and get us all some drinks. I tried to go with Ethan but Josh pinned me down and then the door closed. Once we were alone, he tried to get me to do stuff, forcing himself on me and grabbing at my clothes. He didn't rape me or anything, but he was touching me everywhere and I was trying to get him off.'

I feel as though I'm about to throw up. Josh was fourteen. I'm also fearing what Ethan's role in this was.

Daisy looks at me and it's as though she can see right into my mind. 'Ethan came back in and saw what Josh was doing.'

This is it. Every mother's nightmare.

'He rushed in to try and pull Josh off, but Josh shouted at him to get out. Then he practically forced Ethan out of the door.'

For a second I think I've imagined Daisy saying this. Is she really telling me that Ethan did nothing wrong, that he tried to help her?

There are tears in her eyes now. Three years later, this incident is still so raw for her. 'The rest is a blur but somehow I managed to get out before Josh did anything else. I rushed out and ran home. I didn't see Ethan again – I think he must have left by himself.'

Helen moves closer to Daisy and puts her arm around her. 'Why didn't you tell us? You had to deal with all this on your own.'

'I was... ashamed, I think. I thought it was my fault, that somehow I'd let him do it. Maybe given off the wrong signals.

But now I know different. I had never even given Josh the tiniest reason to think I would be interested in him. And he'd seen me with Ethan only seconds before. He must have known we were getting together.'

'He didn't care,' I say. 'He just took whatever he wanted. I'm sorry you went through that, Daisy.'

She turns to me. 'I'm sorry I didn't tell you before. I just couldn't bring myself to speak about it until now because I was... scared.'

'Of what, Daisy? You know we'd have helped you in any way.' Tony has finally found his voice.

'Let me finish telling you everything first,' Daisy says. 'The next time we were at school I was desperate to talk to Ethan. He told me I should tell the police, or at least my parents, what had happened, but I just shouted at him that I didn't want anyone to know – ever. I told him it would ruin my life. He seemed shocked but eventually promised he'd never say a word. Then he just asked if I was okay and told me we'd better stay away from each other.' She looks at me. 'I don't really understand it. He was standing up to Josh and then suddenly it was as if he wanted nothing more to do with me. That really hurt. Probably even more than what Josh had done. Anyway, that was the last time we really spoke. But Ethan kept his promise to me.'

'I'm sorry he acted that way,' I say. 'I wish we could know why.' My head is spinning; at least now I know a likely reason why the boys fell out, and my theory about Josh wanting to retaliate has become even more plausible. It just doesn't make sense when Ethan didn't do anything but try to pull him off Daisy. There must be more to this.

'I just think, well, it must have been peer pressure,' says Daisy. 'We were all just kids, weren't we? He still tried to help me, and I'll always remember that about him.' She offers me a small smile, which I'm grateful for. 'Anyway, I was so angry at the time, not just about the violation but because Josh had messed things up for me and Ethan. So I did something, even though I'd told Ethan I didn't want anyone to know what had happened. I went to Josh's house to tell his parents.'

'So his mum knew?' I ask, already planning the conversation I will have with Roberta about this.

'I don't think so. When I went round to his house only his dad was in. Horrible man. But I let him know what had happened and told him I would go to the police.'

Helen gasps while Tony reaches for his daughter; they're both clinging on to her now.

'But he just grabbed me and said that if I did, or if I ever told a single person, then he would hunt me down and make me pay. I was terrified. That's why I haven't said anything up until now. But your friend, that Tim guy, he made me see that I shouldn't be afraid of speaking the truth and that there will always be people to support me. I know I told him I didn't want to talk to you, but after he'd gone I couldn't stop thinking about everything you've been through, and that your other son is missing, so if you hadn't contacted me earlier I would have come to talk to you anyway, Mrs Monaghan.'

'Thanks, Daisy. I appreciate that.'

'I've thought about going to the police now, about Josh's dad, but what would be the point? Josh is dead and in a way that's punishment for both of them, so there's no point in dragging it all up now, is there?'

I suppose she is right, as much as I'd like Adrian to pay for threatening a child. 'There's just one thing I'm confused about, Daisy. When I went to see Mr Keats, your old head of year, he told me he'd seen you and Josh in the corridor together. He was convinced you were boyfriend and girlfriend.'

She shakes her head. 'No way. That wasn't me.' She pauses for a moment. 'But Josh was kind of seeing this girl, Natasha, who I guess looked like me from the back. We had the same colour hair.

He could have just thought she was me. Plus, Mr Keats wasn't the most observant person – he was always making mistakes and getting kids muddled up.' She laughs and turns to her mum. 'Do you remember when we went to that parents' meeting and he kept calling me Natasha?'

Helen smiles. 'Oh, yes. I kept correcting him but he still kept saying it.'

That explains things, and I stand up to leave. 'Thank you so much for your time, Helen and Tony. And Daisy, thank you for telling me everything. I'll leave you all to it. I'm sure you've got a lot to talk about.'

Daisy walks with me to the front door. 'That Tim, he said your other son being missing might be tied to Ethan's death? He didn't go into detail, but I just want you to know that I honestly don't know anything else about what was going on with Ethan and Josh. I would tell you if I did.'

Thanking her, I leave the house and head back to London, driving too quickly up the A3 so I can get home and let Tim know this information. I'm filled with pride for Ethan for trying to help Daisy, but now I'm convinced this is what led to his death. But why was Josh so angry with him? Did Ethan speak to him afterwards, maybe threaten to tell someone?

I also need to know if Roberta has known this all along.

But more than anything, I need to find Harley.

FIFTY-THREE

Here I am, standing across from his house in the middle of the night. I know he will be tucked up in bed by now; I'm only here because I'm compelled to be close to him. His house is on a secluded lane and I'm hidden by shadows and overgrown trees, so I'm not worried about being caught.

This isn't the first time I've done this. No, I've been following him for weeks, ever since he ended things so cruelly and abruptly. Did he really think I'd stand back and take it? After all the effort I've put into being with him?

I don't have a plan for what I will do — I will just follow and observe, and I believe an opportunity will present itself sooner or later. I've got nothing but time on my hands, so I can wait as long as it takes.

He's left me feeling hollow and empty inside, though not through guilt — I don't regret anything. I am unable to focus at work, and in no state to properly attend to Mum when she needs me. I curse him, yet I am desperate for him at the same time. Is this what it feels like to lose your mind?

The last thing I'm expecting tonight is for the front door to open, but it does, and I watch the figures as they leave the house.

Now this is interesting; it's way past midnight.

Quickly and silently I follow behind, excitement building at this unusual turn of events.

FIFTY-FOUR

Roberta

This time when she wakes up next to Lewis, she knows exactly what she's told him, and it feels as though the weight of a continent's been lifted from her chest. Now she can breathe again.

And she's ready to face the consequences of what she's done. Whatever will be, will be.

They've spent the night in her car, parked up near Wimbledon Common. Neither of them has any association to this place, so it seemed like a good location to ensure they were off Adrian's radar. Her back aches and she longs to stretch her legs, to iron out the cramp surging through them, but at least they are somewhere Adrian won't be able to track them down.

Beside her in the driver's seat, Lewis is already awake and tapping something on his phone. 'What time is it?' she asks.

He puts down his phone. 'Nearly eight. I've been up for hours but didn't want to wake you. You looked so shattered last night – I suppose that's not surprising, though.'

Roberta is touched by his kindness. 'Well, we got through one night, so that's something, and I'm going to make sure neither of us ever have to run or hide from that man again.' She feels stronger than she's ever felt before, despite what her future will undoubtedly hold.

'What's your plan for that?' Lewis asks.

This, she has thought long and hard about. 'I'm going to go to the police and tell them the truth. It's the only way you'll ever be free, and actually, in a funny way I'll be free too. I've been hiding from this for so long and I won't do it any more. I actually feel good, having talked about it.'

Lewis takes her hand. 'I'm glad you said that. It's the right thing to do. I've spent the last few hours trying to work out how to convince you to go to them, but I didn't think you'd agree.' He moves back the hair that's fallen across her face. 'Despite everything, you're a good person, Roberta. I just want you to know that.'

'Tell me something,' she says. 'If I wasn't going to the police myself, would you have called them?'

He stares at her, his dark eyes carefully studying her face. 'I'm sorry, Roberta, but yes. I would have had to.'

She's about to respond and tell him that she understands when her phone rings from the back seat. Lewis reaches back and passes it to her and she stares at the screen, not recognising the mobile number.

'Hello?' She's prepared for the worst; perhaps it's the police already, and she'll never get to do the right thing and go to them first.

'Hi, Roberta Butler? Sorry to ring so early. My name's Tim Ellroy and I'm helping Zoe Monaghan find her son. I just wondered if we could have a quick chat?'

This must be a prank. 'What do you mean find her son? He's... he's dead.'

'I'm not talking about Ethan. Her other son, Harley, disappeared on Friday night and I've reason to believe it could be tied up in the deaths of Ethan and your son, Josh.'

Roberta gasps at the mention of his name, and Lewis grabs her hand again. Tim's voice is so loud through her phone that she's sure Lewis is catching every word. 'I'm sorry to hear that. Can I speak to Zoe? There are some things I, um, need to tell her. It's important.'

'I'm not with her at the moment but we could meet up in a few hours at her house?'

Roberta nods, even though the man she's speaking to can't see her. 'That's fine.' It will give her time to get her head around talking to Zoe before she goes to the police, to get used to how things are about to change for her.

'Can I just check something?' Tim asks. 'Do you have Josh's mobile phone, by any chance?'

Roberta frowns. 'No, it was never recovered from the river.'

'Okay. Well, I'll see you at Zoe's house later. But before I go, is there anything you can tell me that you haven't mentioned to Zoe already about your son and Ethan? Anything at all? It's even more important now because we need all the help we can get to find Harley.'

She has to pause while she attempts to calm her nerves. 'Did you say you were a police officer?' For the first time it dawns on her that she doesn't know who exactly she's speaking to.

'Ex-police. Now I just help people in ways the police may not be able to, if that makes sense.'

'You mean like a private detective.'

'Not exactly, but something like that. Now, do you think there's anything at all you can tell me?'

Plenty, Roberta thinks, but where does she start? It will need to be right from the beginning to have any hope of people understanding. 'I... I lied to Zoe. I know exactly why the boys had fallen out, and the truth is that I didn't even know Josh was staying at Ethan's that night. He told me he was with a different friend.'

A sharp intake of breath. 'Okay, good. This means we can make some progress. Take your time and tell me everything you can remember. So what exactly did the boys fight about?'

FIFTY-FIVE

Zoe

I've left a message on Tim's phone, explaining that I've just met up with Daisy Carter, at her invitation, and she's finally told me the truth. I didn't go into detail but I urged him to come over as quickly as possible. I also tried Roberta's phone but it went straight to voicemail. Again, I left a message, asking her to call me urgently.

It's a relief when the doorbell rings so soon after leaving the message on Tim's phone, and I rush to answer it, throwing the door open to see a familiar face I can't quite place. She looks familiar but strange at the same time.

'Zoe? I don't know if you remember me, but I'm Liam's sister, Cara.'

Now she's said it, I immediately remember. She looks so different, not the glamorous woman who always trots around the office in stilettoes, despite being tall enough not to need any extra height. Today she's wearing loose jogging bottoms, an oversized T-shirt and white trainers, and it doesn't seem to suit her. Her usually big hair is scraped back into a tight bun and she looks as though she's wearing the remains of make-up she must have had on yesterday.

'Are you okay? Has something happened? Is Liam all right?'

She looks around her, tries to peer into the house. 'Are you alone?'

I'm surprised she's asking this. Surely she and Liam must know that Jake has moved out? 'Yes, it's just me here. Why?'

'Can I come in?'

This is getting stranger by the second. 'Of course.'

Once she's inside, she remains in the hallway, huddled so closely against the front door that it feels like she'll disappear right through it at any moment.

'We can go in the living room?' I suggest, but she immediately shakes her head.

'No, it's okay. This won't take long.'

'What's going on, Cara? And are you okay? You don't look well. Can I get you some water or something? I really think you should sit down.'

She eyes the stairs but doesn't move. 'No, I don't want any water. I came here to tell you something.'

My whole body freezes. This is about Harley – it has to be – and from the state of Cara, it can't be good news. I just can't fathom how on earth Cara is tied up in this. 'You might not need to sit down, but I think I do.' I walk off, leaving her no choice but to follow me into the living room.

She doesn't take a seat but hovers near the door, as if she needs to be close to it so she can make a quick exit.

'Where's Jake?' she says, her eyes fixed on the hall.

I frown. 'He doesn't live here any more. You must know that?'

Her eyes widen. 'I didn't. Can't say I'm surprised, though.'

'What does that mean? Look, what's going on, Cara? What do you know about my son?'

'Your son? What are you talking about?'

'You mean you're not here about Harley?'

'Ha, don't tell me he's in trouble as well? Like father, like son, eh?' Her tone is suddenly bitter and angry, and she no longer looks like a victim.

'Just tell me where Harley is.'

'How should I know? This has got nothing to do with your son – I'm here about Jake.' Her voice, quiet up until now, has risen a few decibels.

'Jake?'

She moves a little closer but stays standing. 'Yes. Your husband. Ha, that's a joke, isn't it? He doesn't deserve that title.'

None of what she's saying makes any sense. Unless she's talking about Leanne. But why would Jake have spoken to her about that? 'What are you saying, Cara? Just tell me.'

'Your husband raped me.'

Her words are a whisper yet they seem to freeze time, freeze everything, explode into a thousand pieces.

I'm too shocked to say anything. An image of Daisy Carter flashes through my mind, how traumatised she was about what Josh did to her.

'Did you hear what I said? Jake raped me. Last Monday. We were both working late at the office.' She's speaking quietly again now, almost nervously, yet her words pierce my eardrums.

I don't want to believe her; no part of me, despite what Jake has done, can comprehend him doing something like this. It feels like she's acting, putting on a show, yet I need to hear her out.

'Is that why you left him?' she asks, when I still haven't spoken. 'Did he tell you what he'd done?'

Finally, I find my voice. 'No, of course not. I would have gone to the police. Have you, by the way? Have you reported it?' I need to act as though she is talking about someone else and give her the same help and advice I would any other woman in this situation.

She shakes her head. 'I've been too scared to report it. And it's my brother's business too, isn't it? This affects him.'

I can see her predicament. 'Have you at least told Liam, though?'

'No. You're the first person I've told.'

'Why are you telling me? I don't understand. It's the police you should be talking to.'

'Because I want my job back.'

This is not what I expected to hear. 'What do you mean?'

'Jake fired me, didn't he? Straight after it happened. Liam is happy to go along with it, but I want my job back, Zoe. I don't deserve to be fired after what he did to me. It's not right.'

Everything shifts with her words; it all becomes clear. 'So let me get this straight – if Jake gives you your job back then you won't go to the police? Even after what he did?'

She stares at me as if this shouldn't need clarifying. 'Yes. As much as I want him to pay for what he did, I want my job back more. I've already suffered enough, haven't I? Why should I also lose a job I love?'

'And you want me to convince Jake to take you on again?'

'Yes. I had no idea you were separated, but he might still listen to you.'

I've heard enough now. Standing up, I grab her by her arm and lead her to the front door.

'Hey, what are you doing?' she protests. 'You're hurting my arm.'

'Get out of my house, Cara.' I push her out of the front door. 'But... but—'

'Call the police if you think they'll believe your lies, but I don't have time for this.'

After slamming the door, I watch her walk down the drive. She's already pulling out her hairband and letting her hair fall around her shoulders while she clutches her phone to her ear.

I contemplate phoning Jake and warning him of her lies, but then change my mind. He can sort out his own mess.

In the kitchen, I force down some toast, even though eating is the last thing I want to do. I need to be physically strong, and Cara's visit, together with my lack of appetite, has left me drained of energy.

The doorbell rings again. Seething with anger at Cara's audacity, I fling it open, ready to let loose – then I realise it's Roberta Butler standing on my doorstep.

'Do you know where Harley is?' I demand, before she's had a chance to speak. Even though there's so much I want to say to her, this is the first thing that comes out.

'No, and I'm so sorry he's gone missing. Tim Ellroy called me this morning. He said he'd meet us here, but I wanted to speak to you alone first. It's really important.'

Tim hasn't returned my call yet, but I was so caught up with Cara's nonsense just now that maybe I missed him. I tell Roberta I need a second and check my phone, finding two missed calls and a voicemail message. How could I have been so careless? It could have been Harley trying to call.

I quickly listen to the message. It's Tim, telling me that he got my message, that he has some news provided by Roberta, which he's looking into, and that she will meet us both at my house.

'Come in,' I tell Roberta. Outside, I glimpse Roberta's car parked by the kerb, and there's someone in it, although it's too far away for me to get a good look. 'Is that Adrian?' I ask, disappointed that Roberta has gone back to him.

'No, of course not. That's my friend, Lewis, but he's got nothing to do with this, so he's waiting for me in the car.'

Inside the house, I feel a sense of déjà vu as I lead Roberta into the living room and watch her sit on the sofa. This time, though, I am armed with more knowledge, and ready to confront her about what her son did to Daisy and how it affected his friendship with Ethan. I open my mouth to speak but she beats me to it.

'This is probably the most difficult thing I've ever had to do in my life,' she says. 'And please, just let me get it out without saying anything then I promise I'll answer any questions you may have.'

Even though she's about to tell me what I was ready to confront her with, I'm filled with dread; is she also about to tell me she knows where Harley is and it's all too late? My stomach starts to squirm.

'Just tell me what's happened to Harley. Just start with that. Please tell me he's okay? I don't care if you've been sending those messages – all I want now is my son back.'

She frowns. 'Zoe, you've got it all wrong. This isn't about Harley, it's about Josh and Ethan. And... well, some other things. You see, I lied to you before, when I said I didn't know why the boys had fallen out. Well, I do know, and it's all to do with me.'

This doesn't make sense. 'Go on,' I urge.

'I already told you that I'd overheard the boys arguing. Well, I heard more than I let on. Josh said to Ethan, "You know what they did." Those were his exact words, and he was talking about me and Adrian.'

I'm riddled with confusion. What's this got to do with Daisy? 'But what was Josh talking about? What did you and Adrian do?'

She takes a deep breath and begins. Every word she says leaves me struggling for breath.

'A couple of weeks before their accident in the river, Adrian and I had been invited out to his workmate's leaving dinner. Adrian never usually wanted me to go to these things, but he insisted I had to be there. I think it was because he knew I'd hate every second of it, and it would just add to the torture he liked to inflict on me. I've never had much to do with any of his colleagues and I certainly didn't know any of their wives or partners. As you probably know, I'm not the most comfortable of people in social situations. So it was all to make me feel even worse about myself. He liked to do that.'

I want to interrupt her and ask how she could have let him do that to her for all those years, strip away at what little self-esteem she may have had, but that's not important now.

'Anyway,' she continues, 'the food was okay and I ended up speaking to this woman called Sophie who was actually really nice to me. She took my mind off everything and made the evening more tolerable. And the whole time, Adrian was taking great pleasure in ignoring me and acting as though I wasn't even there. I'm sure people must have noticed.'

I'm getting impatient now, but I need to hear everything she's got to say.

'When we left,' she continues, 'I was actually feeling okay. I'd met a nice woman who maybe, just maybe, I could end up being friends with, and Adrian wasn't abusing me in the car on the drive home. Well, more fool me. I should have known better than to actually think that things were okay for once.'

'What did he do to you, Roberta?'

'Adrian? Oh, nothing. Not to me. He ignored me all the way home. He wasn't supposed to have been drinking, but I'm sure he'd had a few. I tried to tell him I'd drive but he wouldn't let me. Anyway, we were driving through Shere and the roads were so quiet but then suddenly this bike appeared from nowhere, right in front of us. I screamed at Adrian that he was going too fast, but it was too late. He smashed straight into the cyclist.'

Tears are flooding from her eyes as she recalls this. 'The roads are so narrow,' she explains.

I'm filled with horror. 'Was the cyclist okay? Please tell me he was okay, Roberta.'

One look at her distraught face tells me he wasn't.

'No. He went flying over to the other side of the road and smashed against the concrete. It all happened so quickly, but I can see it so clearly in my mind, as if it happened seconds ago.' Her loud sobbing makes it hard for me to hear her clearly.

Even before she says anything else, I know how this story ends and I'm sick to my stomach. So much about their marriage is starting to make sense now. 'Adrian killed him, didn't he? And now I remember a story in the local paper about a hit-and-run in Shere. That was you two.'

'Please don't look at me like that,' she says, turning away from me. 'I tried to convince him to call the police, but he refused. He said his life would be over and that I should think about Josh. How could I let Josh have a father in prison? That's what he said. It took a while, but he managed to convince me.'

'Oh God, Roberta, that's awful. You must see how heinous this is. What did you do?'

'He told me we had to get out of there before anyone came along and saw us, so we just left. You have no idea how much I hate myself for that. I'd do anything to go back to that moment and change everything. I would force Adrian to let me drive, no matter what it took.' She buries her head in her hands. 'Every single day since I've regretted my decision to go along with it. For days afterwards I thought of calling the police, but then I would look at Josh and I just couldn't do it to him.'

'I assume, because you're telling me this now, that you're finally going to the police?'

She nods. 'Yes, it's long overdue, but I'm going to do what I should have right at the beginning. That poor man. He was only twenty-four. He was about to get married. His poor fiancée.' Her tears come hard and fast now, but I'm finding it hard to feel sorry for her.

There are still so many pieces of the puzzle I need to fit together. 'I'm not sure how Josh and Ethan fit into this?' I say.

She tries to wipe away her tears. 'Things were really strained at home afterwards, and I kept talking to Adrian about it and trying to get him to change his mind about the police, especially after reading the story in the paper.' She shakes her head. 'He wouldn't have any of it, though, and would get loud and vocal about it – abusive, even – forgetting that Josh's bedroom is right next to ours. Now, Josh never said anything to us but he must have heard and told Ethan about it – you know how close they were. I know that's what they were talking about when they argued. *You know what they did.* I can only assume that Ethan was threatening to tell you and Jake, and Josh was trying to convince him not to. I don't know how he did that…' She looks at me, her eyes glazed with sadness. 'Ethan always was a good boy. He just wanted to do the right thing so I can't blame him for that.'

'So why do you think Josh stayed the night at our place?' I ask. 'If they'd argued about something so terrible, why would Josh want to be anywhere near Ethan?' I already know the answer to this, but I want to hear Roberta say that maybe he wanted to harm my son.

'It's so hard to get my head around this, but I think maybe Josh wanted to make sure Ethan wasn't saying anything to you and Jake.'

'Threatening him, in other words.'

Roberta nods. 'I'm so sorry, Zoe. Josh lied to me and told me he was staying with a different friend, Harry. I had no idea that he'd been at your house until the police knocked on my door that morning.'

My head feels like it's about to explode. 'So why would the boys go down to the river?'

Josh wanted Ethan dead. It has to be that. My heart feels like it's being ripped apart.

'I have no idea why they went there,' Roberta says. 'And I don't know how they both ended up in the river. But I swear to you, Zoe, I've told you everything I know, and it's nothing but the truth.'

Despite all her lies, I believe her. And it appears she doesn't know anything about Daisy Carter. 'So you haven't been sending those messages? And you really don't know where Harley is?'

'No!' She pauses. 'Why do you think Harley's disappearance has anything to with the boys' accident?'

I explain about the last text message. *Two down, none to go.*

She looks horrified. 'But that would mean that whoever it is thinks Ethan did something that deserves some sort of retribution?'

I tell her this is exactly the conclusion I've reached. 'And if Ethan had done something to Josh – maybe blackmailing him or threatening to tell the police about what you and Adrian had done – then the only people who would send me those messages would be you or Adrian. And if it's not you…'

She stares at me. 'Adrian has many faults, Zoe, but I really don't think it's him.'

'Really? How can you be sure? He's already killed someone and kept it from the police – I would say that makes him capable of anything.' Not to mention threatening a fourteen-year-old girl.

'You're right,' Roberta admits, 'but I never told him about what I heard Josh saying to Ethan. I couldn't let Adrian know that Josh had overheard us – I just wanted him kept out of our mess. Adrian scared me too much for me to want him to know anything.'

My heart sinks. Once again, I'm wrong.

'Do you happen to have Josh's mobile phone?' I ask. If we can just check it, then it might confirm everything Roberta's said. It might even lead to something else.

She shakes her head. 'No. That man, Tim, asked me too and I told him it was never recovered from the river.'

So that's that then.

For a moment I consider telling Roberta what Josh did to Daisy Carter, just like I'd planned, but I think better of it. She's already got enough to deal with so I will wait for a better time, if that ever comes. Instead, I decide to tell her we should still get the police to question Adrian, but then my phone beeps with a text message.

We need to meet. Come to this address. 86 Norton Avenue, Kingston. No police.

FIFTY-SIX

Zoe

Standing outside this unfamiliar address makes me shiver, despite the mugginess of the late afternoon. All the way to Kingston, I've wondered if it is Adrian I'm about to come face-to-face with, if somehow he has rented a different house, in a different place. I stare up at the windows and wonder if Harley is in there. Has he been given any food? Is he thirsty? Scared? I hope he knows how hard I'm searching for him, and that I've risked coming here alone in the hope that I can talk Adrian out of harming him. If it's not too late.

One son down, one to go.

The words spin around my head, threatening to crush my skull. I can't be too late. I can't lose another son.

The small front garden is overgrown and the door looks flimsy, barely secure, as if even a gentle kick will break it down. I step forward and knock loudly, holding my breath while I wait.

When it swings open, I stare at the person standing there, convinced I've got the wrong house. The woman before me is almost bent double, leaning on a walking frame, her skin wrinkled and sun-damaged. She winces and clutches her back, clearly in pain. Although at first I assumed she must be elderly, on second glance she appears to be no more than sixty.

'I'm so sorry, I think I've got the wrong house.' I've been sent on another wild goose chase and anger seethes within me.

'No, Zoe, you haven't. Come in.'

I'm so stunned to hear her say my name that I'm frozen to the spot for seconds, possibly minutes, until again she urges me to come inside. What the hell is going on? This woman can't have Harley. There's no way.

I don't move. 'Is it you who's been sending me the messages? I don't understand.'

She half smiles. 'No, dear, it's not me. I only sent you the last one, asking you to come here, but I think I know who might be involved in all of it.'

Confused, I look past her to the walls of her hallway. There are no personal pictures anywhere, only prints of flowers and landscapes. There's nothing to give away who this woman is, nothing to shed any light on anything.

'Who? Tell me. And who are you?'

'Come in,' she urges. 'I need to show you something, and then we need to go somewhere, but I'll need help to get there. I get so out of breath, you see, and it's a struggle to talk sometimes. I've got MS, dear, which means driving is out of the question for me.'

Everything screams at me to be careful; this is a stranger's house, no matter how vulnerable she appears to be. But I cannot hesitate. For Harley and Ethan's sake, I swallow my fear and step inside.

'There's something you need to see,' she says, handing me a piece of paper. 'And then I'll tell you everything once we're in the car and on our way.'

It takes me a moment to register what she's just passed to me: a piece of A4 paper, the back of it facing me. I turn it over and my legs almost give way beneath me. It's a printout of a photograph.

And it's my son's face I'm staring at.

FIFTY-SEVEN

I don't feel bad about what I've done. He's messed with my head, drilled a screw deep into my skull, and I'm no longer the same person. He has to pay for what he's done to me, has to know that it's not acceptable to treat people the way he treated me.

I watch him now; he's finally succumbed to sleep and I can get some peace from his questions and desperate pleas. 'All in good time,' I told him. Soon enough, he will know everything. For now, though, I need silence, so that my head is clear to think, to make sure I do this right; I can't afford to make any mistakes.

He still looks beautiful, despite the fear and anxiety he must be feeling.

I'm having a cup of tea when he wakes up, his eyes shooting open, staring at me as if he doesn't remember being here. The horror is dawning on him all over again.

Good. I want him to suffer.

'Why are you doing this?' he asks. 'Just let me go.' His voice is hoarse, and I revel in the discomfort it must be causing him to speak.

'Really?' I ask. 'You don't know? No idea whatsoever? I thought you were more intelligent than that.'

'This is because I ended our... whatever it was we had? You can't be that messed up.'

I laugh. 'We're all human, and none of us are straightforward, are we? We all have our little flaws.'

He tries to pull himself to a sitting position, but the drug I've given him prevents him from moving properly. 'Little flaws? You're a straight-up psycho!'

'Insulting me won't do you any favours, will it, Harley?' I marvel at how much he's changed, how confident he's become. Unfortunately, it does nothing to lessen my attraction to him. I don't think anything ever will.

'Neither will being nice to you, I'm sure,' he says. 'You've already decided what you're going to do to me here. I just want to know why.'

I smile. 'Of course… you don't know the full picture, do you? You think I'm only doing this because I'm some crazy stalker who hasn't been able to get you out of my head for three years. If only it were that simple.'

'Well, that's the truth, isn't it?'

Again, I smile. 'Only a small, minuscule part of the truth. There's a whole lot more to it, though. Things are never just black and white, are they?' I'm enjoying messing with his head.

'Yeah, right.' He turns his head to face the wall.

'I wonder if I can still make you excited, Harley? Shall we find out?' I move across to the bed and reach under the sheet I've covered him in, but there is no response. Perhaps he is too traumatised to feel anything. Never mind; it's probably for the best. I can't help but feel disappointed, though. It would have been nice to know I still had some power over him, even after all this time. Never mind, I will try again later, once the effects of the drug have lessened.

'So what are you going to do? Kill me? Because I really don't think I care any more. Just do it. Believe me, there's nothing worse than the thought that I actually slept with you.'

His cruel words slice into me, but I don't respond.

I can see this makes him frustrated. 'You do realise you'll just be hurting my mum, don't you? All those messages — I know they were you. I've known all along. There was nobody else they could have been from. I tried to find you. I went to your house but your mum said you'd moved out. I had no way to find you.'

'Well, luckily for you, I found you in the end. Kyle Andrews. Did you really think it was him? What did you think he was going to say if you knew all along it was me?'

He shrugs. '*I dunno. But I had to see. I had to make sure nobody else knew about us. Part of me thought that you'd turn up at the bar, but nobody showed.*'

'*No, but I wasn't going to let you go.*'

'*Why did you wait until I'd left the bar to approach me? And you drugged me to get me here, didn't you? There's no other way you could have done it.*'

'*You've got even smarter with age, haven't you? CCTV, Harley. I couldn't risk confronting you until I was sure we were away from any cameras. And clearly we were, because it's been two days now and nobody's found you. They never will.*'

His eyes widen. '*And Alissa? Where is she?*'

'*I thought you might have worked that one out by now, Harley. Maybe you're not as smart as I thought. Alissa is right here in this room.*' I wave at him.

'*You?*'

'*Every email, every text message – they were all from me. I was the girl you fell for. Well, with the help of some photos I found on the Internet. How does that make you feel?*'

He ignores me, but I can tell my revelation is torturing him.

'*You're sicker than I thought,*' he says, after a few moments. '*And all that pain you're causing my mum… She's done nothing to you. You've never even met her. She's a good person and doesn't deserve this.*'

'*Yes, I agree that is unfortunate. Can't be helped, though. Perhaps if she'd brought you up differently you wouldn't have become such an evil person. You wouldn't have hurt people the way you have.*'

'*You really need to get over this,*' he says, mocking me. Surely he knows I have the upper hand? '*Look, I was only sixteen, I was a kid. Please think about my mother. She's already lost one son; think what this would do to her. What if it was your mum?*'

'*Well, it's funny you should mention your brother.*'

He frowns. '*What are you talking about?*'

'Such a shame about what happened to him, isn't it? A terrible accident.' I make the expression on my face one of pity.

'Yes, it was, so I don't know why you're trying to make my mum think otherwise. You really are a nasty piece of work.'

He's too cocky now – another change from the sixteen-year-old boy I knew. That only makes this easier.

'An accident. Are you sure about that, Harley?'

'Yes, it was,' he says, trying to move again.

I let silence fall between us before I respond. This is my big moment, the one I've been waiting for. 'I was there, Harley. At the river that night. I saw everything that happened.'

He turns a shade paler. 'No. You're lying.'

I stand up. I've rehearsed this in my mind, have pictured myself walking around the room like a lawyer in a courtroom. A lawyer who knows without a doubt that he will win the case.

'I was outside your house that night, when your brother and his friend appeared, and then moments later you followed, keeping your distance so they didn't know you were there. It was all a bit strange and intriguing – I just had to know what you were all doing.'

His jaw drops but he says nothing.

'When we got to the river, I heard the two of them arguing. In fact, arguing is an understatement – it was a full-blown fight, I'd say. I couldn't hear every word, as I had to stay back in case any of you saw me, but I got the gist of it. Oh yes, I completely understood, and then it all made sense. You suddenly breaking it off with me – all of it.'

I wait for him to say something but he stays silent. I relish how sick he looks, as if he's about to lose the contents of his stomach, which won't be much because I've barely given him any food.

'Josh was mocking Ethan about the kind of person his older brother likes to sleep with, and threatening to tell your parents and everyone at school about us, to show them a photo of us down by the river weeks before. He'd seen us, hadn't he? And that's why you got freaked out. I can only assume that's why you ended it with me.'

Again, I'm greeted with silence.

'That boy, Josh, was really angry with Ethan, wasn't he?' I continue. 'Wow, it was like he detested him. He mentioned something about a girl – Daisy Carter – but I couldn't hear it properly.'

Harley moans. Perhaps he's trying to say something, but it's inaudible.

'There was so much shouting, and then suddenly you rushed out of your hiding place and pushed Josh, didn't you? It's not like he was trying to hurt your brother, but you still went for him. And then it was like it was happening in slow motion: he began to lose his balance and stumble, falling into the river, but then Ethan grabbed hold of him to try and help. It was too late, though, wasn't it, Harley? Both of them went in. Splash! I'll never forget how it sounded. What I don't understand is why you just stood there for so long – I mean, what was it? Seconds? Minutes? – before you jumped in to try and help them. Or help your brother, at least. You might have had a chance to save them both if you'd acted faster. I'd love to know what was going through your head. I read much later that although Josh couldn't swim, Ethan could, so he really should have been able to save himself.' I smile at him, showing him that I know him inside out. 'Only you know what happened down there. I couldn't see much more from where I was. Anyway, I waited until you'd got out and then I left, sickened by your actions. I'd spent so much time and energy on you, and you turned out to be a murderer.'

'I'm not!' Harley shrieks. 'It was an accident!'

'Really? Why don't you tell me all about it, help me change my mind about you? Because I don't want to believe you're such a heinous person.' I don't tell him this, but I want him to somehow justify his actions, to show me that he is worthy of my devotion.

It takes a while, but eventually he starts talking. 'I was in turmoil. I didn't want anyone finding out about us. It sickened me.'

I'll let that one slide; at least he is opening up now.

'And when Josh showed me the photo he'd taken of me and you by the river, I knew it was only a matter of time before it all came out. I just couldn't handle that. Then Ethan asked me about it and I couldn't deny it, could I? The photo clearly showed us doing stuff together. He said it was disgusting and that Dad would be ashamed of me.' He's crying now, barely able to get his words out. 'And then he had a go at me for ruining his friendship with Josh. He said they'd never argued before but now they were always fighting because Josh wanted to tell everyone and Ethan had no choice but to defend his brother, no matter what he thought of me.'

'How noble,' I say. 'What a saint he was.'

'I… I couldn't let Dad know what I'd done. I was forever trying to please him and make him proud of me, even though he never said that he was, and this would have just destroyed everything.'

'Well, that's all very sad, isn't it, but don't you think people should pay for their sins?'

'So I deserve to die? Doesn't that make you a hypocrite? Who's going to make you pay for killing me?'

'It doesn't work like that, Harley. And anyway, who said I was going to kill you? I just want you to suffer. I want your life to be over, just like mine is.'

'Why did you wait three years for this?'

'I'll answer that after you answer one of my questions. Why did you follow Ethan and Josh to the river that night? What were they doing there? It's something I've never been able to understand.'

I don't expect him to indulge me by answering, and I'm surprised when he does.

'I'd been on edge ever since they'd found out, and I had to be alert to what they were doing. I didn't know if Josh had convinced Ethan to say anything, so I had to know what they were up to. I think they both just liked hanging out there and they went there to have it all out, away from our parents.'

'Hmmm. It still seems a strange place to go in the middle of the night, though.' He doesn't know what I'm hinting at, even though it's staring him in the face. 'The river is where Josh saw us, isn't it? So it *was a bit like rubbing it in Ethan's face. His brother's dirty secret.' I smile at him. 'Or perhaps Josh wanted to lure Ethan away. Maybe he'd planned to do something to him.'*

Harley shakes his head. 'You mean he wanted to hurt Ethan? No. No way. They were friends. Josh isn't you. He wasn't sick and twisted.'

Again, I ignore his insult. 'His actions say something different, though, don't they? And we'll never know the full truth, will we?'

'You're just trying to mess with my head. I'm not listening to you. And answer my question – why did you wait three years to bring all this up?'

I suppose now is as good a time as any to explain things. 'That wasn't intentional. I tried to move on afterwards – I mean, I hated you most of the time, so it should have been easy, but I just couldn't make it work with anyone else. There were lots of men, of course. Real men – not little boys like you'd been, but men who knew how to have a relationship. Unfortunately, they just weren't for me. Now here I am, alone, with no life other than work, so why should you be heading off to medical school without a care in the world?'

'Without a care in the world? Are you sick in the head? I lost my brother and it was all my fault. That's something I'll have to live with for the rest of my life.'

'It's not enough. Not nearly enough.'

'Then what the hell is?'

'Seeing your family destroyed by your actions. Your whole world crumbling and falling apart, bit by bit. You know, I really thought your mum would have worked it all out. I was actually going to tell her myself, but do you know what? It'll be much better if you do it.'

He frowns as he tries to get his head around this. I know what question will come next before he even speaks. 'But you could have gone to the police if you were there at the river. You could have told them what you'd seen.'

'Oh no. There was no way I was getting involved. How could I? They would have asked all sorts of questions about what I was doing

there and about my connection to you. I couldn't have them prying into my business. I wanted nothing to do with it.'

He stares at me, frightened. 'Please, you don't need to get my mum involved in this.'

'It's too late; she already is. And you being forced to tell her what you did, while I watch, is poetic justice for me. That's just for starters, of course. Then there'll be the police to deal with, and hopefully you'll go to prison. Even if you do get away with it, your life is well and truly over. Forget about medical school. And—'

The sound of the bedroom door opening behind me stops me in my tracks. I spin around and see my mother standing there, clutching the arm of Zoe Monaghan.

'Scott!' she cries, her voice hysterical, as she takes in the scene before her. 'What are you doing?'

FIFTY-EIGHT

Zoe

Beside me, Diana Holbrook is screaming at her son, but all I can do is stare at Harley, lying on the bed, flat on his back, not moving, even though he isn't restrained in any way. My boy.

I rush over to him and pull him up, wrapping him in my arms, while he stays limp and lifeless.

'Mum, I need to get out of here,' Harley says, his voice quiet.

I assure him we will, and then I turn to Scott. 'What have you done to my son?' I shout.

He must be in shock to see his mother and me here, but he's doing a good job of hiding it. 'I don't think you should be asking what I've done to him – more like what has *he* done. To your other son, Ethan.' He smirks, reminding me of Roberta's husband. Another evil man.

'What are you talking about?'

Diana shuffles slowly towards Scott. She's clearly in pain, but has done this for me. I feel sorry for her; not only does she have to deal with her multiple sclerosis, but she's just found out that her son is a monster. I, too, have a lot to get my head around – seeing Harley and this man together in that photo, all over each other, has been a complete shock for me. Only it's worse for her because Harley has been a victim in all this, preyed upon by a much older man. The thought of it rips my heart apart. I had no idea what he was going through.

'I think that's for Harley to tell you, isn't it? he says, pointing towards the bed. 'There's a lot he needs to fill you in on.'

I stare at this man and feel physically sick. He would look quite pleasant if he didn't have a nasty sneer on his face, but it's his age that causes me anxiety. Diana told me he is thirty-eight, almost the same age as Jake and I, so he's old enough to be Harley's dad. And Harley only looked around sixteen in the photo Diana showed me. He was a child. A child who thought he had an adult's mind. This appalling man took advantage of my son, manipulated him.

'Scott, you need to stop this now,' Diana says. 'We called the police before we got here and they're on their way. What have you done to this young man? Why can't he move?'

'The drugs will wear off soon enough. Don't any of you people understand that this isn't the point here? You're missing the big picture.'

'I don't care,' Diana says. 'What's happened to you? He was just a *boy*, Scott. That picture… it's… sickening.'

Scott ignores her, keeping his eyes fixed on Harley. 'How did you find me here?'

'You've been acting strangely for ages. Disappearing all the time. So I searched your room and found a tenancy agreement for this flat. But you still live at home so it didn't make any sense. Then I went on your computer and found that photo. I didn't know who it was until this nice detective came to see me about a missing young man. He showed me a recent photo, and although he looked older, I recognised it as the same boy from the photo.'

For the first time since I stepped into this room, Scott Holbrook's smug expression drops from his face.

'You didn't think I'd ever get up the stairs on my own, did you?' Diana continues, 'let alone know how to use a computer. I'm just useless, aren't I, Scott? A burden.'

'Yes, you bloody are!' Scott yells. 'I never had a chance of a normal life – looking after you every day, trying to keep you positive after Dad left. I was too old to be living with my mother!'

Diana's face crumples. 'You didn't have to stay with me, Scott. I always told you that. All I wanted was for you to meet a nice young man and settle down. *Man*, not boy.'

'He was sixteen.'

'He was still at school!' I yell. 'You were the adult. You should have been responsible.'

Scott walks over to the bed, and for a terrible moment I think he will raise his fist to batter Harley. Instead, he crouches down. 'Tell them, Harley. Tell them that you wanted to do everything we did. That I never forced you. You wanted to be with me.'

I grab Harley's hand and squeeze it tightly to show him I support him, whatever has gone on.

'I didn't,' he says. 'He gave me alcohol. I didn't know what I was doing. I was a child, Mum!' His voice quivers.

My hand makes a fist and I ram it into Scott Holbrook's face. He falls backwards. Quickly, I look up at Diana but she is nodding her approval.

'You're a liar,' Scott says, pulling himself off the floor. 'Tell the truth, Harley. All of it. Because as soon as the police get here, that's what I'm going to do.'

'I don't know what he's talking about, Mum,' Harley says, his voice almost a whisper.

'Don't worry about it now,' I say. 'We just need to get you out of here.'

As soon as I've said that, footsteps thud up the stairs and two officers appear in the bedroom doorway, immediately making their way over to Scott.

I don't hear anything they say because Harley is crying into my shoulder, his tears soaking through my T-shirt. One of the officers drags Scott away while the other assures us the ambulance will be here any second.

Diana makes her way slowly to the bed and sits down at the end. She cries as she tries to speak. 'I'm so sorry about this. And

I'm so sorry he dragged your other son into it. He obviously wanted to torment you all and get back at Harley. I can't believe he's done this.'

'It's not your fault,' I assure her, placing my hand gently on her shoulder. 'And thank you for bringing me here before you called the police. You didn't have to do that, and I really appreciate it.'

'I'm a mother too,' she says. 'I would have wanted the same chance.'

'We bring them up the best we can, don't we? And then they're on their own, making their own decisions – good or bad. You are not responsible for what your son's done. Please know that.'

'Thank you,' she says, before bursting into tears.

FIFTY-NINE

Jake

He sits across from Leanne, staring into his gin and tonic. 'I'm sorry,' he says. 'I should never have doubted you. You've always been a good friend to me and I can't believe I turned on you.'

'I understand,' she says, lifting her wine glass to her lipsticked mouth. She's pretty, he thinks, and has grown more beautiful with age. This just makes him sad; he never thought he'd be thinking of any other woman like this.

Zoe. His heart still aches for her, even though he knows it's over between them, and that it's all down to him. At least they're on speaking terms now, although that's taken a few weeks.

'How's Zoe doing?' she asks, as if aware of his thoughts. Leanne has always been intuitive. Zoe still won't speak to her, even after finding out that Leanne is the one who was ultimately responsible for us finding Harley.

'We don't talk much, but I think she's fine. She's just happy to have Harley back and to have closure, to know that Ethan's death was definitely an accident, after all those days wondering.'

'So it was all Scott. He wanted to mess with her head, to get back at Harley?'

I sip some gin. 'Seems so. That sick bastard. If I could track him down, I'd…' He lets the thought go.

Leanne reaches over and takes his hand. 'I can't believe he didn't end up in prison.'

Jake shakes his head, the hand that's not cradling his glass becoming a fist. 'In the end, Harley didn't want to press charges. Said he couldn't bear the thought of a court case, having to be exposed like that, and that's even if they decided to prosecute. And it happened three years ago and there was no evidence either way, so I doubt it would have gone to court. If nothing else, he groomed my son, made him believe he wanted to do what he did.'

'I believe that,' Leanne says. 'But it's so hard to remember Harley telling me about him.'

Jake takes another, much longer, sip of gin, wanting to shut out Leanne's words but at the same time needing to hear them.

'Do you think he knew exactly what he was doing then? At sixteen?'

Leanne takes a moment to think about this. 'It's so complicated, Jake. I don't think Harley ever thought he was gay, but perhaps he really did fall for Scott.'

'Only because that man pretended to be a woman to start with.'

'Perhaps. But then Harley got to know him for who he actually was. And he still slept with him.'

Jake goes cold inside, wants to scream at her to stop. He'd be fine if it had been a boy Harley's age, he knows he would. But a thirty-five-year-old man? That's just too difficult to get his head around.

'So when he spoke to you and told you about this man he'd met, what did he say exactly?'

'First off, he never said anything about a man. He told me it was a boy who went to a different school. You know I would have told you and Zoe otherwise. I had no idea this was a grown man.'

'But you think Harley liked him? Wanted to do what they did?'

'I have to be honest with you, Jake – yes, I do. At least when he first told me about it. I don't know what happened after that, but it didn't last long and he refused to talk about it once their relationship, or whatever you want to call it, ended. I don't know,

I just got the feeling that Harley was ashamed. Regretted it. And he had girlfriends after that.' She squeezes Jake's hand, must know how difficult this is for him.

Jake shakes his head. 'I wish he'd been able to talk to me about it. It breaks my heart that he thought I'd be ashamed of him or something, just for being attracted to another male.'

'He was sixteen, Jake. Plus, you two have never had that kind of bond.' She offers an apologetic smile. 'Sorry, but it's true.'

'Zoe then. He should have talked to Zoe.'

'And said what? Hey, Mum, I'm sleeping with a thirty-five-year-old man, can I have your approval please?'

Despite everything, Jake manages a smile. 'Well, when you put it like that.'

Leanne leans back in her seat, her eyes following a young couple walking into the bar. 'Look, I think you should just focus on the future now. Harley's going to medical school, there'll be no more messages from that man, and, well, you've still got me.'

He lifts her hand and kisses it. 'And I'm grateful for that. And thank you for talking to Tim Ellroy – it made all the difference, and we might not have Harley back if you hadn't told Tim everything.'

'You do understand why I couldn't say anything to you or Zoe? I'd made a promise to Harley and I just couldn't break it, not until I realised it might help find him if I spoke up.'

'I get it. I'm just glad that Harley opened up to you all those years ago, otherwise we would never have found him. And who knows what that psycho would have done to him?'

'It was just lucky that Harley mentioned him name once. I don't know if he realised he'd even said it at the time, but I remembered it and I could let Tim know.'

Leanne stares at him and he knows there's something she wants to ask him. 'Did you ever tell Zoe?'

He knows what she's talking about without her having to mention it. 'No. I just don't see what good it would do.'

'But it's just more lies, isn't it, Jake? I thought you wanted an end to all that.'

He does, but how can he bring himself to tell Zoe when it's even worse than sleeping with Leanne? He has to continue living with his guilt. Guilt because he could have prevented the boys going to the river that night. Guilt that he heard a noise as he lay in bed, was sure it was the front door but convinced himself in his daze that it couldn't have been, and was too tired to move or even give it much thought. So while he turned over and fell back to sleep, his son was heading towards his death.

He shakes his head. 'No, I can't tell her.'

'Well, I'm glad you were able to share it with me – eventually,' Leanne says. Jake had only told her the other day, and it did help relieve some pressure to have it out in the open. 'You didn't know what was happening. If you'd had any idea you would have rushed downstairs.'

Yes, he would. Knowing that doesn't make him feel any better, though. But he's lived with it for three years, so he'll just keep on living with it, until eventually it might be the end of him.

Leanne tactfully changes the subject and they spend the rest of the evening talking about her new promotion at work and how many new clients Jake has secured in the last few weeks.

Leanne is right: he needs to try to focus on the future now.

SIXTY

Roberta

She's been released on bail, but still there is a lightness in her step as she walks around her new flat, taking in the clean, modern minimalism. It's rented – she won't be able to buy a place until she and Adrian have sold their house – but at least it's somewhere she can call home, and it's a lot nicer than the B & B she'd spent those nights in. Besides, Roberta doesn't know what the future holds, so it doesn't make sense to rush into buying a property.

The intercom buzzes and she rushes to see who it is on the camera. Lewis. She presses the button to open the main door downstairs. She feels secure here, safe from Adrian, even though she knows he didn't get bail and that it is very likely he will be spending a very long time in prison. This makes her feel content, despite the fact that she might also be charged.

'How are you doing?' Lewis asks, his smile warming her heart. After everything he went through because of her, she's grateful to have his friendship, even though she will always yearn for more. She understands why he can't give her any more than his emotional support, and she's come to terms with this.

They meet up at least once a week, and although they aren't in a relationship, spending time with him has made her understand just how awful her marriage was, how terrible Adrian was, even before the hit-and-run, before they had Josh. She had thought there'd been a few good years then, but no, just having Lewis as a friend has proved her wrong in only a short space of time.

While she makes coffee – she cannot bear the thought of drinking wine any more – they chat about their respective days. They have both made a vow to each other to not talk about, or worry about, the pending charges against her, and this is easy for her to do when she's in Lewis's presence.

Besides, her solicitor says there are extenuating circumstances which will have to be taken into consideration. For years, she was abused by Adrian, so it's no wonder she was too afraid to stand up to him and go to the police as soon as it had happened. And then they'd lost Josh. It all gives her hope that she will keep her freedom, or at the very least get a shorter prison sentence.

One thing she is grateful for is that now everything's out in the open, it doesn't appear that Josh knew about the hit-and-run after all. At least she can be comforted in the thought that he died not knowing what a monster his dad was, and not thinking that she supported Adrian's terrible decision to keep quiet about that poor cyclist.

Zoe keeps in touch and has been to visit her, and this is another thing that keeps Roberta feeling positive. Finally, they are forming a friendship, and can take comfort from one another, both of them having suffered the same loss.

'Why do you bother with me?' Roberta blurts out to Lewis, while they're drinking their coffee and watching television.

'What's brought all this on?'

'I just need to know. After everything, why do you make so much effort with our friendship?'

He takes her hand. 'Because, Roberta, you are one of the strongest women I know. I know you don't believe it, but you are. Look what you've been through – and you're still here, fighting to have a life. Come on, woman, you need to give yourself some credit.'

And this fills her up, validates how she has already started to feel about herself after all those years of being a victim.

Leaning forward, she tries her best to push aside the urge to kiss him, and instead squeezes his hand, hoping he will know how lucky she feels to have him supporting her.

Maybe she'll end up alone, but that's okay. She will cherish every day, every minute of her life, and fight for her freedom.

SIXTY-ONE

Zoe

It was months before the truth came out, and when it finally did, I believe it was by accident. Unintentional. Harley had already kept it hidden for three years, so I think he found it easier to simply carry on the lie.

I also think he struggled to come to terms with what he had done with Scott, and it was all tied to Ethan and Josh. The lie grew bigger until he just couldn't cope with it any longer.

Harley had come home from medical school for the weekend and I was talking about Ethan over dinner, how glad I was that I could once again put him to rest and grieve normally, once again accept that fact that it was just a terrible accident. Harley was quiet as usual – something I had put down to nerves about being out in the world on his own – and at first I didn't notice that he was crying. He did it so silently that, until I look at him, there was nothing to alert me to his distress.

His whole body shook as he told me the truth about how the boys ended up in the river that night, and what they'd been fighting about. His words were the second most painful thing I've ever had to hear in my life, and I held him tightly as they poured out, even though I was being ripped apart inch by inch.

Afterwards, when he'd cried it all out, I said that I'd go with him to the police, and be there for him whatever happened.

I will never forget the look on his face; it will haunt me for the rest of my days.

Neither Jake or I have ever been prejudiced against anyone for their beliefs, sexual orientation or anything else, and all we ever wished for our sons was that they never hurt anyone. So why couldn't Harley tell us that everything that happened with Scott had been consensual?

Jake sits across from me in the café we've agreed to meet in. He looks much older now, even though not that much time has passed, and his stubble is speckled with dots of grey, much more than he had only months ago. It suits him.

I haven't seen him since I first took Harley home after finding him in Scott's flat, and he can't believe I've agreed to meet. We are both Harley's parents, though, and we're in this together.

'It's my fault,' he says. 'He thought I'd be disappointed or something. Disgusted. Why would he think that? What did I ever say to make him believe that?'

'He was sixteen,' I say. 'He was confused about everything and not thinking straight. I think a lot of it was to do with Scott's age, rather than him being male.

'And he still insists he doesn't like men?'

I nod. 'Yes. He says he just liked Scott. He fell for him as a person, I suppose, and that was what was important.'

'Hmmm.' Jake's not convinced. 'The fact that Scott had been talking to him online as *Alissa*? I call that grooming, Zoe.'

'It's time to let this rest now, Jake. It's best if we all put it behind us. Harley already feels bad enough about it. About what happened to Ethan.'

'Yes, that's a lot to live with,' Jake agrees. 'He couldn't save his brother.' He pauses and lifts his coffee cup to his mouth. 'He did try, didn't he?'

'Yes,' I say. 'Of course he did.'

I swallow the large lump in my throat that appears whenever I think about this. The only way it disappears is when I remind myself that we try our best for our children, teach them everything we want them to learn and then set them free, hoping they make the right decisions.

'At least he's made a good start at medical school. He is happy there, isn't he? I still can't get much out of him, so I can't be sure how he feels about anything.'

I explain to him that it will take time to form a bond with Harley that should have been there in the first place. Such a lot has happened; he needs to relax and let it happen naturally. Both he and Harley just need to be themselves around each other; that's the only way it can work.

'So anyway, how's Tim?' Jake asks.

'We're not together,' I say. 'We're just friends. Good friends.'

'For now,' Jake says, and I believe I see a hint of a smile. We've come a long way in such a short space of time.

'How's Leanne?' I ask, still finding it hard to mention her name without it causing me pain.

A hint of redness flushes Jake's cheeks. 'We're mending our friendship. Slowly getting back on track.' He pauses. 'She'd love to see you again.'

'No. Not yet. I'm not saying never, but just not yet. Tell her I said thank you again, though, for finally telling Harley's secret.'

'Oh, Zoe, she misses you so much. Won't you even think about meeting up with her?'

There is barely a day when I don't think about this, when I don't miss the two of them, but sometimes things are irreparable, and it would do more damage to try and fix them. 'I don't think so,' I say. 'Maybe one day. Just not yet. What about that mess with Cara? Did you sort it all out?'

Jake shakes his head. 'That bloody woman. Yes, thankfully she told the truth to Liam in the end. I mean, what a disaster that would have been if she'd actually gone to the police. It would have been her word against mine, wouldn't it? And even if it didn't get as far as court, I'd be tainted just by the accusation. No smoke without fire and all that.'

We all need to be more open-minded, I think. Take each situation on its own and not be so quick to judge. 'I've had enough of secrets and lies,' I tell Jake. 'Why can't we all just be open and honest?'

'You are,' he says, smiling. He knows I'm not having a dig at him. 'Don't ever change, Zoe.'

I watch Jake as he leaves the café, the lump returning to my throat, threatening to choke me. I will have to get used to it; it's the price I have to pay for keeping Harley's secret.

A LETTER FROM KATHRYN

Thank you so much for choosing to read my seventh book, *The Warning*. I'm extremely grateful for your support and really hope you have enjoyed reading it, and that it took you by surprise. I always try my best to put a twist in the tale!

If you did enjoy it, and haven't already signed up, then you can keep up-to-date with my latest releases by using the following link:

www.bookouture.com/kathryn-croft

I always say this but reviews are so important to authors so I would really appreciate it, if you did like *The Warning*, if you could spare a moment to post a quick review on Amazon to let others know your thoughts. I'd also greatly appreciate any recommendations to friends and family!

I'm always thrilled to hear from readers to find out how you are engaging with my characters and stories, so please feel free to contact me via Twitter, my Facebook page or directly through my website.

Thank you again for all your support!
Kathryn x

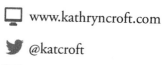 www.kathryncroft.com

@katcroft

authorkathryncroft

ACKNOWLEDGEMENTS

I can't believe I've done this seven times now, and once again I'm grateful to all the people who have helped to make *The Warning* the best book it can be. Being pregnant at the time of writing it, I am also truly thankful for all the support I've had in bringing the seed of an idea to life. My fabulous editors, Keshini Naidoo and Lydia Vassar-Smith – thank you for your input and advice. Madeleine Milburn, my wonderful agent, thank you, as always, for everything you've done for me and for all your input with this book.

Thank you to Hayley Steed, Alice Sutherland-Hawes and Giles Milburn at the Madeleine Milburn Literary, TV & Film Agency for the amazing work you do for all your authors.

To the whole Bookouture team, including Kim Nash and Noelle Holten, thank you for all your hard work and dedication.

Thank you to all my readers – I wouldn't be doing the job that I love without your support so I really appreciate you reading my books.

Another special thank you to all book reviewers and bloggers who take the time to read any of my books – I really appreciate this.

Thank you to my wonderful family for your continued support. I am now truly blessed to be a mum of two and my little son and daughter already keep me strong and motivated. Everything I do is for you two! And, of course, my amazing husband, Paul.

CPSIA information can be obtained
at www.ICGtesting.com
Printed in the USA
FSHW022000210621
82579FS